Perspectives on Behavioral Medicine

VOLUME 2

Neuroendocrine Control and Behavior

Perspectives on Behavioral Medicine

VOLUME 2
Neuroendocrine Control and Behavior

Edited by

REDFORD B. WILLIAMS, Jr.

Department of Psychiatry
Behavioral Physiology Laboratory
Duke University Medical Center
Durham, North Carolina

1985

ACADEMIC PRESS, INC.

Harcourt Brace Jovanovich, Publishers

Orlando   San Diego   New York   Austin
London   Montreal   Sydney   Tokyo   Toronto

WITHDRAWN

ACADEMIC PRESS, INC.
Orlando, Florida 32887

United Kingdom Edition published by
ACADEMIC PRESS INC. (LONDON) LTD.
24–28 Oval Road, London NW1 7DX

LIBRARY OF CONGRESS CATALOGING-IN-PUBLICATION DATA

Main entry under title:

Perspectives on behavioral medicine.

  (Perspectives on behavioral medicine)
  "Genesis in the program of the annual meeting of
the Academy of Behavioral Medicine Research, held in
Charlottesville, Virginia, in June, 1980."—
  Includes index.
  1. Psychoneuroendocrinology.   I. Williams,
Redford Brown, DATE-   II. Academy of Behavioral
Medicine (U.S.)   III. Series.
QP356.45.N48   1985   612'.814   85-9136
ISBN 0-12-532102-3 (alk. paper)
ISBN 0-12-531954-1 (paperback)

PRINTED IN THE UNITED STATES OF AMERICA

85 86 87 88   9 8 7 6 5 4 3 2 1

Contents

**PART II
APPLIED PSYCHONEUROENDOCRINOLOGY**

Contributors

Numbers in parentheses indicate the pages on which the authors' contributions begin.

ANDREW BAUM (201), Medical Psychology, Uniformed Services University of the Health Sciences, School of Medicine, Bethesda, Maryland 20814

EVERETT W. BOVARD (103), Department of Social Sciences, Queensborough Community College, The City University of New York, Bayside, New York 11364

DANIEL L. COLLINS[1] (201), Medical Psychology, Uniformed Services University of the Health Sciences, School of Medicine, Bethesda, Maryland 20814

M. A. FITZMAURICE (149), Pacific Northwest Research Foundation, Seattle, Washington 98104

RAYMOND FLEMING (201), Medical Psychology, Uniformed Services University of the Health Sciences, School of Medicine, Bethesda, Maryland 20814

WILLIAM F. GANONG (25), Department of Physiology, University of California, San Francisco, California 94143

DAVID C. GLASS (189), Research and Graduate Studies, Laboratory Office Building, State University of New York at Stony Brook, Stony Brook, New York 11794

ALBERTO GRIGNOLO (183), Department of Pharmacology, Duke University Medical Center, Durham, North Carolina 27710

---

[1]Present address: Testing Function, U.S. Air Force Human Resources Laboratory, Brooks AFB, Texas 78231.

DAVID A. HAMBURG[2] (1), John F. Kennedy School of Government, Harvard University, Cambridge, Massachusetts 02138

G. JEAN KANT (53), Neuroendocrinology and Neurochemistry Branch, Department of Medical Neurosciences, Division of Neuropsychiatry, Walter Reed Army Institute of Research, Walter Reed Army Medical Center, Washington, D.C. 20307-5100

JOHN P. KOEPKE (183), Department of Psychiatry, University of North Carolina, School of Medicine, Chapel Hill, North Carolina 27514

GEORGE F. KOOB (39), Division of Preclinical Neuroscience and Endocrinology, Scripps Clinic and Research Foundation, La Jolla, California 92037

CYNTHIA M. KUHN (133), Department of Pharmacology, Duke University Medical Center, Durham, North Carolina 27710

C. RAYMOND LAKE (201), Psychiatry and Pharmacology, Uniformed Services University of the Health Sciences, School of Medicine, Bethesda, Maryland 20814

ALAN W. LANGER (183), Department of Psychiatry, University of North Carolina, School of Medicine, Chapel Hill, North Carolina 27514

ROBERT H. LENOX (53), Neuroscience Research Unit, Department of Psychiatry, University of Vermont College of Medicine, Burlington, Vermont 05405

KATHLEEN C. LIGHT (183), Departments of Psychiatry and Physiology, University of North Carolina, School of Medicine, Chapel Hill, North Carolina 27514

JAMES L. MEYERHOFF (53), Neuroendocrinology and Neurochemistry Branch, Department of Medical Neurosciences, Division of Neuropsychiatry, Walter Reed Army Institute of Research, Walter Reed Army Medical Center, Washington, D.C. 20307-5100

EDWARD H. MOUGEY (53), Division of Neuropsychiatry, Walter Reed Army Institute of Research, Walter Reed Army Medical Center, Washington, D.C. 20307-5100

PAUL A. OBRIST (183), Department of Psychiatry, University of North Carolina, School of Medicine, Chapel Hill, North Carolina 27514

LEE L. PENNINGTON (53), Division of Neuropsychiatry, Walter Reed Army Institute of Research, Walter Reed Army Medical Center, Washington, D.C. 20307-5100

VERNON RILEY[3] (149), Pacific Northwest Research Foundation, Seattle, Washington 98104

[2]Present address: Carnegie Corporation of New York, New York, New York 10022.
[3]Deceased.

MARC A. SCHAEFFER (201), Medical Psychology, Uniformed Services University of the Health Sciences, School of Medicine, Bethesda, Maryland 20814

SAUL M. SCHANBERG (133), Department of Pharmacology, Duke University Medical Center, Durham, North Carolina 27710

G. RUFUS SESSIONS[4] (53), Division of Neuropsychiatry, Walter Reed Army Institute of Research, Walter Reed Army Medical Center, Washington, D.C. 20307-5100

DARREL H. SPACKMAN (149), Pacific Northwest Research Foundation, Seattle, Washington 98104

REDFORD B. WILLIAMS, JR. (71), Department of Psychiatry, Behavioral Physiology Laboratory, Duke University Medical Center, Durham, North Carolina 27710

[4]Present address: USAFA/DFBL, U.S. Air Force Academy, Colorado Springs, Colorado 80840-5941.

Preface

At a meeting held at the Institute of Medicine of the National Academy of Sciences in April, 1978, a group of some 35 behavioral and biomedical scientists formulated this definition of behavioral medicine:

> Behavioral medicine is the *interdisciplinary* field concerned with the development and *integration* of behavioral *and* biomedical science and techniques relevant to health and illness and the application of this knowledge and these techniques to prevention, diagnosis, treatment and rehabilitation.[1]

The field of behavioral medicine is perhaps best known for its accomplishments relating to the application of biofeedback techniques in the treatment of a wide variety of physical disorders and the demonstration that the Type A behavior pattern is a risk factor for coronary heart disease. Both of these accomplishments have a direct bearing on important clinical issues in biomedicine. It is important to realize, however, that there are also areas of research in the basic medical sciences which also help to provide the scientific base for the field of behavioral medicine. In no area is this contribution more evident than in the recent explosive growth of knowledge in the neurosciences. Discoveries concerning the CNS mechanisms of neuroendocrine control offer great promise for helping us to understand the basic mechanisms whereby behavioral and psychosocial factors contribute to health and illness. To achieve this goal, it is clear that the new knowledge regarding neuroen-

---

[1]Schwartz, G. E., and Weiss, S. M. (1978). Behavioral medicine revisited: An amended definition. *Journal of Behavioral Medicine, 1,* 249–251.

docrine control mechanisms must be integrated with existing knowledge regarding the role of behavioral and psychosocial factors in illness. The outcome of such integrative efforts should be testable hypotheses which will advance our understanding of the role of behavioral and psychosocial factors in health and illness.

The purpose of this book, then, is to provide the reader with a selective overview of important recent developments in the neurosciences related to neuroendocrine control mechanisms which have important implications for major areas of interest in behavioral medicine. In his general introductory chapter, David Hamburg presents a synthesis of related developments in the biomedical and behavioral sciences which have played an important role in the emergence of the field of behavioral medicine, with particular emphasis on developments in behavioral biology concerned with neuroendocrine control. In view of his key role, as President of the Institute of Medicine, in sponsoring a series of conferences on recent developments in the biobehavioral sciences relevant to the health of the American people, Hamburg is eminently well qualified to provide us with this integrative overview.

Following this introduction, Part I, "Basic Mechanisms," provides a general introduction to recent developments concerning neuroendocrine control, as well as a consideration of general implications of such developments for the stress field. In his chapter, Ganong presents a concise summary of recent developments in basic neuroendocrinology at the cellular and biochemical levels. Then follows a review by Koob of the most up-to-date information concerning the recent characterization of the molecular structure of corticotropin-releasing factor (CRF) and its biological significance as a mediator of the effects of stress on behavior. Continuing the consideration of brain mechanisms mediating responses to stress, Meyerhoff and colleagues present some interesting data concerning the differential effects of varying forms of stress on brain and pituitary nucleotides in the rat. In the next chapter, Williams extends the discussion to a consideration of different neuroendocrine response patterns elicited by different types of behavioral stress in humans and considers the possible role of such response patterns in the pathogenesis of disease. The final chapter in this section, by Bovard, comes at the issue from another direction: the CNS–neuroendocrine mechanisms responsible for the health-promoting effects of social support.

Part II, "Applied Psychoneuroendocrinology," shows how the integrative efforts of the first section might be applied toward improving our understanding of the role of behavioral and psychosocial factors in several specific illnesses. Schanberg and Kuhn review their elegant research program delineating the underlying psychoendocrine mediation of the role of maternal deprivation in psychosocial dwarfism. Next, Spackman, Fitzmaurice, and the late Vernon Riley provide a review of a large body of research which emphasizes the importance of neuroendocrine mechanisms in mediating the influences of stress on neoplastic process. Obrist and coworkers review their research into the beta-adrenergic mediation of behavioral influences on renal function in animal models. The chapter by Glass provides an overview of the possible pathophysiological mechanisms mediating the increased coronary disease risk observed among persons exhibiting the Type A, coronary-prone behavior pattern. Finally, in the last chapter of this section, Baum and colleagues present some recent data in what might be termed the new field of "socioneuroendocrinology": the effects of chronic stress on neuroendocrine function among those living in the near vicinity of the Three Mile Island nuclear accident.

While still a relatively young field, behavioral medicine already has many exciting accomplishments to its credit. At the same time, its evolution is still in progress, and the likely future developments offer considerable promise of real solutions to some of today's most serious and perplexing health problems. It seems clear that the integration of new knowledge of neuroendocrine control mechanisms with behavioral medicine theory and research will be essential if this promise is to be realized. This book will make a useful contribution to this process by reviewing the progress to date in this area and by pointing the way to the future work.

This book had its genesis in the program of the annual meeting of the Academy of Behavioral Medicine Research, held in Charlottesville, Virginia, in June, 1980. Of this volume's eleven chapters, six were presented at the 1980 Academy meetings, one has been extensively revised and updated from the material presented at the meeting, and four are entirely new material commissioned specifically for this volume to ensure that, while selective, the overview presented touches upon the most important recent research trends. For example, the chapters by Koob on behavioral effects of CRF and by Baum and colleagues on neuroendocrine correlates of stress at Three Mile Island are both based on very recent research, some of which is as yet unpublished elsewhere, though submitted to archival journals.

In editing this book I have been fortunate to have the able assistance of several individuals who gave unselfishly of their time and energies. Logan Wright, Camille Wortman, John Mason, and Neil Schneiderman, through their work on the program committee of the Academy for the 1980 meeting, helped to ensure that the areas covered touched upon the most important research developments. Jerry Singer and Peg Bang of the Academy secretariat helped both to prod our contributors and keep the paper flowing. Special thanks are due to those who contributed the additional chapters: George Koob, Everett Bovard, and Andrew Baum.

Finally, to my wife, Virginia, and to Lloyd and Jennifer go my appreciation for their patience with a spouse and parent who still has not learned well enough how to say no to outside commitments.

1

Toward a Conjunction of Biomedical and Behavioral Sciences

DAVID A. HAMBURG

The Burden of Illness

At the Institute of Medicine's annual meeting in 1976, Rice, White, and Feldman gave a paper which has had strong impact by clarifying the total burden of illness in the United States (Rice, Feldman & White, 1976). They examined such dimensions as potential years of life lost compared with an appropriate population measure of life expectancy, inpatient days, work loss days, limitations on major activities, economic costs, and other measures. Their analysis gives results similar to those of Lalonde (1974) in Canada. There is a burden of illness characteristic of industrialized, affluent nations. In the Canadian analysis, using an average life expectancy of 70 years, motor vehicle accidents accounted for about 13% of years of life lost because so many of them occur early in life, usually in adolescence and young adulthood. Cardiovascular diseases accounted for about 12% of the years of life lost, while other accidents apart from motor vehicles accounted for about 11% of years lost. Respiratory diseases, particularly lung cancer, accounted for 8% and suicide, about 4%. That profile of illness, early death, and related long-term disability in the industrial, affluent countries has major behavioral components—for example, the risk of smoking in cardiovascular diseases and cancer, the many damaging effects of heavy alcohol use, and the role of risky driving in serious accidents. Moreover, poor and socially depreciated people do not benefit adequately from biomedical advances—for example, from the powerful preventive potentiality of early prenatal and perinatal care, much of which is also behavioral in nature.

PERSPECTIVES ON BEHAVIORAL MEDICINE, Vol. 2
Neuroendocrine Control and Behavior

Collaboration

In the context of this newly emerging and highly promising inter-disciplinary organization, I want to say a word about the vital matter of *collaboration* in the health sciences and professions—so plainly crucial for progress in behavioral medicine (Hamburg, 1980).

As knowledge in the life sciences has accumulated during the 1960s and 1970s, a remarkable transformation has occurred. The amount of information and its complexity overwhelms anything we might have imagined at the time when the great expansion of research began, short-ly after World War II. In order to gain sufficient technical depth to make significant contributions, research workers must specialize and hyper-specialize. They must dig deeply into a narrow area in order to master the complexities and add to existing knowledge. One field in which this has occurred with great success is behavioral neurobiology. Truly as-tonishing illumination is emerging on anatomy, physiology, biochemis-try, pharmacology, pathology, and behavioral aspects of the nervous system. Each of these disciplines subdivided in practice in order to un-tangle the dramatic complexity of the brain and its works. As various components became reasonably clarified, their relation to other compo-nents became a matter of great interest. The subspecialty barriers began to crumble in the face of the need to combine perspectives, to pool technical strengths, and to bring order out of confusion. Thus, an inte-grative trend has become apparent in recent years, concomitant with continuing and essential work in a highly specialized mode. There is an emerging picture of a functioning nervous system in a living organism and some ways in which it can go wrong. This integrative view grows out of many fruitful collaborations across disciplinary boundaries; and, in turn, this view stimulates new collaborations as potentially useful new connections are envisioned. This mutual benefit aspect of collabora-tion is the key to its significance.

Another area of science in which similar trends have emerged is in molecular biology. Deep specialization has led to great progress in bio-chemistry, genetics, ultrasturcture, biophysics, and immunology. Pro-found insights into the nature of moleucles and cells have given power-ful impetus to the life sciences—indeed, a genuine revolution. Yet the living organism is not a bag of molecules. These marvelous components of the organism must "talk to each other, must relate harmoniously in dynamic ways that change over time to make adaptation possible. Thus, in recent years a strong integrative current has emerged that links the structure, function, and regulation of human genes and leads toward a deep understanding of gene–environment interactions in health and disease. In this sphere, as in neurobiology, a richness and diversity of collaborations has built strength, linking concepts, methods, and perspectives that altogether provide one of the most important developments of our time.

Thus, in major research areas, progress is being made toward achieving both depth and breadth, both specialization and integration. This is done by creating a tapestry of collaborations that can obtain knowledge otherwise impossible to obtain.

Another arena of collaboration that is highly salient to future health improvement lies in disease prevention and health promotion. Now, to take effective action in disease prevention anywhere in the world involves reaching beyond the medical care system. Some effective action is now being taken within this system and more can be done in the future. But to fulfill the potentiality of modern disease prevention—taking into account the rapidly growing body of knowledge of risk factors and underlying mechanisms pertinent to cardiovascular disease, cancer, respiratory disease, infectious disease and more—the health sector will have to learn how to collaborate more effectively with other sectors. This involves such diverse and complex sectors of modern society as education, media, transportation, and industry.

The Emergence of Behavioral Biology

In my view, one crucial linkage of the biomedical and behavoioral sciences occurs in what I am tempted to call a final common pathway: the brains' control, or at least strong regulatory influence, over the endocrine and autonomic nervous systems. Since the 1950s, much has been learned about the endocrine and autonomic nervous systems. The adaptations involved in stressful circumstances refer to the flow of changes in environmental conditions which affect the organism at all levels of biological organization. If those changes are drastic, they tend to be experienced as difficult and distressing. That is what we usually mean by stressful conditions. There is a broad biology of stress which is being revived in a new context, with new techniques that make possible advances that were virtually unimaginable when the term *stress* first came into common use several decades ago.

One area of creative ferment is that concerned with transmission of information in the brain and, also, between the brain and other tissues. Whereas during the 1960s we had a bare minimum of information on neurotransmitters in the brain, we now know that about a dozen amino acids and monoamines have vitally important roles in neurotransmission, either directly as transmitters at the synapse, or as modulators of information flow between neurons (Bloom, 1979; Usdin, Hamburg, & Barchas, 1977). Especially important in this connection are norepinephrine, dopamine, serotonin, and gamma-amino-butyric acid. Each transmitter substance is differentially distributed in the brain. Certain circuits rely primarily on one substance for transmission of information from cell to cell. Thus, it is meaningful to speak of a dopaminergic circuit or system. In fact, dopaminergic systems have been shown to have high relevance for Parkinson's disease and schizophrenia.

Of special importance for behavioral medicine are the transmitter systems of the great hypothalmic–limbic–midbrain circuits first elucidated by Nauta. These circuits exert strong regulatory influence on the endocrine system and autonomic nervous system and, hence, on the cardiovascular and gastrointestinal systems. They also are involved substantially in mediating adaptive functions of memory, appraisal, and motivational–emotional responses. Acting in concert with the enormously developed neocortex in humans, these circuits play a vital role in appraising the functional significance of ongoing events and thereby paving the way for adaptive responses.

When a change occurs in environmental conditions—as must necessarily happen hour-by-hour, day-by-day, sometimes drastic, sometimes not—an organismic appraisal occurs, mostly automatically but sometimes with careful deliberation. Such appraisals may be freely translated into a set of questions whose relevance to adaptation is apparent. What is it? What does it mean for me? How can I respond? Will action be required? If so, what action would be effective in meeting the challenge? Such questions are answered, even if vaguely formulated, in ways that produce a coordinated set of metabolic and cardiovascular changes that prepare the organism for action. The course of action is guided by the brain as reappraisal proceeds in light of ongoing feedback. Thus, these hypothalmic–limbic–midbrain circuits mediate crucial integrative processes of organismic biology that have been highly relevant to survival for millions of years in human evolution (Guillemin, 1978; Hamburg, 1962; Schally, 1978).

These circuits are influenced by steroid hormones—influences which are highly pertinent to effective stress responses and to reproduction and, hence to survival of the species. More recently, we have learned that these circuits are peculiarly influenced by neuropeptides. Some of these effects are measured not in milliseconds like the conventional neurotransmitters, but in minutes or perhaps even hours. It appears that some neuropeptides stay on the cell membrane longer than other substances and modulate the flow of information. This may constitute a kind of "fine tuning" which appears highly relevant to mood. This is a new and exceedingly stimulating field.

The discovery of the hypothalamic hormones, and the significance of this discovery deserves emphasis here. G. Harris discovered what came to be called the "portal system," a strange, special, rich network of blood vessels. Those blood vessels could, in principle, carry chemical messengers. Where previously we had thought only of electrical messages, we now came to recognize there could be chemical messages by which the brain could control the anterior pituitary and the rest of the body by a chemical route.

Meanwhile, we and others were investigating the possibility that psychological stress in humans could influence the adrenal cortex and the thyroid. When one becomes very upset, anxious, angry, or depressed for a long enough period, changes are found in the function of the adrenal cortex and, in some people, the thyroid. We also investigated reproductive hormones. It developed that our early assumptions were correct—there are effects of stressful experience on all the glands controlled by the anterior pituitary.

But how were these effects mediated? What molecules were the messengers? Isolating, purifying, and characterizing those substances seemed almost impossible. But Guillemin and Schally and their collaborators had the characteristics required to take on this task: vision, teamwork, courage, the ability to organize a very complex enterprise involving semi-industrial methods, and to persist in the face of disappointment over many years. In due course, they characterized several hypothalamic hormones and received the Nobel prize for this achievement in 1977.

The basic insight has to do with coordination of the body. The cells must communicate with each other in some way. The components of the organism must be coordinated in a functioning whole, especially in relation to changes in conditions from day-to-day or year-to-year. To use an analogy with an automobile engine, it will not do to have cylinders if the cylinders do not work together. It would be worse still if the cylinders did not work together with the other parts of the engine. The engine must work in a coordinated way if it is to make the vehicle move. So, too, with the human organism.

The great coordinating systems are two: the nervous system, and the endocrine system. What Schally and Guillemin and their collaborators have done is to show us specifically and tangibly *the coordination of the coordinators.* They have tied together the two great coordinating systems of the body, and that is a momentous achievement. Clinically, the delineation of these compounds which control so much of the coordinating functions of the body already offers promise in respect to all of the functional systems regulated by those hormones and their peripheral targets.

The research on hypothalamic hormones not only provided profound new insights but also a remarkable technology for peptide analysis. Taken together, these advances—coinciding with the discovery of receptors in the brain and other related advances—have produced an "explosion" of neuropeptide discoveries during the late 1970s and early 1980s. In addition to their intrinsic worth, these discoveries have strong implications for clinical pharmacology and other therapies in the remainder of this century, based not only on the new technologies but also on a deeper understanding of adaptation.

Further advances are on the horizon. New drugs in the 1980s and 1990s will be more specific in action, built upon substances mediating specific functions in humans, for example, the modulation of pain. The elucidation of pain pathways, their transmitters, receptors, modulators, and behavioral correlates, constitutes a major advance in biology. So, too, does the utilization of physical and organic chemistry to make biological substances. These analoges may intensify or otherwise usefully modify the activities of a natural substance—for example, the hypothalamic hormone LHRF (luteinizing hormone releasing factor).

The new recombinant DNA technology opens up a new vista for production of peptides and already has been applied on a small scale to somatostatin and growth hormone.

A vivid example of progress in this field has been provided by Avram Goldstein, who discovered a natural brain endorphin, dynorphin, that is 200 times more potent than morphine and 50 times more potent than any other known endorphin (Goldstein, Tachibana, Lowney, Hunkapillar, & Hood, 1979). Its extraordinary potency indicates that it binds with great specificity to pain receptors.

It is of special interest that pituitary secretion of endorphins is closely linked to the secretion of adrenocorticotropic hormone (ACTH; Rossier, Bloom, & Guillemin, in press). Indeed, there is a common precursor, pro-opiocortin. Thus, ACTH and endorphins are secreted together under conditions appraised by the organism as stressful. In my judgment, this suggests that they mediate a closely related set of adaptive functions. They must facilitate the organism's ability to respond to stress, withstand pain, mobilize for activity, and do what is necessary to cope with the stressful challenge.

Another peptide of great interest is LHRF, the hypothalamic hormone which controls the reproductive system in both sexes (McAdoo et al., 1978). It is found fairly widely distributed in the brain. When administered systemically to healthy young men, by our group, it had effects on alertness, sexual motivation, and resistance to fatigue. Whether these were direct effects, or secondary to the stimulation of testosterone release, we cannot say, but there is nonhuman experimental evidence that LHRF has some direct effects on behavior in mammals in the absence of the gonads. Recent evidence also indicates that LHRF has a transmitter role in the sympathetic nervous system. Synthetic analogues of LHRF have been prepared, including both super-potent and super-inhibitory molecules. The latter may be useful in contraception, and clinical trials are underway. Vale has prepared a long-acting analogue. Such long-acting preparations simplify the problem of adherence to a therapeutic regimen, which is so difficult in chronic diseases and of special importance in developing countries.

Other neuropeptides are also of great interest for research in behavioral medicine (Krieger & Liotta, 1979; Motta, Crosignani, Martini, 1975; Simantov, Childers, & Synder, 1977). Somatostatin, another of the hypothalamic hormones, has potent inhibitory effects on secretory cells of the pancreas, and it also inhibits activity of the sympathetic nervous system. Indeed, its widely ramifying, inhibitory effects deserve exploration in a variety of functional systems.

Substance P, a compound discovered by von Euler, evidently participates in the transmission of pain impulses. Antagonists to substance P would be of great interest for possible use in analgesia and anesthesia.

Cholecystokinin was discovered in the intestine and has been known for many years. But it takes on new interest by virtue of the discovery that it is present in high concentration in the cerebral cortex. Yalow has found that this peptide occurs in smaller amounts in the brains of genetically obese mice than in those of normal mice. Perhaps cholecystokinin mediates a satiety signal—though not necessarily the only one. This is under active investigation now. If confirmed, it will doubtless spur research on the important behavioral–biomedical problem of obesity—for example, whether a deficiency of this peptide may predispose one to obesity by weakening satiety responses. This in turn raises the possibility that cholecystokinin or an anologue may be useful for some obese people in the future. Here again, the heuristic value of research on neuropeptides, behavior, and disease is striking. By the same token, the attraction of outstanding investigators into the area is encouraging.

ACTH, the pituitary peptide so crucial in stress responses, has been of interest in other ways. It is found in many neurons in various brain regions, illustrating the general point that a variety of peptides have functions throughout the brain, so that it is reasonable to consider them neuroregulators—transmitters or modulators or both, depending upon circumstances.

Moreover, a molecular fragment of ACTH, ACTH 4-10, facilitates learning and remembering in some animal experiments, though the findings in humans are less clear. Other interesting work with peptides and amino acids is proceeding in the broader context of the neurochemistry of memory. This is of special interest in relation to the formidable problem of memory deficits in the elderly.

The work on *releasing factors* that led to the profound discoveries in the hypothalamic hormone area began in the 1950s in the search for the ACTH-releasing factor in trying to understand the psychobiology of stress. It is ironic that this hypothalamic hormone has been the most difficult to characterize chemically. At this writing, there are encouraging indications that the problem has finally been solved, though the results are not yet published. This could open up a set of possibilities for clarifying the mechanisms of stress response, and developing drugs to modify those responses, akin to the possibilities already sketched for LHRF.

Thus, neuropeptides have foreseeable implications for our understanding and ability to make useful interventions in diverse domains of behavior, health and disease: sex, alertness, pain-relief, sense of well-being, relief of anxiety and depression, regulation of appetite, lowering of blood pressure, learning and memory, and a variety of cardiovascular and gastrointestinal effects. The stimulating potential of this work for behavioral medicine deserves strong emphasis.

Peptides are not the only molecules of interest in current work on brain function, behavior, and disease. The earlier work on monoamines, amino acids, and steroid neuroregulators is still full of potentialities. And, as has happened before, exploration of mechanisms of action of effective drugs may open new doors to knowledge. For example, the benzodiazepine group of CNS-active compounds has already proven to be of value in antianxiety, sleep-promoting, and anticonvulsant drugs. In 1980, a benzodiazepine receptor was identified in mammalian brains. Following the sequence that proved so rewarding in the opiate–endophin line of inquiry, investigators in several laboratories are now trying to characterize the natural ligand that binds to these receptors.

So, an unprecedented array of molecules, cells, circuits, systems, techniques, and concepts are now available for research on problems of central interest to behavioral medicine. It is reasonably safe to predict a transforming effect on the field in the remainder of this century.

This neurobiobehavioral science area is one that has very far-reaching ramifications as basic science, and it is pregnant with clinical implications in the 1980s. The dynamic emergence of this field has been seen in a set of disciplines that coalesce under the rubric of behavioral biology, that is, the behavioral aspects of neurobiology, genetics, endocrinology, biochemistry, pharmacology, physiology, and evolution. In turn, behavioral biology has had a very stimulating impact on a wider range of behavioral sciences, including the study of psychosocial variables in their own right—segments of psychology, anthropology, sociology have been stimulated. Where there has been contact between those conerned with biological variables and those concerned with psychosocial variables, a great deal of mutual benefit has occurred. One of the key problems for future advancement is how to provide the conditions under which sustained interaction can occur between those who work with biological, and those who work with psychosocial, variables. This is not easy. The emergence of this new, broadly composed, scientific society is one constructive response to this challenge.

Cardiovascular Diseases

One dynamic area of conjunction between biomedical and behavioral sciences lies in cardiovascular research. There are, indeed, promising biobehavioral lines of inquiry bearing directly upon the heavy burden of illness manifested in what is in fact the largest public health problem of industrialized, affluent countries. One major current of such inquiry draws upon principles of learning linked to social psychology and modern communications research in efforts to reduce cardiovascular risk factors (Eliot, 1979; Hamburg, 1979; Rose, 1980; Weiner, 1977).

Hypertension

Basic research in physiology, biochemistry, pharmacology, genetics, and behavior—applied to renal, cardiovascular, endocrine, and nervous systems—has increased understanding of hypertension, though much still remains in doubt. Out of past basic research came small-scale clinical explorations and then well-designed, large-scale clinical trials, so that effective pharmacological treatment is now available. High blood pressure can be controlled, and this reduces the risk of stroke, renal failure, and heart failure. This important finding has been extended to mild hypertension. Yet the problem is not solved—even with the next generation of still more effective drugs.

People who do not know they have high blood pressure cannot treat it; at least half of Americans with high blood pressure are unaware of their condition. Many of those who are aware do not adhere to therapy; this is of course a general problem in chronic disease. Nevertheless, the National High Blood Pressure Education Program has increased by many millions the number of people using effective treatment measures.

As in many other therapeutic regimens, about half of the patients simply do not adhere to the prescribed course of treatment. It is important to ascertain, through behavioral research, why patients do not take medication that is manifestly good for their health.

A certain amount of clarification has emerged. Failure to take medication depends partly on such factors as (1) long waiting time for the doctor and at the pharmacy, (1) inadequate follow-up by doctor and clinics, (3) over-complicated and confusing dosage schedules, (4) unsatisfactory doctor–patient relationships, and (5) inadequate explanation of possible side effects. The latter is particularly significant to patients who had no symptoms prior to medication. There has been some careful work utilizing learning principles on the utility of nonphysician medication counselors who focus specifically on these issues. They can considerably enhance adherence to therapeutic regimens.

Coronary Artery Disease

Coronary artery disease and subsequent angina, myocardial infarction, heart failure, or arrhythmia is of course based on atherosclerosis and so has stimulated research on the underlying processes. Coronary artery disease accounts for 650,000 deaths annually, two-thirds of the cardiovascular disease mortality, and it is the nation's largest cause of death.

Sudden death occurs as the first "symptom" in at least one-fourth of those with coronary disease and more than half the deaths occur before hospitalization. This is a powerful stimulus to research on primary prevention. Increasingly, attention is turning to the detection of cardiovascular risk factors and efforts to diminish them before disease becomes clinically apparent. The cardiovascular risk factors include age, male sex, elevated blood pressure, cigarette smoking, elevated plasma cholesterol, (especially, elevated low-density lipoprotein), elevated blood glucose, overweight, sedentary way of life, family history of heart disease before age 65, personality type A, and severe stress. Taken together, these risk factors can predict at least two out of three untoward coronary events.

Interest in modifying risk factors is high, but the task is difficult. It requires significant educational and social changes. Still, there are encouraging indications that altering firmly established patterns of behavior (such as smoking, diet, exercise, work habits, and coping with stress) is possible. The relation of such behavior changes to health outcomes is under active investigation. This will be a research area of intensified activity in the years immediately ahead.

Significant changes in risk factors have occurred in the U.S. in the past

15 years, at least in part because of public concern with health, and education regarding health-promoting behavior. Consumption of tobacco products, milk, cream, butter, eggs, and animal fats have all diminished in the adult population. The decline tends to be greater in the more educated segments of the population, and is especially strong among health professionals. These changes coincide with an accelerating decline in cardiovascular mortality. While this may be a coincidence, it deserves further investigation. The most searching examination of epidemiological evidence indicates that a substantial part of the decline in cardiovascular mortality is probably due to the changes in health-relevant behavior. But the burden of illness is still heavy in cardiovascular disease, and health-damaging behaviors are still highly prevalent. Progress, yes, but there is a long way to go.

The Stanford Heart Disease Prevention Program, an interdisciplinary research effort in behavioral medicine has shown that decreasing risk factors associated with cardiovascular disease is possible through media-based health education. The risk factors addressed in this 2-year community program were cigarette smoking, high plasma cholesterol concentrations, and high blood pressure. The experiment involved three communities in California: one with a mass media education program, one with a mass media program supplemented with face-to-face counseling for high risk individuals, and one control community with no special programs (Farquhar, 1978; Farquhar *et al.*, 1977).

Key aspects of the experiment were as follows:

1. The design of the campaign was based on an analysis of the knowledge deficits and the media-consumption patterns of the intended audience, that is, meeting the needs of the local people in a comprehensible way.
2. The mass media approaches and the face-to-face instruction were based on established principles and methods of behavioral science relevant to this problem, that is, especially those of social learning.
3. The mass media materials were devised to teach specific behavioral skills—for example, preparation of a palatable low-fat diet—as well as offering health-relevant information and motivating people to use that information for their own benefit.

There was a 30% reduction of overall cardiovascular disease risk, almost all of which was achieved in the first year of the program and sustained through the second year.

These and other findings have implications for planning similar programs. A well-planned mass media effort may be effective by itself, but it takes longer to achieve results than when mass media communications are combined with intensive individual instruction of high-risk persons. Effects are probably better sustained if community leaders and family members are involved, thus building a social support network that can provide continuing reinforcement for health-promoting behavior. This project suggests the utility of combined efforts of biomedical research, public health, and behavioral science. New projects of this sort have begun and older ones are approaching fruition. If such findings are replicated in other communities, then a pervasive and sustained change in the methods of health education is likely to follow, drawing upon the cumulative record of community-based prevention research. In my judgment, several issues deserve special attention as foci of bio-behavioral research in this area: (1) specific, culture-sensitive information regarding the nature of the threat to health, (2) specific, culture-sensitive information regarding the skills helpful in coping with the risk factors, (3) prompt reinforcement of early changes in behavior toward health-promoting patterns, (4) community organization in such ways as to provide respected models of health-promoting behavior and long-term social reinforcements for such behavior; (5) family involvement in health education activities, and (6) formulation of educational messages in such ways as to link health-promoting behavior with self-respect and motivations fundamental to survival. These issues are pertinent to a wide range of research on health and behavior—from cardiovascular risk factors in affluent countries to health-promoting practices involving water and sanitation in poor, developing countries.

Another study in this vein, of larger size and longer duration, is of great interest here. The purpose of this ongoing study is to establish the effectiveness of cardiovascular disease risk factor reduction in decreasing the incidence of heart attack and stroke (McAlister *et al.*, 1980; Puska, 1978). It has been in progress in North Karelia, Finland, for more than 6 years. The intervention program includes (1) health education through a variety of community resources, including local newspapers and radio, and (2) hypertension screening with intensive group health education directed at high-risk individuals.

The result of these combined efforts is that annual incidence rates of acute myocardial infarction, which has been increasing in Finland for many years, have reversed their historical trend. Apparently, there also has been a change from the more severe heart attack toward less severe attacks. The annual incidence of strokes had also fallen by the third year of the program.

The experiences in California and Finalnd will provide a stimulus for community-based prevention research in the future. For example, the

Pennsylvania study of Stunkard (1980) is a good example, especially in its systematic procedures for community organization in the service of risk factor reduction (Hjermann, 1980; Strunkard, 1980). The follow-up measures of behavior change achieved under these conditions will be of special interest. Such investigations will need to be based on the best available biomedical data—for example, to determine the priority of risk reduction efforts—and must explore ways to elicit cooperation of public and private sectors in facilitating health-promoting behavior. Such public education and community organization efforts hold much promise for lifelong disease prevention and health promotion in developing countries, especially regarding maternal and child health, nutrition, family planning, and sanitation.

A report from the important Oslo study (Hjermann, 1980) gives further encouragement in this regard. The purpose of the study is to determine whether dietary lowering of blood lipids and cessation of smoking are possible in healthy men at relatively high risk of coronary disease, whether such modifications in risk factors can be maintained for many years, and whether such modifications lead to lowering of the incidence of coronary disease. The Oslo investigators found that dietetic-hygenic interventions succeeded in reducing cigarette smoking and also in reducing blood lipid levels. It will be useful to learn in more detail the nature of the behavioral interventions, especially if it turns out that the incidence or severity of coronary disease is diminished in the invervention group.

Biobehavioral Science and Disease Prevention in Adolescence

Consideration of cardiovascular risk factors draws attention to formative factors that shape the health-damaging behavior patterns characteristic of several major risk factors. The characteristic exploratory, risk-taking behavior of adolescence comes to mind in this context (Institute of Medicine, 1978a; Jessor & Jessor, 1977; Kandel, 1975; Kelley, 1979). There is a worldwide need for intensified research on adolescence from biological and social science perspectives (Hamburg & Hamburg, 1976). Also, the emergence of behavioral pediatrics offers new opportunities for clinical research on adolescent problems, after a long period of neglect in which this critical phase of the life cycle feel between pediatrics and internal medicine, between child and adult psychiatry, and between different research approaches lacking a developmental perspective.

The onset of adolescence is a critical period of biological and psycho-social changes for the individual. Puberty is one of the most far-reaching physiological upheavals in the life span. For many, it involves a drastic change in social environment as well: the transition from elementary to secondary school. These years are highly formative for health-relevant behavior patterns such as smoking of cigarettes, the use of alcohol or other drugs, the driving of automobiles and motorcycles, habits of food intake and exercise, and patterns of human relationship including high-risk pregnancy and sexually transmitted disease. Advances in fields such as endocrinology, psychology, and epidemiology now offer the opportunity to obtain deeper insights into adolescent development if they are used in collaboration (Hamburg & Hamburg, 1975).

Adolescents are rapidly learning how to become adults. They can benefit from anticipatory guidance in respect to vital matters of human biology, health, disease, and behavioral adaptation. Before health-damaging patterns are firmly established, there is a crucial opportunity for preventive intervention.

But how is it possible to reach adolescents in credible ways that are likely to diminish health-damaging behavior? Is it feasible to reach out to them where they spend their time and capture their interest and imagination in ways that fit their own orientations? For examples, clues from the population-based cardiovascular prenention studies can be useful in formulating mass media approaches to health-relevant behavior in adolescence.

One approach to adolescent problems, peer counseling programs for junion and senior high school students, rests upon an analysis of developmental tasks and coping strategies (Hamburg & Varenhorst, 1972). Utilizing the credibility of peers in adolescence, the program trains students to help other students. It does so largely by clarifying the tasks and strategies characteristic of this phase of the life cycle in a particular setting, by providing information on the processes of interpersonal relationship, and by providing continuing supervision to the student counselors. Findings suggest that the program is useful for both coun-selees and counselors.

This approach is now being tested in a study of systematic peer leadership to discourage onset of tobacco dependency. This is a field experiment in which a model curriculum has been designed to improve skills for resisting influences toward smoking. These skills, for example, resistance to peer pressure, are communicated by 16-year-olds to 12-year-olds. Hundreds of students in matched experimental and control schools are compared on cigarette smoking rates at baseline and follow-up periods of up to 2 years. So far, the results indicate much less smoking among the adolescents exposed to the peer counseling program than among the controls (McAlister, 1979; McAlister, Perry, & Maccoby, 1979). Other studies utilizing special films, which emphasize somewhat different themes, are also underway and include some long-term follow-ups (Botvin, 1980; Evans, 1979; Evans, Henderson, Hill, & Raines, 1979; Evans et al., 1978; Hurd et al., 1980; Leventhal & Cleary, 1980).

This area of inquiry, with its strong potentiality for disease prevention and life span benefits, deserves sustained attention in research on behavioral medicine.

Health and Behavior in Aging

In the past century, human life expectancy has increased dramatically. With the origin of agriculture 10,000 years ago, both the size of the human population and the average length of life increased, but the age of the oldest people changed very little (Washburn, 1981). The average length of life is affected by many environmental factors that have changed in the modern era, especially in the twentieth century. The result is a situation that is an authentic evolutionary novelty—a very large number of human beings living to ages far beyond those which were characteristic of the species. In human evolution, there never was natural selection for healthy old people; the ability to live to old age is a by-rpoduct of selection for evolutionary success at much younger ages. Less than 5% of precontact Australian aborigines lived past 50; about half died before age 20.

In industrialized nations, the primary demographic fact of the next several decades will be a rapidly aging population (Institute of Medicine, 1977, 1978b). The number of Americans 65 and over has risen from 4% of the population in 1900 to 11% of today's population. More than 50% of those who have ever been over the age of 65 are alive today. We must learn how to adapt.

Research shows that senile dementia, which is severe in 5% and moderate in 10% of those 65 and over, has pathological features distinct from normal aging. Biological research on senile dementia has focused especially on changes in choline acetyltransferase, an enzyme responsible for production of acetylcholine in cholinergic neurons. Acetylcholine is one of the most important neurotransmitters. Although this enzyme declines in normal aging, the decrease is much greater in patients with senile dementia of the Alzheimer type, compared with age-matched controls. A key fact is that the receptors for acetylcholine are present in normal quantity even in the absence of the enzyme. This raises the possibility of finding a substance that can activate these receptors and alleviate the disorder. Other neurobiological research has demonstrated age-related changes in neurotransmitter uptake which may contribute to the higher incidence of Parkinsonism in older patients.

Psychosocial approaches are also important in elucidating problems of aging. Research has shown that incompetent behaviors of elderly people are often contingent on social factors (Rodin, 1980). Many elderly persons who are placed in a mutual aid, social support network with meaningful tasks and a basis for self-respect can function effectively at advanced ages. Since much ingenuity is manifest in psychoscoial interventions pertinent to care of the elderly in Europe, valuable opportunities exist in this sphere (as in others) for international scientific cooperation for health.

Differential Susceptibility to Disease

Everyone is exposed to harmful agents and stressful experiences. For any noxious agent (biological or psychosocial), there is marked individuality in response. Both genetic and enviornmental factors pertinent to such individuality of response are beginning to be clarified, and this approach will deserve our attention in the years ahead (Vogel & Motulsky, 1979).

Studies of the influence of genetic factors on responses to environmental agents are now of great interest. Such work requires that genes involved in susceptibility and resistance to particular diseases be identified. The interactions of such genes with specific environmental factors may point the way to sharply focused preventive techniques. These investigations are likely to concentrate on substances that are widespread—as in diet, medication, occupation—and to which a relatively large fraction of the population is genetically susceptible—for example, genetics of lipid metabolism in relation to diet. Similar considerations apply to toxic constituents of cigarette smoke and to reactions to alcohol (Institute of Medicine, 1980). Linkages of genetics, biochemistry, psychology, and clinical medicine will be important in sorting out these interactions.

Only some of those genetically predisposed actually become ill. Another set of factors pertinent to differential susceptibility lies in the social environment. From numerous epidemiological studies of varying design—using different populations, health outcome measures, and stress indicators—there has come considerable convergence of evidence indicating that many disorders are precipitated by environmental stressors (such as moving, unemployment, bereavement). The extent of community disintegration, a family's lack of social supports, and the number of stressful events in the life of an individual have been found to affect illness-related work and school absences (Cassel & Tyroler, 1961), the occurrence of complications of pregnancy (Nuckolls, Cassel, & Caplan, 1972). and, indeed, life expectancy.

A report of unusual interest helps to clarify these phenomena (Berkman & Syme, 1979). The relationship between social ties and mortality was assessed using the 1965 Human Population Laboratory survey of random sample of about 7000 adults in California and a subsequent 9-year mortality follow-up. People who lacked social ties were more likely to die in the follow-up period than those with more extensive contacts. The age-adjusted relative risks for those most isolated when compared to those with the most social contacts were 2.3 for men and 2.8 for women. The association between social ties and mortality was independent of self-reported physical health status at the time of the initial survey, year of death, socioeconomic status, and health practices such as smoking, alcoholic beverage consumption, obesity, physical activity, and utilization of preventive health services.

Natural support systems can be effective in buffering stressful experience. They also can influence the use of health services and compliance with medical regimens. This is pertinent to the requirements for behavior change in smoking cessation, weight control, or long-term adherence to anti-hypertensive medication.

Social support systems facilitate the development of coping strategies that help people contain distress within tolerable limits, maintain self-esteem, preserve interpersonal relationships, meet the requirements of new situations, and prepare for the future (Hamburg & Killilea, 1979). An interesting area for future research would be the experimental construction of social support networks where natural ones are lacking.

A Model of Coping Behavior

Some recurrent findings of coping studies over a quarter century suggest a general model of coping behavior (Coelho, Hamburg, & Adams, 1974; Hamburg & Adams, 1967; Hamburg & Hamburg, in press). This model is not fully comprehensive, does not delineate consistent individual differences in preferred coping modes, and does not adequately cover the long-range development of coping behavior in the individual life span (though it has some implications for long-range development). Nevertheless, it appears to have considerable applicability to both threatening and psychosocial transitions. It refers to individual strategies and their social context. It aims to stimulate new work with more refined techniques now possible (Levine & Holger, 1980; Miller, 1980). The elements listed below are roughly sequential. They focus on the individual in the process of working out a coping strategy or an interrelated set of strategies, that is, what people tend to do under stress, whether they realize it or not. The time scale is usually months. Generally, this sequence of events is fully observable within a year of a person's life after onset of a major transition.

Each element of the model subsumes a variety of specific patterns. The elements are as follows:

(1) People under stress tend to regulate timing and dosage of awareness of threats, which assures gradual transition from avoidance to recognition if threat is highly distressing. (2) If multiple, concurrent stresses are occurring, people under stress tend to sequence processing so as to deal with them one at a time. (3) People under stress seek information regarding the task from multiple sources. (4) People under stress formulate expectations, hopeful ones if possible. (5) People under stress delineate units that are manageable, and focus on intermediate goals that are visible and probably reachable. (6) People under stress rehearse task-specific behavior, and practice in a safe situation (e.g., restoration of an affectionate, respectful relationship.) (7) People try out this behavior in actual task-specific situation, preferably of no-more-than moderate risk. (8) They appraise feedback regarding their performance and their satisfaction. (9) They try more than one approach, typically formulating predominant and subsidiary approaches. (10) Ultimately, most people make a commitment to one promising approach and puruse it with vigor. (11) Usually there are buffers against disappointment and contingency plans for the inevitable disappointments of living.

Much of this involves improvising by individuals in working out an implicit strategy to meet a set of difficult tasks. But it almost always occurs in a social context—and that context makes a difference.

Under stress, the first response is often one of seeking affiliation. While established attachments are most highly valued under these conditions, many other affiliations are useful—and, indeed, if the experience is sufficiently difficult, almost any affiliation will do, at least for a little while. With such human anchorage established, information seeking can proceed in a supportive context.

Affiliation in stressful circumstances may serve a variety of functions that tend to be adaptive: (1) mutual protection ("If you can't do it yourself, I'll help you"); (2) bonds of special significance are forged in the heat of stressful experience—these are rewarding attachments; (3) models of effectiveness (I'll show you how to meet the task''); (4) access to a pool of coping strategies; and (5) feedback regarding the probable utility of exploratory ventures and provisional efforts.

The further development of coping research in the context of behavioral medicine may help to clarify differential susceptibility to stressful experience and, hence, suggest useful therapeutic and preventive interventions.

Broadening the Spectrum of Health Research and Education

As we learn more about the burden of illness, the importance of behavioral factors for health becomes increasingly clear. But the point is more general. As the burden of illness changes, the sciences needed to lessen the burden also change. Similarly, as new scientific opportunities arise, their relevance to disease must be sought by those responsible for the health of the nation. New gardens of science must be cultivated, old biases discarded, conventional wisdoms set aside in the face of new observations, fresh ideas, and neglected social responsibilities. It was not so long ago that the emerging discipline of biochemistry was viewed with suspicion by chemists as weak chemistry and by biologists as weak biology. Today this hybrid discipline has become the central discipline of biomedical research. It was not so long ago that most leaders in medicine were very doubtful that genetics would have any practical significance for health in the twentieth century. Today, genetics is one of the most dynamic areas of medicine. The same story holds for neurobiology. These lessons should be borne in mind in the years ahead, as the health sciences adapt to new problems and new opportunities—indeed, unprecedented opportunities. In the present context, one of the crucial areas for health progress certainly lies in the conjunction of beavioral and biomedical sciences.

Let us seek more effective and diverse modes of collaboration in research and education aimed toward measurable improvement in health outcomes. In this important and difficult task, let us try hard to help each other, to share our difficulties, to pool our information and ideas, to learn from each other, and maintain a decent respect in the face of differences. Whether or not these efforts will be of direct benefit to us now, they will surely be of benefit to people everywhere in the decades to come.

References

Berkman, L. F., & Syme, S. L. 1979). Social networks, host resistance, and mortality: A nine-year follow-up study of Alameda Count residents. *American Journal of Epidemiology, 109,* 186–204.

Bloom, F. E. (1979). Is there a neurotransmitter code in the brain? In P. Simon (Ed.), *Advances in pharmacology and therapeutics: Vol. 2. Neuro-Transmitters.* New York: Pergamon Press.

Botvin, G. (1980). Preventing the onset of cigarette smoking through life skills training. *Preventive Medicine, 9,* 135–143.

Cassel, J., & Tyroler, H. A. (1961). Epidemiological studies of culture change: I. Health status and recency of industrialization. *Archives of Environmental Health, 3,* 25–33.

Coelho, G., Hamburg, D., & Adams, J. (1974). *Coping and adaptation.* New York: Basic Books.

Eliot, R. S. (1979). *Stress and the major cardiovascular disorders.* Mount Kisco, NY: Futura Publishing Company.

Evans, R. I. (1979). Smoking in children and adolescents: Psychosocial determinants and prevention strategies. In *Smoking and health: A report of the Surgeon General* (DHEW Publication No. (PHS) 79-50066). Washington, DC: U.S. Government Printing Office.

Evans, R. I., Rozelle, R. M., & Mittelmark, M. B., *et al.* (1978). Deterring the onset of smoking in children: Knowledge of immediate physiological effects and coping with peer pressure, media pressure, and parent modeling. *Journal of Applied Psychology, 8*(2), 126–135.

Evans, R. I., Henderson, A. H., Hill, P. C., & Raines, B. E. (1979). Current psychological, social, and educational programs in control and prevention of smoking: A critical methodological review. In A. M. Gotto & R. Paeoletti (Eds.), *Atherosclerosis reviews* (Vol. 6). New York: Raven Press.

Farquhar, J. W. (1978). The community-based model of life style intervention trials. *American Journal of Epidemiology, 108*(2), 103–111.

Farquhar, J. W., Maccoby, N., Wood, P. D., *et al.* (1977). Community education for cardiovascular health. *The Lancet, 2,* 1192–1195.

Goldstein, A., Tachibana, S., Lowney, L. I., Hankapiller, M., & Hood, L. (1979). *Dynorphin-(1-13), an extraordinarily potent opioid peptide. Proceedings, National Academy of Sciences, 76,* 6666–6670.

Guillemin, R. (1978). Peptides in the brain: The new endocrinology of the neuron. *Science, 202*(4366), 390–402.

Hamburg, B., & Hamburg, D. A. (1975). Stressful transitions of adolescence—endocrine and psychosocial aspects. In L. Levi (Ed.), *Society, Stress and Disease* (Vol. 2, pp. 93–106). London: Oxford University Press. pp. 93–106.

Hamburg, B., & Hamburg, D. A. (1976, December). Becoming mature. *World Health* pp. 12–17.

Hamburg, B., & Killilea, M. (1979). Relation of social support, stress, illness, and use of health services. In *Healthy people: The Surgeon General's report on health promotion and disease prevention. Background papers.* (DHEW Publication No. (PHS) 79-55071A, pp. 253–276). Washington, DC: U.S. Government Printing Office.

Hamburg, B., & Varenhorst, B. (1972). Peer counseling in the secondary schools: A community mental health project for youth. *American Journal of Orthopsychiatry, 42,* 566–581.

Hamburg, D. A. (1962). The relevance of recent evolutionary changes to human stress biology. In S. Washburn (Ed.), *Social life of early man* (pp. 278–288). Chicago: Aldine Publishing Co.

Hamburg, D. A. (1979). Health of the American people. In *Science and technology: A five-year outlook* (pp. 381–435). San Francisco: Freeman.

Hamburg, D. A. (1980). Toward increasing collaboration among health professions. *Journal of Medical Education,* in press.

Hamburg, D., & Adams, J. (1967). A perspective on coping behavior: Seeking and utilizing information in major transitions. *Archives of General Psychiatry, 17,* 277–284.

Hamburg, D., & Hamburg, B. (in press). A lifespan perspective on adaptation and health. In B. Kaplan & M. Ibrahim (Eds.), *Family and health: Epidemiological approach* (Vol. II). Chapel Hill: University of North Carolina Press.

Hjermann, Ingvar. (1980). Smoking and diet intervention in healthy coronary high risk men. Methods and 5-year follow-up of risk factors in a randomized trial—*The Oslo Study. Journal of the Oslo City Hospital, 30,* 3–17.

Hurd, P., Johnson, C. A., Pechecek, T., Bast, L. P., Jacobs, D. R., & Leupker, R. V. (1980). Prevention of smoking in seventh grade students. *Journal of Behavioral Medicine, III* (in press).

Institute of Medicine. (1977). Report of the conference May 17–19 sponsored by the Institute of Medicine and the Royal Society of Medicine, *Care of the elderly: Meeting the challenge of dependency.* ISBN 0-8089-1055-8, available from Grune and Stratton, New York.

Institute of Medicine. (1978a). *Conference on adolescent behavior and health: A summary.* IOM PUb. No. 78-004. Washington, DC.

Institute of Medicine. (1978b). *Aging and medical education.* Report of a study by a committee of the Institute of Medicine, September 1978. Available from National Institute on Aging, Building 31, Room 5C36, 9000 Rockville Pike, Bethesda, Maryland 20205.

Jessor, R., & Jessor, S. L. (1977). *Problem behavior and psychosocial development: A longitudinal study of youth.* New York: Academic Press.

Kandel, D. (1975). Stages in adolescent involvement in drug use. *Science, 190,* 912–914.

Kelley, J. G. (1979). *A psychological study of coping and adaptation.* Hillsdale, NJ: Erlbaum.

Krieger, D. T., & Liotta, A. S. (1979). Pituitary hormones in brain: Where, how, and why? *Science, 205,* 366–372.

LaLonde, M. (1974). *A new perspective on the health of Canadians: A working document.* Ottowa, Canada: Government of Canada.

Leventhal, H., & Cleary, P. D. (1980). The smoking problem: A review of the research and theory in behavioral risk modification. *Psychological Bulletin.*

Levine, S., & Holger, U. (Eds.). (1980). Coping and health. New York: Plenum.

McAdoo, B., Doering, C., Kraemer, H., Dessert, N., Brodie, H., & Hamburg, D. (1978). A study of the effects of gonadotropin-releasing hormone on human mood and behavior. *Psychosomatic Medicine, 40,* 199–209.

McAlister, A. L. Tobacco, alcohol, and drug abuse: Onset and prevention. In *Healthy people: The Surgeon General's report on health promotion and disease prevention. Background papers.* DHEW Publication No. (PHS) 79-55071. Washington, DC: U.S. Government Printing Office.

McAlister, A. L., Perry, C., & Maccoby, N. (1979). Adolescent smoking: Onset and prevention. *Pediatrics, 63,* 650–658.

McAlister, A., Puska, P., Kostella, K., Pallones, U., & Maccoby, N. (1980). Mass communication and community organization for public health education. *American Psychologist, 35,* 375–379.

Miller, N. E. (1980). Coping and health: A perspective on the effects of stress and coping on disease and health. In S. Levine & H. Ursin (Eds.), *Coping and health* New York: Plenum.

Motta, M., Crosignani, P. G., & Martini, L. (Eds.). (1975). Hypothalamic hormones: Chemistry, physiology and clinical uses. New York: Academic Press.

Nuckolls, C. B., Cassel, J., & Caplan, B. H. (1972). Psychosocial assets, life crises and the prognosis of pregnancy. *American Journal of Epidemiology, 95,* 431–441.

Puska, P. (1978). In Institute of Medicine, Vol. 2, Summaries, *Conference on health promotion and disease prevention.* Washington, D.C.: National Academy of Sciences.

Rice, D., Feldman, J., & White, K. (1976). *The Current Burden of Illness in the United States* (Occasional Paper of the Institute of Medicine). Washington, DC: National Academy of Sciences.

Rodin, J. (1980). Managing the stress of aging: The role of control and coping. In S. Levine & H. Ursin (Eds.), *Coping and health.* New York: Plenum.

Rose, R. M. (1980). Endocrine responses to stressful psychological events. *Psychiatric Clinics of North America, 3*(2).

Rossier, J., Bloom, F. E., & Guillemin, R. (in press). Endorphins and stress. To be published in *Selye's guide for stress research.* The Salk Institute, La Jolla, California, ed. H. Selye. Florence, Kentucky: Van Nostrand Reinhold.

Schally, A. V. (1978). Aspects of hypothalamic regulation of the pituitary gland. *Science, 202*(4363), 18–28.

Simantov, R., Childers, S. R., & Snyder, S. (1977). Opiod peptides: Differentiation by radioimmunoassay and radioreceptor assay. *Brain Research, 135,* 358–367.

Stunkard, A. J., Schechter, C., Taylor, A., Marconi, K., Norman, S., & Stolley, P. (1980). *The Pennsylvania Community Health Intervention Project,* Lancaster, PA: Lycoming County Medical Society.

Usdin, E., Hamburg, D. A., & Barchas, J. (Eds.), *Neuroregulators and psychiatric disorders.* New York: Oxford University Press.

Vogel, F., & Motulsky, A. G. (1979). *Human genetics: Problems and approaches.* New York: Springer-Verlag.

Washburn, S. L. (1981). Longevity and primates. In J. L. McGaugh & S. B. Kiesler (Eds.), *Biology, behavior and aging* (Vol. 3). New York: Academic Press.

Weiner, H. (1977). *Psychobiology and human disease.* New York: Elsevier North-Holland.

PART I

Basic Mechanisms

2
Changing Concepts
of Neuroendocrine Control*

WILLIAM F. GANONG

Introduction

Neuroendocrinology is concerned with the way cells communicate with one another. The four generally recognized means of intercellular communication are via (1) gap junctions (direct transfer), (2) synaptic junctions (neural communication), (3) circulating body fluids (endocrine communication), and (4) interstitial fluid (paracrine communication). Gap junctions permit movement of molecules from one cell to another without entering the extracellular fluid. Communication mediated by extracellular chemical messengers occurs by way of synapses, by way of circulating body fluids, and by way of the interstitial fluid. Not many years ago, it was believed that neural and endocrine communication were separate and different, and that they were mediated by different types of chemical compounds. Neural communication was private, with chemical messengers released at nerve endings traversing the 20-nm gap between the pre- and postsynaptic elements. Endocrine communication was viewed as public, with the messages spread throughout the body and received only by those cells with appropriate receptors. This belief in the separation of the two systems has now broken down to the point that it seems more appropriate to think in terms of neuroendocrine communication, with subspecialization along a spectrum from neurons to gland cells.

*This chapter includes results of research in the author's laboratory supported by USPHS Program-Project Grant AM06704.

PERSPECTIVES ON BEHAVIORAL MEDICINE, Vol. 2
Neuroendocrine Control and Behavior

Hypothalamic Hormones

The first challenge to the separation of the neural and endocrine systems came from Scharrer and Scharrer (1954), who argued on morphological grounds that neurons secrete hormones. From work done on mammals, they presented evidence that the supraoptic and paraventricular neurons in the hypothalamus secreted the posterior pituitary hormones, oxytocin and vasopressin, into the general circulation. They also argued that these hormones were manufactured in the cell bodies of the supraoptic and paraventricular neurons and migrated down the axons of these neurons to their endings in the posterior lobe of the pituitary. Their views have turned out to be essentially correct. Oxytocin and vasopressin are synthesized in separate neurons. Current concepts of supraoptic and paraventricular function (Brownstein, Russell, & Gainer, 1980) hold that each peptide is synthesized along with its neurophysin as a pre-prohormone in the endoplasmic reticulum of the cell bodies. The complexes are packaged in the Golgi apparatus to form granules, and the granules migrate by axoplasmic flow to the nerve endings, with additional processing during migration. Release of posterior pituitary hormones along with their neurophysins from the endings is initiated by action potentials in the neurons and occurs by calcium-dependent exocytosis.

The secretion of the hormones of the anterior lobe of the pituitary is also regulated by hormones produced in the hypothalamus. The seven accepted hormones of the anterior pituitary are summarized in Figure 2.1. Prolactin stimulates milk secretion in the female breast; the gonadotropins, follicle-stimulating hormone (FSH) and luteinizing hormone (LH), are responsible for the formation of germ cells and the secretion of gonadal hormones; thyroid-stimulating hormone (TSH) regulates the secretion of the thyroid gland; growth hormone produces growth by way of somatomedin, a peptide secreted by the liver; and adrenocorticotropic hormone (ACTH) regulates the secretion of part of the adrenal cortex. β-lipotropin (β-LPH) is secreted with ACTH. This peptide includes in its structure the amino acid sequences of the naturally occurring opioids β-endorphin and methionine enkephalin. The opioid peptides have important and widespread effects in the brain, but the degree to which they penetrate the blood–brain barrier is limited, and it is uncertain how much if any of the circulating opioids are formed from β-LPH. Consequently, the function of circulating β-LPH remains uncertain.

There are no functionally important, direct neural connections between the hypothalamus and the anterior pituitary, but there is a special

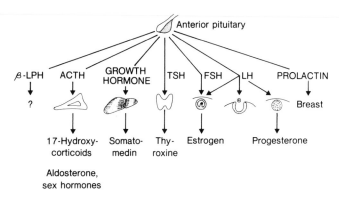

FIGURE 2.1 Hormones secreted by the anterior lobe of the pituitary (modified from Ganong, 1979).

system of blood vessels connecting the two. This system of hypophyseal portal vessels arises in capillaries on the ventral surface of the median eminence of the hypothalamus and passes directly to the anterior lobe (Figure 2.2). It provides a short, direct pathway by which hormones can pass from the brain to this portion of the pituitary.

There are at least seven hypothalamic hypophysiotropic hormones (releasing factors) secreted in the hypophyseal portal circulation (Figure 2.3). Corticotropin-releasing hormone (CRH) stimulates the secretion of ACTH and β-LPH. Thyrotropin-releasing hormone (TRH) regulates the secretion of TSH. The luteinizing hormone-releasing hormone (LHRH) stimulates the secretion of LH and FSH. It seems likely that LHRH is the

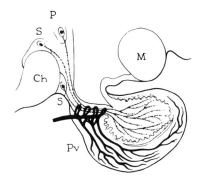

FIGURE 2.2 Hypophyseal portal vessels (Pv). The vessels originate from capillary loops and capillaries on the ventral surface of the median eminence of the hypothalamus (primary plexus) and pass directly to the anterior lobe. Ch, chiasm; S, supraoptic nucleus; P, paraventricular nucleus; M, mammillary body (from Ganong, 1979).

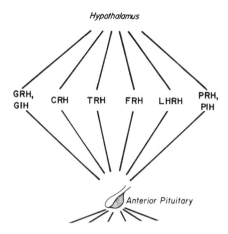

FIGURE 2.3   Hypothalamic hypophysiotropic hormones. See text for discussion.

only gonadotropin-releasing hormone (GnRH) but there is some evidence for an additional follicle-stimulating hormone-releasing hormone (FRH). Prolactin is doubly regulated, with its secretion inhibited by a prolactin-inhibiting hormone (PIH) and stimulated by a prolactin-releasing hormone (PRH). Similarly, the secretion of growth hormone is inhibited by a growth hormone-inhibiting hormone (somatostatin), and stimulated by a growth hormone-releasing hormone (GRH).

Six of these hypophysiotropic hormones have been chemically characterized and synthesized; TRH is a tripeptide, LHRH is a decapeptide, somatostatin is a tetra-decapeptide, and PIH is the catecholamine, dopamine. All have been demonstrated by immunocytochemical or other techniques to be produced by neurons in and near the hypothalamus, rather than by ependymal cells or glia (Ajika, 1980; Elde & Hökfelt, 1978). CRH and GRH are larger peptides, and it seems reasonable to postulate that PRH is also a polypeptide, although proof awaits its isolation and characterization. Thus, neurons in the hypothalamus secrete a variety of different hormones. In the case of the neurons that enter the posterior pituitary, the hormones enter the general circulation, whereas in the case of the neurons ending in the median eminence, the hormones enter the hypophyseal portal circulation (Figure 2.4).

The cell bodies of the neurons secreting TRH are located in and near the dorsomedial nuclei and perifornical area of the hypothalamus, and the axons of these cells end in the medial portion of the external layer of the median eminence. LHRH-secreting neurons have cell bodies in the preoptic and other portions of the hypothalamus and axons that end in

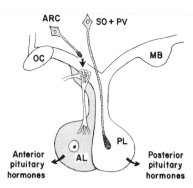

FIGURE 2.4   Diagrammatic summary of the secretion of hormones by hypothalamic neurons. Supraoptic and paraventricular neurons (SO + PV) release oxytocin and vasopressin into the general circulation in the posterior lobe of the pituitary (PL), whereas arcuate (ARC) and other neurons secrete hypophysiotropic hormones into the hypophyseal portal vessels with transport to the anterior lobe (AL). OC, optic chiasm; MB, mammillary body (from Rose & Ganong, 1976; reprinted by permission from Figure 1, page 88, Chapter 4 in Current Developments in Psychopharmacology, Volume 3 by W. B. Essman and L. Valzelli, Eds. Copyright 1976, Spectrum Publications, Inc., New York).

the lateral portions of the external layer of the median eminence. Somatostatin-secreting neurons have their cell bodies located in large part in the periventricular nuclei above the optic chiasm, and their axons terminate throughout the external layer of the median eminence. The dopamine that regulates prolactin secretion is produced by the tuberoinfundibular neurons (Figure 2.5), which have cell bodies in the arcuate nucleus of the hypothalamus and axons that terminate primarily in the lateral portions of the external layer of the median eminence.

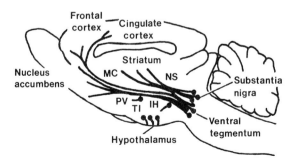

FIGURE 2.5   Dopaminergic systems in the brain. IH, incerto-hypothalamic system; MC, mesocortical system; NS, nigrostriatal system; PV, periventricular system; TI, tuberoinfundibular system (from Ganong, 1979).

Control of Hypophysiotropic Hormone Secretion

Secretion of the hypophysiotropic hormones is controlled in part by feedback of adenohypophyseal, adrenocortical, gonadal, and thyroid hormones and in part by afferent input from a variety of neural pathways. Neurons in these pathways undoubtedly secrete many different synaptic transmitters. However, the aminergic pathways have received the most attention, partly because they have been mapped in detail with immunocytochemical and fluorescent techniques, and partly because they are affected by drugs that are commonly used in medical and psychiatric practice. The aminergic inputs are dopaminergic, noradrenergic, adrenergic, and serotonergic (Ganong, 1979; Moore & Bloom, 1978; Moore & Bloom, 1979).

The dopaminergic neurons in the brain are shown diagrammatically in Figure 2.5. The periventricular and incerto-hypothalamic systems as well as the tubero-infundibular system may be involved in hormonal regulation (Weiner & Ganong, 1978). Dopaminergic neurons with cell bodies in the arcuate nucleus innervate the posterior lobe of the pituitary as well as the median eminence, but the role of dopamine in the regulation of the secretion of posterior pituitary hormones is unknown.

The noradrenergic neurons in the brain are shown diagrammatically in Figure 2.6, and the epinephrine-secreting neurons in Figure 2.7. The locus ceruleus system only innervates part of the hypothalamus, whereas the lateral tegmental system projects to all parts of the hypothalamus. The epinephrine-secreting cells also project to the hypothalamus. Noradrenergic discharge inhibits ACTH secretion and stimulates the secretion of LH, TSH, and growth hormone (Weiner & Ganong, 1978). However, at least in some instances, the role of the noradrenergic system is permissive rather than primary, with other mechanisms producing the actual increase in hormone secretion. The function of central epinephrine in the regulation of endocrine function is uncertain at present, but the adrenergic fibers are in an anatomical position to regulate endocrine function.

The serotonergic neurons in the brain are diagramed in Figure 2.8. There is a prominent serotonergic input to the suprachiasmatic nuclei, and these nuclei function as a biological clock, regulating endocrine and other circadian rhythms (Moore, 1978). Therefore, it is not surprising that drugs which modify serotonergic discharge alter endocrine rhythms (Weiner & Ganong, 1978). In addition, central release of serotonin stimulates prolactin secretion, apparently by stimulating the secretion of PRH.

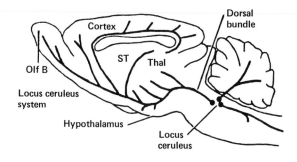

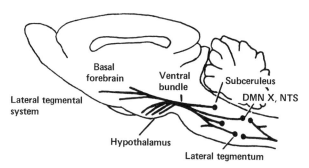

FIGURE 2.6   Noradrenergic systems in the brain. The locus ceruleus system is shown on top and the lateral tegmental system on the bottom. DMN X, dorsal motor nucleus of vagus; NTS, nucleus tractus solitarius; Olf B, olfactory bulb; ST, stria terminalis; Thal, thalamus (from Ganong, 1979).

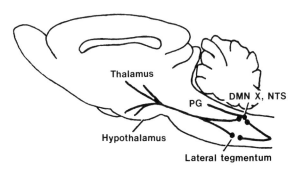

FIGURE 2.7   Epinephrine-secreting (adrenergic) neurons in the brain. See legend for Figure 2.6. PG, periaqueductal gray (from Ganong, 1979).

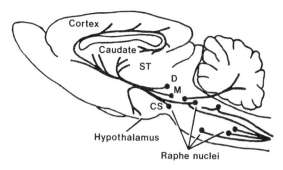

FIGURE 2.8   Serotonin-secreting neurons in the brain. D, M, CS, dorsal, medial, and central superior raphe nuclei; ST, stria terminalis (from Ganong, 1979).

Chemical Messengers that Are both Neurotransmitters and Hormones

An important discovery made possible by the availability of synthetic hypothalamic hormones and immunocytochemical techniques has been the demonstration that a single substance can be a neurotransmitter, a neural hormone, and a hormone secreted by gland cells. Somatostatin is a good example. This peptide was discovered in the median eminence of the hypothalamus, where it is clearly a neural hormone secreted into the hypophyseal portal vessels. Elsewhere in the brain, it is present in nerve endings and appears to function as a neurotransmitter. This is especially true in the substantia gelantinosa, where abundant somatostatin-positive granules are located in the endings of primary afferent neurons (Elde & Hökfelt, 1978). In addition, somatostatin is secreted along with substance P by primary afferent neurons in tissue culture (Mudge, Fischbach, & Leeman, 1977). The pancreas and gastrointestinal tract also contain somatostatin, but the peptide in these organs is in D cells, which are typical endocrine cells. Somatostatin is secreted into the general circulation from the gastrointestinal tract, and apparently plays an endocrine role in the regulation of gastrointestinal function (Schusdziarra *et al.*, 1980).

Another example is dopamine. There is abundant evidence that this substance is a neurotransmitter in the caudate nucleus and elsewhere. It is also a neural hormone that regulates prolactin secretion and is secreted into the hypophyseal portal circulation in the median eminence. In addition, dopamine is found in the circulating blood. Of the circulating dopamine, 30–50% is believed to be of adrenal medullary origin (Kvetňanský, Weise, & Kopin, 1979), and it is presumably released from gland cells in this organ. Circulating dopamine affects the circulation in the kidneys and other organs (Goldberg, 1972).

Norepinephrine is a neurotransmitter in the brain and a hormone secreted by the adrenal medulla. It also diffuses into the circulation from noradrenergic endings in various tissues, and in this sense, it is a neural hormone.

Epinephrine has not been shown to be a neural hormone, but it appears to be a transmitter in the brain, and it is the principal hormone in the adrenal medulla.

LHRH has not been demonstrated to be produced by gland cells, but it is a neural hormone secreted by neurons in the median eminence. In addition, evidence is accumulating that it is the neurotransmitter responsible for the late, slow excitatory postsynaptic potential (EPSP) in frog sympathetic ganglia (Jan, Jan, & Kuffler, 1979). The late, slow EPSP produced by electrical stimulation of preganglionic neurons can be exactly duplicated by injection of LHRH. In addition, a competitive antagonist of LHRH blocks the response to injected LHRH and to electrical stimulation. This discovery is important because the sympathetic ganglia represent a simple system in which the role of a peptide transmitter can be studied in detail.

TRH is clearly a neural hormone, but it is also present in nerve endings in many different parts of the brain (Elde & Hökfelt, 1978). In these locations, it probably functions as a neurotransmitter. TRH is also present in the gastrointestinal tract, although it is not known whether it is present in nerve or gland cells in this location (Morley, Garvin, Pekary, & Hershman, 1978).

Oxytocin and vasopressin, the archetypes of neural hormones, are also present in the endings of axons that project from the supraoptic and paraventricular nuclei to the nucleus tractus solitarius, other nuclei in the brain stem, and the intermediolateral gray column in the spinal cord (Kozlowski, Brownfield, & Hostetter, 1979; Swanson, 1977; Swanson & McKellar, 1979). It has not been proved that the peptides function as neurotransmitters in these locations, but on the basis of morphology, they probably do.

Somatostatin and TRH are by no means the only hormonal peptides common to the brain and the gastrointestinal tract. Vasoactive intestinal peptide (VIP) is present in gland cells in the gastrointestinal tract and in nerve endings in the brain. It is also found in nerves in many different peripheral tissues (Said, 1980). Cholecystokinin-pancreozymin (CCK) is secreted by gland cells in the gastrointestinal tract and appears to be a neurotransmitter in a variety of different locations in the brain. Enkephalins are found in neurons in the brain and in the gastrointestinal

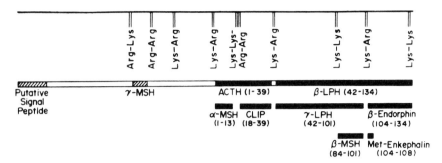

FIGURE 2.9 Diagrammatic representation of pro-opiocortin and its derivatives. CLIP, corticotropin-like intermediate lobe peptide. Numbers refer to the amino acid residues reading from the start of ACTH toward the C terminal. The Lys–Arg and similar bonds that are commonly hydrolyzed in prohormones are shown at the top (modified from Nakashini *et al.*, 1979).

tract. They are also found in the adrenal medulla (Schultzberg *et al.*, 1978), and there is evidence that metenkephalin is secreted by this gland (Clement-Jones *et al.*, 1980). Glucagon is present in neurons in the hypothalamus as well as in gland cells in the pancreas and the stomach (Vranik, personal communication, 1980), and a variety of other peptides have been found in the brain and the gastrointestinal tract (Said, 1980).

To make matters more complex, the hormones secreted by gland cells in the anterior lobe of the pituitary are also present in nerve endings in the brain (Krieger & Liotta, 1979). ACTH, β-LPH, and related hormones are formed in the pituitary from a large precursor molecule now often called pro-opiomelanocortin. The structure of this precursor molecule has been elucidated by use of recombinant DNA techniques (Figure 2.9). At its C terminal, this molecule has the sequence of β-LPH preceded by the sequence of ACTH (Nakashini *et al.*, 1979). In the secretion granules of the corticotrops in the anterior lobe of the pituitary, these two hormones are separated from the prohormone and secreted in equimolar amounts when the contents of the granules are extruded. In the intermediate lobe, processing proceeds further with the formation of β-endorphin, α-MSH, and two other peptides. ACTH and α-MSH are found in the brain as well as in the pituitary, and it seems clear that pro-opiomelanocortin is manufactured not only in the anterior pituitary but in the cell bodies of neurons located in the arcuate nucleus. The pro-opiomelanocortin-containing cells project to the thalamus, septum, and related areas near the diencephalon (Krieger & Liotta, 1979). Immunoreactive ACTH has also been would in gland cells in the gastric mucosa (Kendall & Orwoll, 1980), but its state and function in this latter location are unknown.

There is one report of prolactin-like activity in neurons (Fuxe, Hökfelt, Eneroth, Gustafsson, & Skett, 1976), and LH may be present as well (Emanuele, Kirsteins, & Lawrence, 1979; Brownfield, personal communication, 1980). Growth hormone activity has also been reported in the brain, and cells of the amygdala have been reported to make growth hormone in tissue culture (Pacold, Kirsteins, Hojvat, Lawrence, & Hagen, 1978).

It is worth noting that amines and peptides may mediate paracrine as well as neural and endocrine communication. Somatostatin inhibits the secretion of insulin and glucagon, and it may diffuse through the interstitial fluid from D cells to insulin-secreting and glucagon-secreting cells in the pancreatic islets (Orci & Unger, 1975). In the brain, many of the varicosities in terminals of amine-secreting cells are not associated with synaptic junctions, and norepinephrine, epinephrine, dopamine, and serotonin may diffuse through brain extracellular fluid to act on neurons that are some distance away (Descarries, Watkins, & Lapierre, 1977; Swanson, Connelly, & Hartman, 1978). A peptide which might function in a paracrine fashion in the brain is angiotensin II. This peptide increases the release of norepinephrine from hypothalamic tissue (Chevillard, Duchene, Pasquier, & Alexandre, 1979). All the components of the renin–angiotensin system are present in the brain, and spinal fluid contains renin substrate and angiotensin II (Ganong, Rudolph, & Zimmerman, 1979). However, paracrine communication is easy to postulate but hard to prove.

Conclusions

In summary, many different chemical messengers serve multiple functions (Table 2.1). This includes both peptides and catecholamines. The same substance can be secreted in one location as a nerve transmitter mediating synaptic communication, in another as a neural hormone produced by neurons, and in a third as a typical endocrine product secreted by gland cells. Therefore, it seems appropriate to think in terms of a neuroendocrine integrating system with morphological specialization rather than rigidly separate nervous and endocrine systems. The phylogenetic evidence fits this view; when nervous systems first evolved in hydra and sponges, the cells in them were both endocrine and neural (Said, 1980). In more complex animals, many neurons are specialized for synaptic communication, and many endocrine products come from typical gland cells. However, there are numerous intermediate situations, as outlined above. There is even some degree of interconvertibility between endocrine and gland cells. For example, pheochrom-

TABLE 2.1
Neuroendocrine Messengers: Substances that Function as Neurotransmitters, Neural Hormones, and Classical Hormones

	Neurotransmitter (present in nerve endings)	Hormone secreted by neurons	Hormone secreted by endocrine cells
Dopamine	+	+	+?
Norepinephrine	+	+	+
Epinephrine	+		+
Somatostatin	+	+	+
LHRH	+	+	
TRH	+	+	
Oxytocin	+	+	
Vasopressin	+	+	
VIP	+		+
CCK	+		+
Glucagon	+		+
Enkephalins	+		+
Pro-opiocortin derivatives	+		+
Other anterior pituitary hormones	+?		+

ocytoma cells from the adrenal medulla grow neurites when exposed to nerve growth factor in tissue culture (Bradshaw, 1978). Thus, it seems appropriate to think in terms of neuroendocrine communication with interactions and subspecialization along a spectrum from neural to endocrine tissue.

References

Ajika, K. (1980). Relation between catecholaminergic neurons and hypothalamic hormone-containing neurons in the hypothalamus. In L. Martini & W. F. Ganong (Eds.), *Frontiers in neuroendocrinology* (Vol. 6, pp. 1–32). New York: Raven Press.

Bradshaw, R. W. (1978). Nerve growth factor. *Annual Review of Biochemistry, 47*, 191–216.

Brownstein, M. J., Russell, J. T., & Gainer, H. (1980). Synthesis, transport, and release of posterior pituitary hormones. *Science, 207*, 373–378.

Chevillard, C., Duchene, N., Pasquier, R., & Alexandre, J-M. (1979). Relation of the centrally evoked pressor effect of angiotensin II to central noradrenaline in the rabbit. *European Journal of Pharmacology, 58*, 203–206.

Clement-Jones, V., Lowry, P. J., Pullan, P. T., Corder, R., Rees, L. H., & Besser, G. M. (1980). Purification and chemical characterisation of methionine enkephalin from a human adrenal pheocromocytoma. Program and Abstracts, *Sixth International Congress of Endocrinology* (p. 528). Melbourne, Australia.

Descarries, L., Watkins, K. C., & Lapierre, Y. (1977). Noradrenergic axon terminals in the cerebral cortex of rat. III Topometric ultrastructural analysis. *Brain Research, 133,* 197–222.

Elde, R., & Hökfelt, T. (1978). Distribution of hypothalamic hormones and other peptides in the brain. In W. F. Ganong & L. Martini (Eds.), Frontiers in neuroendocrinology (Vol. 5, pp. 1–33). New York: Raven Press.

Emanuele, N., Kirsteins, L., & Lawrence, A. M. (1979). Brain LH: Localization, response to hypophysectomy and ovariectomy. *Clinical Research, 27,* 250. (abstract).

Fuxe, K., Hökfelt, T., Eneroth, P., Gustafsson, J-A., & Skett, P. (1976). Prolactin-like immunoreactivity: Localization in nerve terminals in rat hypothalamus. *Science, 196,* 899–900.

Ganong, W. F. (1979). *Review of medical physiology* (9th ed.). Los Altos, CA: Lange Medical Publications.

Ganong, W. F., Rudolph, C. D., & Zimmermann, H. (1979). Neuroendocrine components in the regulation of blood pressure and renin secretion. *Hypertension, 1,* 207–218.

Goldberg, L. I. (1972). Cardiovascular and renal actions of dopamine: Potential clinical applications. *Pharmacology Review, 24,* 1–29.

Jan, Y. N., Jan, L. Y., & Kuffler, S. W. (1979). A peptide as a possible transmitter in sympathetic ganglia of the frog. *Proceedings of the National Academy of Sciences, USA, 76,* 1501–1505.

Kendall, J., & Orwoll, E. (1980). Anterior pituitary hormones in the brain and other extrapituitary sites. In L. Martini & W. F. Ganong (Eds.), Frontiers in neuroendocrinology (Vol. 6, pp. 33–65). New York: Raven Press.

Kozlowski, G. P., Brownfield, M. S., & Hostetter, G. (1979). Neurosecretory supply to extrahypothalamic structures: choroid plexus, circumventricular organs, and limbic system. In W. Bargmann, A. Oksche, A. Palenov, & B. Scharrer (Eds.), *Neurosecretion and Neuroendocrine Activity* (pp. 217–227). Berlin: Springer Verlag.

Krieger, D. T., & Liotta, A. S. (1979). Pituitary hormones in the brain: Where, how, and why? *Science 205,* 366–372.

Kvetňanský, R., Weise, V. K., & Kopin, I. J. (1979). The origins of plasma epinephrine, norepinephrine and dopamine levels in stressed rats. In E. Usdin, I. J. Kopin, & J. Barchas (Eds.), *Catecholamines: Basic and clinical frontiers* (Vol. 1, pp. 684–686). Oxford, England: Pergamon Press.

Moore, R. Y. (1978). Central neural control of circadian rhythms. In W. F. Ganong & L. Martini (Eds.), Frontiers in neuroendocrinology (Vol. 5, pp. 185–206). New York: Raven Press.

Moore, R. Y., & Bloom, F. E. (1978). Central catecholamine neuron systems: Anatomy and physiology of the dopamine systems. *Annual Review of Neuroscience, 1,* 129–169.

Moore, R. Y., & Bloom, F. E. (1979). Central catecholamine neuron systems: Anatomy and physiology of the norepinephrine and epinephrine systems. *Annual Review of Neuroscience, 2,* 113–168.

Morley, J. E., Garvin, T. J., Pekary, A. E., & Hershman, J. M. (1978). Thyrotropin-releasing hormone in the gastrointestinal tract. *Biochemical Biophysical Research Communications, 79,* 314–318.

Mudge, A. W., Fischbach, G. D., & Leeman, S. E. (1977). The release of immunoreactive substance P and somatostatin from dissociated cell cultures. *Seventh Annual Meeting of The Society for Neuroscience:* Abstract 1306; p. 410.

Nakashini, S., Inoue, A., Kita, I., Nakamura, M., Chang, A. C. Y., Cohen, S. N., & Numa, S. (1979). Nucleotide sequence of cloned cDNA for bovine corticotropin-β-lipotropin precursor. *Nature 278,* 423–427.

Orci, L., & Unger, R. H. (1975). Functional subdivision of islets of Langerhans and possible role of D cells. *Lancet II,* 1243–1244.

Pacold, S. J., Kirsteins, L., Hojvat, S., Lawrence, A. M., & Hagen, T. C. (1978). Biologically active pituitary hormones in rat brain amygdaloid nucleus. *Science 199,* 804–806.

Rose, J. C., & Ganong, W. F. (1976). Neurotransmitter regulation of pituitary secretion. In W. F. Essman & L. Valzelli (Eds.), *Current developments in psychopharmacology* (pp. 87–123). Holliswood, NY: Spectrum Publications.

Said, S. I. (1980). Peptides common to the nervous system and the gastrointestinal tract. In L. Martini & W. F. Ganong (Eds.), Frontiers in neuroendocrinology (Vol. 6, pp. 293–331). New York: Raven Press.

Scharrer, E., & Scharrer, B. (1954). Hormones produced by neurosecretory cells. *Recent Progress in Hormone Research, 10,* 183–240.

Schultzberg, M., Lundberg, J. M., Hökfelt, T., Terenius, L., Brandt, J., Elde, R., & Goldstein, M. (1978). Enkephalin-like immunoreactivity in gland cells and nerve terminals of the adrenal medulla. *Neuroscience, 3,* 1169–1186.

Schusdziarra, V., Zyznar, E., Rouiller, D., Boden, G., Brown, J. C., Arimura, A., & Unger, R. H. (1980). Splanchnic somatostatin: A hormonal regulator of nutrient homeostasis. *Science, 207,* 530–532.

Swanson, L. W. (1977). Immunohistochemical evidence for a neurophysin-containing autonomic pathway arising in the paraventricular nucleus of the hypothalamus. *Brain Research, 128,* 346–353.

Swanson, L. W., Connelly, M. A., & Hartman, B. K. (1978). Further studies on the fine structure of the adrenergic innervation of the hypothalamus. *Brain Research, 151,* 165–174.

Swanson, L. W., & McKellar, S. (1979). The distribution of oxytocin- and neurophysin-stained fibers in the spinal cord of the rat and monkey. *Journal of Comparative Neurology, 188,* 87–106.

Weiner, R. I., & Ganong, W. F. (1978). The role of brain monoamines and histamine in the regulation of anterior pituitary secretion. *Physiological Review, 58,* 905–976.

3

Stress, Corticotropin-Releasing Factor, and Behavior

GEORGE F. KOOB

The Stress Response

After nearly 30 years of intense effort, a corticotropin-releasing factor (CRF) with great potency and intrinsic activity for *in vitro* and *in vivo* stimulation of adrenocorticotropic hormone (ACTH) and β-endorphin has been characterized and synthesized by Vale and associates (Vale, Spiess, Rivier, & Rivier, 1981). A 41-residue peptide, CRF is presumably the long sought after hypothalamic neurohumor with the specific function of releasing ACTH from the anterior pituitary, and thus may be considered the final common pathway for the neurohumoral control of ACTH.

The significance of the chemical identification of CRF can perhaps be best understood in terms of classical stress theory. Initially formulated by Selye in 1936, the general concepts of stress theory have undergone some refinement over the past 40 years. Nevertheless, a generally accepted definition of *stress* is that "stress is the nonspecific (common) result of any demand upon the body" (Selye, 1980), and probably the most reliable indication that a state of stress exists is variation in the production of ACTH. Internal or external demands are conveyed in the form of stimuli to the anterior pituitary via neurohumoral means (presumably CRF), and the pituitary responds with a secretion of ACTH. ACTH, in turn, stimulates the adrenal cortex to secret glucocorticoids, which have widespread effects on metabolism such as gluconeogenesis, hyperinsulinemia, lysis of lymphoid tissue, increased gastric secretion, and reduced inflammatory and antibody responses. These physiological

PERSPECTIVES ON BEHAVIORAL MEDICINE, Vol. 2
Neuroendocrine Control and Behavior

changes in response to increased hypothalamic–pituitary action are paralleled by alterations in behavior that have been associated with increases in alertness and attention (De Wied, 1977).

Efforts to identify the antecedent physiological mechanisms of the hypothalamic–pituitary "stress-response" have defined two means by which the pituitary can be activated. In one, systemic stress, ACTH is released by a direct action on the pituitary, presumably by a direct hormonal action on the median eminence; alternatively, a neurogenic stress can activate ACTH release by an indirect action on the pituitary via neural connections. This distinction is based on the observation that complete or partial hypothalamic deafferentation or localized hypothalamic lesions can abolish or reduce the adrenocortical response to photic, acoustic, olfactory and sciatic nerve stimulation, whereas such lesions do not alter the adrenocortical response to systemic stresses such as ether stress or injection of epinephrine (Conforti & Feldman, 1976; Feldman & Conforti, 1977, 1980a, 1980b). Indeed, it is through these CNS pathways to the hypothalamus that, presumably, the adrenocortical response is triggered by psychological factors, and may also be the basis for the autonomic arousal associated with anxiety. Behavioral evidence for this interaction is presented in the next section.

There is, however, an alternative means by which behavioral or physiological responses to stress or anxiety might be mediated by the hypothalamic-pituitary system in an organism, that is, via direct neurotropic action of CRF in the CNS itself. Thus, just as pathways project to the hypothalamus from the limbic areas to activate, via CRF, the pituitary–adrenal axis, so might CRF feedback to these same areas mediate appropriate behavioral responses to stress. Behavioral evidence for a direct neurotropic action for CRF is discussed in the section, "Direct Neurotropic Actions of CRF."

Behavioral Effects of ACTH

Activation of this hypothalamic–pituitary system in an organism has long been associated with the regulation of behavior, particularly behavior involving stressful situations such as behavior motivated by shock. For example, early work showed that completely hypophysectomized rats were severely retarded in the acquisition of active and passive avoidance (Anderson, Winard, & Tam, 1968; Applezweig & Baudry, 1955; De Wied, 1964). Also, ACTH administered during acquisition of an avoidance task delayed extinction of the learned response in adrenalectomized rats (Miller & Ogawa, 1962; Murphy & Miller, 1955). Later, De Wied demonstrated that the rapid extinction produced by removal of the posterior and intermediate lobe of the pituitary could be reversed by ACTH and related peptides (De Wied, 1965). This work established that ACTH and ACTH analogs not only influenced adaptive behavior through actions of the adrenal hormones, but they also exerted behavioral influences which were independent of endocrine activity (De Wied, 1980). Subsequent work, however, has established that ACTH and ACTH analogs have little effect on the acquisition of learned responses in normal animals (Bohus, Nyakas, and Endroczi, 1968; Guth, Levine, and Seward, 1971; Hennessy, Cohen and Rosen, 1973; Miller and Caul, 1973), but rather, they produce profound effects on the extinction of learned responses no matter what the valence of the motivation (Bohus, Gispen, & De Wied, 1973; Bohus, Hendrickx, Van Kolfschoten, & Krediet, 1975; De Wied, 1966, 1969, 1974; Garrud, Gray, & De Wied, 1974; Gray, 1971; Greven & De Wied, 1973; Guth et al., 1971; Kastin et al., 1973; Levine & Jones, 1965; Levine, Smotherman, & Hennessy, 1977; Lissak & Bohus, 1972; Sandman, Kastin, & Schally, 1973; Sandman et al., 1972). This is generally interpreted as an effect on attentional processes or as "temporary increases in the motivational significance of environmental cues" (De Wied, 1980); others have suggested that ACTH produces "a more general change in the ability of an animal to alter its behavior in response to unpredictable changes in reinforcement contingencies" (Gray & Garrud, 1977); or ACTH "enhances fear-motivated responding" (Weiss, McEwen, Silva, and Kalkut, 1969). Indeed, there are reports of increases in emotionality with ACTH 4-10 administration (File, 1979).

These above effects appear to be a direct effect of ACTH, itself, on some neural substrate, not yet identified. Where this substrate is located and how pituitary ACTH normally interacts with it is unknown. Some researchers even claim evidence for extra-pituitary ACTH-like material in the brain (Krieger, Liotta and Brownstein, 1977). It will be of some interest to determine whether systemic CRF can mimic these effects, and how much of the behavioral activation of centrally administered CRF can be attributed to an activation of the pituitary–adrenal axis. In fact, dexamethasone pretreatment can produce an attenuation of taste aversion learning (Levine et al., 1977), and this could reflect a down regulation of central or pituitary CRF functions.

Direct Neurotropic Actions of Corticotropin-Releasing Factor

CRF injected intracerebroventricularly (i.c.v.) produces a prolonged elevation of plasma norepinephrine, epinephrine, glucagon, and glucose in rats and dogs (Brown et al., 1982a, 1982b, 1982c). CRF (i.c.v.)

also increases heart rate and blood pressure in rats and dogs (Brown *et al.*, 1982c; Fisher *et al.*, 1982) and suppresses gastric acid secretion (Taché *et al.*, 1983; Taché & Gunion, 1985). Both the metabolic and cardiovascular changes are reversed by chlorisondamine, an autonomic ganglionic blocker, but not by angiotensin or vasopressin antagonists. Hypophysectomy or adrenalectomy also does not block these CRF-induced changes (Fisher *et al.*, 1982). Thus, CRF appears to have a direct neurotropic action in activating the sympathetic nervous system, eventually through an action on peripheral catecholamine systems, an activation observed with many kinds of stress (Brown *et al.*, 1982c).

CRF injected i.c.v. also produces a profound dose-dependent activation of the electroencephalogram (EEG) (Ehlers, Hendrickson, Bloom, Rivier, & Vale, 1982). At a dose as low as 0.0015 nmol, CRF produced increases of 6 to 8 Hz activity in the hippocampus. Doses of 0.015 to 0.15 nmol produced a much longer lasting activation of EEG, and after a 2-hour delay some interictal spikes occurred in the amygdala and hippocampus. Higher doses (1.5–3.75 nmol) were characterized by consistent amygdala interictal spikes and afterdischarges and, after a delay of 4 to 7 hours, some motor seizures. These seizures developed over time in a manner not unlike those produced by amygdala "kindling" paradigms.

At the more cellular level, CRF has been shown to produce a pronounced depolarization and excitation of hippocampal pyramidal cells (Aldenhoff, Gruol, & Siggins, 1983). Using an *in vitro* hippocampal slice preparation, CRF applied by superfusion, depolarized by 3 to 12 mV, all CA1 and CA3 cells tested. This depolarization was accompanied by marked increases in action potential discharge, but no apparent decrease in input resistance. Intracellular recordings demonstrated that the excitation arose from reduction of the afterhyperpolarizations that followed bursts of spikes (Siggins *et al.*, 1985). It was hypothesized that CRF may alter potassium conductance either directly or via a change in calcium conductances. These results may provide a cellular basis for the EEG changes observed following i.c.v. injection.

The autonomic and electrophysiological activation produced by i.c.v. injection of CRF is paralleled by a behavioral activation that is dose and situation dependent. CRF injected i.c.v. in rats produces a dose-dependent locomotor activation (Sutton, Koob, Le Moal, Rivier, & Vale, 1982; see Figure 3.1). This activation, particularly at lower doses (15–150 pmol), is characterized by increased locomotion and sniffing, grooming, and rearing—behavior consistent with a general behavioral arousal; at higher doses (≥1500 pmol of CRF) more bizarre behavioral effects were observed, for example, elevated walking and repetitive locomotion such as moving forwards and backwards in a straight line and pawing rapidly

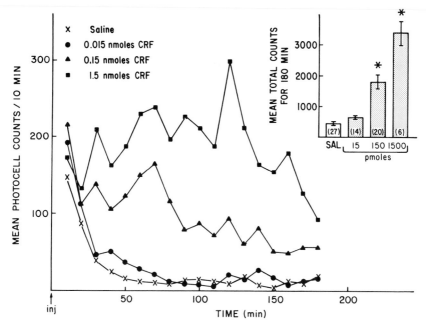

FIGURE 3.1   Locomotor response after i.c.v. infusions of 0.1, 1, and 10 μg corresponding to 0.015, 0.15, and 1.5 nmol of CRF, respectively. Ordinate refers to total photocell counts for each 10-min period of a 3-hour test. *Significantly different from saline, and from each other. Neuman–Keuls test $p < .05$, following ANOVA. Mean total counts for 180 min represent average ± SEM (figure from Sutton *et al.*, 1982; reprinted by permission from *Nature, 297,* 331–333. Copyright © 1982 Macmillan Journals Limited).

against the sides of the cage. These changes are paralleled by a marked activation of the EEG described above for such doses (Ehlers *et al.*, 1982).

Although other peptides such as the endorphins and ACTH have been shown to produce increases in spontaneous behavioral activity, the nature of the CRF response differed substantially from the response observed with these other peptides. For example, CRF does not produce the initial depressant phase followed by bursts of locomotor activity that characterizes i.c.v. injections of opioid peptides (Segal *et al.*, 1979), and the locomotor activation caused by CRF is not antagonized by the opiate antagonist naloxone, or by low doses of the dopamine receptor antagonist alpha flupenthixol (Koob *et al.*, 1984). Nor is this activation reversed by 6 hydroxydopamine lesions of the region of the nucleus accumbens, lesions that reverse the locomotor-stimulating effects of indirect sympathomimetics (Swerdlow & Koob, 1985). Nor has ACTH, itself, been reported to increase activity in various tests of activity and exploration. As described above, peripheral ACTH reduced exploration in a novel environment but did not alter locomotor activity (File, 1978), whereas i.c.v. injection of ACTH 1-24 markedly reduced locomotion (Isaacson & Green, 1978; File & Clarke, 1981). In fact, the behavioral response to i.c.v. injection of ACTH has been characterized as a stretching–yawning syndrome in which the rats display excessive grooming behavior interrupted by bouts of stretching and yawning (Dunn, Green, & Isaacson, 1979; Ferrari, Gessa, & Vargiu, 1963; Gessa, Pisano, Vargiu, Crabai, & Ferrari, 1967; Gispen, Weigant, Greven, & De Wied, 1975; Rees, Dunn, & Juvane, 1976). CRF, in contrast, did not produce the stretching–yawning syndrome, but at the lower doses appeared to exaggerate the normal response of the rats when initially exposed to the photocell-cage environment.

This activation appears to be independent of the pituitary–adrenal system in that hypophysectomized rats chronically treated with rat growth hormone so that they gained 3.5 g/day showed consistent and reliable increases in activity in the photocell cages following i.c.v. administration of CRF, similar to the increases observed in sham-operated animals (Eaves et al., 1985).

Perhaps of more importance for the conceptualization of CRF as a peptide involved in the organism's behavioral response to stress are the experiments showing that CRF can potentiate the effects of exposure to a novel, presumably aversive, environment. Rats tested in a novel, open field following i.c.v. injection of doses of CRF (0.0015–0.15 nmol) show responses that are consistent with an increased "emotionality" or increased sensitivity to the stressful aspects of the situation. Here rats show decreases in locomotion and rearing (see Figure 3.2). In this open field test, a typical saline-injected rat will rapidly circle the outer squares of the open field during the first 3–4 min of the 5-min test. During the last 1–2 min of the test, these saline-injected animals make some forays into the center of the open field, usually accompanied by rearing on the hind legs. Typically, a rat injected with 0.15 nmol of CRF and placed 60 min later in the open field moves hesitantly to the outer squares and then either circles the open field remaining close to the floor or remains in one of the corners grooming or hesitantly moving forwards and backwards.

Similar results have been observed in an open field, conflict test (Britton, Koob, Rivier, & Vale, 1982) previously shown to be sensitive to both anxiolytic drugs as well as treatments which increase neophobia (Britton & Britton, 1981). Here, rats were deprived of food for 24 hours and then placed in a highly illuminated circular open field where a single food pellet was secured to a pedestal in the center of the open field. CRF, again injected one hour prior to the test in doses of 1.5 to 150 pmol,

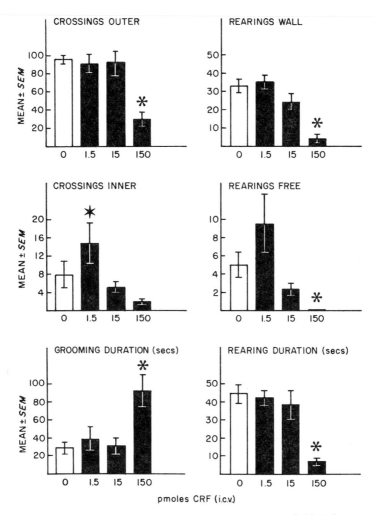

FIGURE 3.2   Effects of CRF (i.c.v.) on behavior of rats in an open field. Values represent mean ± SEM of the total number of observations during the 5-min test. 1.5, 15, and 150 pmol of CRF correspond to 0.01, 0.1, and 1.0 μg/rat. *Significantly different from saline injected rats, Newman–Keuls test $p < .05$ following ANOVA (adapted from Sutton *et al.*, 1982).

produced a dose-dependent change in behavior consistent with an in-crease in the aversiveness of the situation. CRF caused decreases in the number of approaches to the food pellet, decreases in the amount of food eaten per approach to the food pedestal, and an increase in groom-ing (Britton *et al.*, 1982). These results are the opposite to those observed with benzodiazepine treatment and are consistent with the hypothesis that CRF augments the stressfulness of a novel environment.

In a more classical operant test of "anxiety," a conflict test, CRF produced a significant decrease in punished responding, an effect opposite to that observed with benzodiazepines, and this "anxiogenic" effect was reversed by concomitant treatment with a benzodiazepine (Thatcher-Britton *et al.*, 1985). However, this increased sensitivity to aversive events was not paralleled by an increased sensitivity to pain. CRF also decreases food intake and muscimol-, norepinephrine-, dynorphin-, and insulin-induced feeding, effects attributed to a stress-related supression of food intake (Levine *et al.*, 1982; Morley, Levine, & Rowland, 1983).

A wealth of empirical evidence and theoretical treatises suggests that the acquisition of learned behavior can vary with the level of activation or "arousal" of the animal. For example, correlations have been obtained between independent measures of arousal such as exploratory behavior, EEG, and galvanic skin response and the speed of acquisition of a response (Berlyne, 1960). In addition, Berlyne (1960) has proposed that both animals and man strive to maintain intermediate amounts of arousal potential, and that stimuli that evoke such levels of arousal will be pleasant, and stimuli that evoke zero or too much arousal will be unpleasant. It follows that optimal learning will correspond to these optimal levels of arousal. Indeed, more recent treatments of this theoretical issue have centered on arousal as the intervening variable in the incentive–motivation required for all learning (Killeen, Hanson, & Osbourne, 1978). Given that CRF has activating or arousal properties, it also follows that a reflection of this activation would be the ability of an animal to acquire a learned response. Our preliminary results provide support for this hypothesis. CRF administered prior to the daily acquisition of an appetitively motivated visual discrimination task significantly improved acquisition (Koob *et al.*, 1982; see also Koob & Bloom, 1985).

At higher doses, CRF can clearly disrupt behavior. Rhesus monkeys injected i.c.v. with 180 μg of CRF showed behavioral changes associated with arousal but in their home cages withdrew into a combination of huddling and lying down (Kalin, Shelton, Kraemer, & McKinney, 1983). Other behaviorally disruptive effects of CRF at higher doses include a suppressive effect on female sexual behavior (Sirinathsinghji, Rees, Rivier, & Vale, 1983).

Anatomical evidence is also consistent with the behavioral and physiological evidence for a direct neurotropic action of CRF. As expected, immunoreactive fibers staining for CRF were found in rat, sheep, dog, and monkey hypothalamus using antibodies to ovine CRF (Bloom, Battenburg, Rivier, & Vale, 1982; Bugnon, Fellman, Gouget, & Cardot,

1982; Olschowka, O'Donohue, Mueller, & Jacobowitz, 1982; Paull et al., 1982). Cell bodies located in the parvocellular part of the paraventricular nucleus project a dense fiber plexus to the median eminence and other hypothalamic and mesencephalic loci. Subsequent work using the ovine antibody on untreated sheep brain (Battenberg, Bloom, Rivier, & Vale, 1982) and on colchicine-treated rat brain (Swanson, Sawchencko, Rivier, & Vale, 1983) has revealed this same hypothalamic–median eminence projection and a much more extensive extra-hypothalamic distribution. CRF-stained cells were also found in the central nucleus of the amygdala, bed nucleus of the stria terminalis, parabrachial nucleus, laterodorsal tegmental nucleus, substantia inominata, and some neocortical areas, and a few rare cells were observed in the hippocampus. The most densely stained collections of CRF fibers were seen in the median eminence and neurohypophysis. High density was also seen in the medial preoptic area, central and dorsal medial nuclei of the amygdala, the substantia inominata, and the parabrachial nuclei. Thus, the majority of CRF-stained cell groups and pathways are associated predominantly with limbic parts of the telencephalon, with the hypothalamus and brainstem. It appears that a system of CRF-stained pathways interrelates all groups in the basal forebrain, pons, and medulla that are involved in the integration of autonomic and neuroendocrine responses (Sawchenko & Swanson, 1985; Swanson, Sawchenko, Rivier, & Vale, 1983).

Summary

CRF injected directly into the brain ventricular system produces a pronounced behavioral activation. In a familiar photocell-cage environment, CRF increases activity, and at high doses (1500 pmol) it produces bizarre abnormal behavior. In novel, stressful environments, such as open field tests, CRF produces behavioral effects consistent with an increase in the emotionality of the situation, and in a conflict test, CRF produces decreases in punished responding. Finally, CRF can improve acquisition of appetitively motivated tasks, but at higher doses can disrupt behavior.

These results describing neuronal activation, sympathetic activation, EEG arousal, general behavioral activation, and stress-enhancing actions all suggest a possible role for CRF in a fundamental activating system. The functional significance of this system may have developed as a means for an organism to mobilize not only the pituitary–adrenal system but also the CNS in response to environmental challenge. Indeed, the preliminary results in our laboratory suggest that treatment with CRF can improve learning in both aversively and appetitively motivated tasks (see above). Clearly, a hypothetical CNS activation system definitively linked to the pituitary–adrenal system that can improve behavioral performance at low levels of output but attenuate behavioral performance at high levels of output would be of certain survival value. It is not difficult either to imagine a possible role for such a system in clinical disorders such as anxiety, affective disorders, and other psychopathology.

The following summarizes CRF actions:
1. Hypothalamic Pituitary Axis
   a. potent stimulation of the secretion of ACTH
   b. potent stimulation of the secretion of other proopiomelanocortin products such as β-endorphin
2. Autonomic Nervous System
   a. elevation of plasma epinephrine and norepinephrine concentrations
   b. stimulation of blood pressure and heart rate
   c. production of hyperglycemia
   d. suppression of gastric acid secretion
3. Limbic System
   a. production of cellular, electroencephalographic and behavioral activation
   b. improvement in learning
   c. increased responsiveness to stress, including "anxiogenic-like" effects
   d. behavioral pathology at high doses, including disruption of sexual behavior, increased aggressive behavior, and behavioral withdrawal

Acknowledgments

The author gratefully acknowledges the technical assistance of Eva Alwerud, Mary-Ruth Eaves, Janet Morgan, and Jonathan Scheimer in the experiments outlined in this chapter. The author also acknowledges his collaborators in this work: Wylie Vale, Jean Rivier, Richard Sutton, Don Britton, Neal Swerdlow, Karen Thatcher-Britton, Michel Le Moal, and Floyd Bloom. I gratefully thank Nancy Callahan for manuscript assistance.

References

Aldenhoff, J. B., Gruol, D. L., & Siggins, G. R. (1983). Corticotropin releasing factor decreases postburst hyperpolarizations and excites hippocampal neurons. *Science 221*, 875–877.

Anderson, D. C., Winard, W., & Tam, T. (1968). Adrenocorticotrophic hormone and acquisition of a passive avoidance response. *Journal of Comparative and Physiological Psychology, 66,* 497–499.

Applezweig, M. H. & Baudry, F. D. (1955). The pituitary–adrenocortical system in avoidance learning. *Psychological Report, 1,* 417–420.

Battenberg, E. L. F., Bloom, F. E., Rivier, J., & Vale, W. (1982). Corticotropin releasing factor (CRF): Immunoreactive neurons and fibers in rat and primate hypothalamus. *Neurosciences Abstract, 8,* 110.

Berlyne, D. E. (1960). *Conflict arousal and curiosity.* New York: McGraw-Hill.

Bloom, F. E., Battenberg, E. L. F., Rivier, J., & Vale, W. (1982). Corticotropin releasing factor (CRF): Immunoreactive neurones and fibers in rat hypothalamus. *Regulatory Peptides, 4,* 43–48.

Bohus, B., Gispen, W. H., & De Wied, D. (1973). Effect of lysine vasopressin and ACTH 4-10 on conditioned avoidance behavior of hypophysectomized rats. *Neuroendocrinology, 11,* 137–143.

Bohus, B., Henrickx, H. H. L., van Kolfschoten, A. A., & Krediet, T. G. (1975). Effect of ACTH 4-10 on copulatory and sexually motivated approach behavior in the male rat. In M. Sandler & G. L. Gessa (Eds.), *Sexual behavior: Pharmacology and biochemistry* (pp. 269–275). New York: Raven Press.

Bohus, B., Nyakas, C. S., & Endroczi, E. (1968). Effects of adrenocorticotrophic hormone on avoidance behavior of intact and adrenalectomized rats. *International Journal of Neuropharmacology, 7,* 307–314.

Brito, G. N. O., Thomas, G. J., Gingold, S. J., & Gash, D. M. (1981). Behavioral characteristics of vasopressin-deficit rats (Brattleboro Strain). *Brain Research Bulletin, 6,* 71–75.

Britton, D. R. & Britton, K. T. (1981). A sensitive open field measure of anxiolytic drug activity. *Pharmacology, Biochemistry and Behavior, 15,* 577–582.

Britton, D. R., Koob, G. F., Rivier, J., & Vale, W. (1982). Intraventricular corticotropin-releasing factor enhances behavioral effects of novelty. *Life Sciences, 31,* 363–367.

Brown, M. R., Fisher, L. A., Rivier, J., Speiss, J., Rivier, C., & Vale, W. (1982a). Corticotropin-releasing factor: Effects on the sympathetic nervous system and oxygen consumption. *Life Sciences, 30,* 207–210.

Brown, M. R., Fisher, L. A., Spiess, J., Rivier, J., Rivier, C., & Vale, W. (1982b). Comparison of the biologic actions of corticotropin-releasing factor and sauvagine. *Regulatory Peptides, 4*(2), 107–114.

Brown, M. R., Fisher, L. A., Spiess, J., Rivier, C., Rivier, J., & Vale, W. (1982c). Corticotropin-releasing factor: Actions on the sympathetic nervous system and metabolism. *Endocrinology, 111*(3), 928–931.

Bugnon, C., Fellman, D., Gouget, A., & Cardot, J. (1982). Immunocytochemical detection of the CRF-containing neurons in the rat brain. *Comptes Rendus, 294,* 279–284.

Conforti, N. & Feldman, S. (1976). Effects of dorsal fornix section and hippocampectomy on adrenocortical responses to sensory stimulation in rats. *Neuroendocrinology, 22,* 1–7.

De Wied, D. (1964). Influence of anterior pituitary on avoidance learning and escape behavior. *American Journal of Physiology, 207,* 255–259.

De Wied, D. (1965). The influence of the posterior and intermediate lobe of the pituitary and pituitary peptides on the maintenance of a conditioned avoidance response in rats. *International Journal of Neuropharmacology, 4,* 157–167.

De Wied, D. (1966). Inhibitory effect of ACTH and related peptides on extinction of conditioned avoidance behavior in rats. *Proceedings of Experimental Biology and Medicine, 122,* 28–32.

De Wied, D. (1969). Effects of peptide hormones on behavior. In W. E. Ganong & L. Martini (Eds.), *Frontiers in neuroendocrinology* (pp. 97–140). New York/London: Oxford University Press.

De Wied, D. (1974). Pituitary-adrenal system hormones and behavior. In F. G. Schmitt & F. G. Worden (Eds.), *The neurosciences. Third study program* (pp. 653–666). Cambridge, MA: MIT Press.

De Wied, D. (1977). Behavioral effects of neuropeptides related to ACTH, MSH and β-LPH. In D. Krieger & W. Ganong (Eds.), *ACTH and related peptides: Structure, regulation and action* (pp. 263–274). *Annals of New York Academy of Sciences.*

De Wied, D. (1980). Pituitary-adrenal system hormones and behavior. In H. Seyle (Ed.), *Selye's guide to stress research* (Vol. 1, pp. 252–279). New York: Van Nostrand Reinhold.

Dunn, A. J., Green, E. J., & Isaacson, R. L. (1979). Intracerebral ACTH mediates novelty-induced grooming in the rat. *Science, 203,* 281–283.

Eaves, M., Thatcher-Britton, K., Rivier, J., Vale, W., & Koob, G. F. (1985). Effects of corticotropin releasing factor on locomotor activity in hypophysectomized rats. *Peptides,* in press.

Ehlers, C. L., Henriksen, S. J., Bloom, F. E., Rivier, J., & Vale, W. W. (1983). Corticotropin releasing factor produces increases in brain excitability and convulsive seizures in rats. *Brain Research, 278,* 332–336.

Feldman, S. & Conforti, N. (1977). Adrenocortical responses to olfactory stimulation in rats with partial hypothalamic deafferentiations and lesions. *Neuroendrinology, 24,* 162–268.

Feldman, S. & Conforti, N. (1980a). Inhibition of adrenocortical responses following olfactory stimulation in rats with stria terminalis lesions. *Neuroscience, 5,* 1323–1329.

Feldman, S. & Conforti, N. (1980b). Participation of the dorsal hippocampus in the glucocorticoid feedback effect on adrenocortical activity. *Neuroendocrinology, 30,* 52–55.

Ferrari, W., Gessa, G. L., & Vargiu, Z. (1963). Behavioral effects induced by intracisternally injected ACTH and MSH. *Annals of New York Academy of Sciences, 104,* 330–345.

File, S. E. (1978). ACTH but not corticosterone impairs habituation and reduces exploration. *Pharmacology, Biochemistry and Behavior, 9,* 161–166.

File, S. (1979). Effects of ACTH 4-10 in the social interaction test of anxiety. *Brain Research, 171,* 157–160.

File, S. E. & Clarke, A. (1981). Exploration and motor activity after intraventricular ACTH, morphine and naloxone. *Behavioral Brain Research, 2,* 223–227.

Fisher, L. A., Rivier, J., Rivier, C., Spiess, J., Vale, W., & Brown, M. (1982). Corticotropin-releasing factor (CRF): Central effects on mean arterial pressure and heart rate in rats. *Endocrinology, 110,* 2222–2224.

Garrud, P., Gray, J. A., & De Wied, D. (1974). Pituitary-adrenal hormones and extinction of rewarded behavior in the rat. *Physiology and Behavior, 12,* 109–119.

Gessa, G. L., Pisano, M., Vargiu, L., Crabai, F., & Ferrari, W. (1967). Stretching and yawning movements after intracerebral injections of ACTH. *Res. Can. Biol., 26,* 229–236.

Gispen, W. H., Weigant, V. M., Greven, H. H., & De Wied, D. (1975). The induction of excessive grooming in the rat by intraventricular application of peptides derived from ACTH: Structure activity. *Life Sciences, 17,* 645–655.

Gray, J. A. (1971). Effect of ACTH on extinction of rewarded behaviour is blocked by previous administration of ACTH. *Nature, 119,* 52–54.

Gray, J. A. & Garrud, P. (1977). Adrenopituitary hormones and frustrative nonreward. In L. H. Miller, C. A. Sandman, & A. J. Kastin (Eds.), *Advances in biochemical psychophar-*

macology: Vol. 17. *Neuropeptide influences on the brain and behavior* (pp. 201–212). New York: Raven Press.

Greven, M. H., & De Wied, D. (1973). The influence of peptides derived from corticotropin (ACTH) on performance. Structure activity studies. In P. Zimmermann, W. H. Gispen, B. H. Marks, & D. De Wied (Eds.), *Drug effects on neuroendocrine regulation. Progress in brain research* (pp. 429–442). Amsterdam: Elsevier.

Guth, S., Levine, S., & Seward, J. P. (1971). Appetitive acquisition and extinction effects with exogenous ACTH. *Physiology and Behavior, 7,* 195–200.

Hennessy, J. W., Cohen, M. E., & Rosen, A. J. (1973). Adrenocortical influences upon the extinction of an appetitive runway response. *Physiology and Behavior, 11,* 767–770.

Isaacson, R. L. & Green, E. T. (1978). The effects of ACTH 1-24 on locomotion, exploration, rearing and grooming. *Behavioral Biology, 24,* 118–122.

Kalin, N. H., Shelton, S. E., Kraemer, G. W., & McKinney, W. T. (1983). Associated endocrine, physiological and behavioral changes in rhesus monkeys after intravenous corticotropin-releasing factor administration. *Peptides, 4,* 211–215.

Kastin, A., Miller, L., Nockton, R., Sandman, C., Schally, A., & Stratton, L. (1973). Behavioral aspects of melanocyte stimulating hormone (MSH). In E. Zimmerman, W. Gispen, B. Marks, & D. De Wied (Eds.), *Drug effect on neuroendocrine regulation. Progress in brain research* (pp. 461–470). Amsterdam: Elsevier.

Killeen, P. R., Hanson, S. J., & Osbourne, S. R. (1978). Arousal: Its genesis and manifestation as response rate. *Psychological Review, 85,* 571–581.

Koob, G. F., & Bloom, F. E. (1985). Corticotropin-releasing factor and behavior. *Federation Proceedings, 44,* 259–263.

Koob, G. F., Le Moal, M., Bloom, F. E., Sutton, R. E., Rivier, J., & Vale, W. (1982). Corticotropin releasing factor produces behavioral activation and improves learning in rats. *Neuroscience Abstracts, 8,* 145.

Koob, G. F., Swerdlow, N., Seeligson, M., Eaves, M., Sutton, R., Rivier, J., & Vale, W. (1984). CRF-induced locomotor activation is antagonized by alpha-flupenthixol but not by naloxone. *Neuroendocrinology, 39,* 459–464.

Krieger, D. T., Liotta, A., & Brownstein, M. J. (1977). Presence of corticotropin in limbic system of normal and hypophysectomized rats. *Brain Research, 128,* 575–579.

Levine, A. S., Rogers, B., Kwerp, J., Grace, M., & Morley, J. E. (1982). Effect of centrally administered corticotropin releasing factor (CRF) on multiple feeding paradigms. *Neuropharmacology, 22,* 337–339.

Levine, S. & Jones, L. E. (1965). Adrenocorticotrophic hormone (ACTH) and passive avoidance learning. *Journal of Comparative and Physiological Psychology, 59,* 357–360.

Levine, S., Smotherman, W. P., & Hennessy, J. W. (1977). Pituitary-adrenal hormones and learned taste aversion. In L. H. Miller, C. A. Sandman, & A. J. Kastin (Eds.), *Advances in biochemical psychopharmacology:* Vol. 17. *Neuropeptide influences on brain and behavior* (pp. 163–178). New York: Raven Press.

Lissak, K. & Bohus, B. (1972). Pituitary hormones and avoidance behavior of the rat. *International Journal of Psychobiology, 2,* 103–115.

Miller, R. E. & Caul, W. F. (1973). Effect of adrenocorticotropic hormone on appetitive discrimination learning in the rat. *Physiology and Behavior, 10,* 141–143.

Miller, R. E. & Ogawa, N. (1962). The effect of adrenocorticotrophic hormone (ACTH) on avoidance conditioning in the adrenalectomized rat. *Journal of Comparative and Physiological Psychology, 55,* 211–213.

Morley, J. E., & Levine, A. S. (1983). Corticotropin releasing factor, grooming and ingestive behavior. *Life Sciences, 31,* 1459–1464.

Murphy, J. V. & Miller, R. E. (1955). The effect of adrenocorticotrophic hormone (ACTH) on avoidance conditioning in the rat. *Journal of Comparative and Physiological Psychology, 48,* 47–49.

Olschowka, J. A., O'Donohue, T. L., Mueller, G. P., & Jacobowitz, D. M. (1982). Hypothalamic and extra-hypothalamic distribution of CRF-like immunoreactive neurons in the rat brain. *Neuroendocrinology, 35,* 305–308.

Paull, W. K., Scholer, J., Arimura, A., Meyers, C. A., Chang, J. K., Chang, D., & Shimuzu, M. (1982). Immunocytochemical localization of CRF in the ovine hypothalamus. *Peptides, 3,* 183–191.

Rees, H. D., Dunn, A. J. & Juvane, P. M. (1976). Behavioral and biochemical responses of mice to the intraventricular administration of ACTH peptides and lysine vasopressin. *Life Sciences., 18,* 1333–1340.

Sandman, C. A., Miller, L. H., Kastin, A. J., & Schally, A. U. (1972). A neuroendocrine influence on attention and memory. *Journal of Comparative and Physiological Psychology, 80,* 54–58.

Sandman, C. A., Kastin, A., & Schally, A. (1973). Melanocyte-stimulating hormone and learned appetitive behavior. *Experientia, 92,* 372–379.

Sawchenko, P. E., & Swanson, L. W. (1985). Localization, co-localization and plasticity of corticotropin-releasing factor immunoreactivity in rat brain. *Federation Proceedings, 44,* 221–227.

Segal, D. S., Browne, R. G., Arnsten, A., Derrington, D. C., Bloom, F. E., Guillemin, R., & Ling, N. (1979). Characteristics of β-endorphin-induced behavioral activation and immobilization. In E. Usdin, W. E. Bunney, Jr., & N. S. Kline (Eds.), *Endorphins in mental health research* (pp. 307–324). London: MacMillan.

Selye, H. (1980). *Selye's guide to stress research.* New York: Van Nostrand Reinhold.

Siggins, G. R., Gruol, D., Aldenhoff, J., & Pittman, Q. (1985). Electrophysiological actions of corticotropin-releasing factor in the central nervous system. *Federation Proceedings, 44,* 237–242.

Sirinathsinghji, D. J. S., Rees, L. H., Rivier, J., & Vale, W. (1983). Corticotropin-releasing factor is a potent inhibitor of sexual receptivity in the female rat. *Nature* (London), *305,* 230–235.

Sutton, R., Koob, G., Le Moal, M., Rivier, J., & Vale, W. (1982). Corticotropin releasing factor (CRF) produces behavioral activation in rats. *Nature, 299,* 331–333.

Swanson, L. W., Sawchenko, P. E., Rivier, J., & Vale, W. (1983). Organization of ovine corticotropin releasing factor immunoreactive cells and fibres in the rat brain: An immunohistochemical study. *Neuroendocrinology, 36,* 165–186.

Swerdlow, N. R., & Koob, G. F. (1985). Separate neural substrates of the locomotor-activating properties of amphetamine, heroin, caffeine, and corticotropin releasing factor (CRF) in the rat. *Pharmacology, Biochemistry and Behavior,* in press.

Taché, Y., Goto, Y., Gunnion, M., Vale, W., Rivier, J., & Brown, M. (1983). Inhibition of gastric acid secretion in rats by intracerebral injection of corticotropin-releasing factor. *Science, 222,* 935–937.

Taché, Y., & Gunion, M. (1985). Corticotropin-releasing factor: Central action to influence gastric secretion. *Federation Proceedings, 44,* 255–258.

Thatcher-Britton, K., Morgan, J., Rivier, J., Vale, W., & Koob, G. F. (1985). Chlordiazepoxide attenuates CRF-induced response suppression in the conflict test. *Psychopharmacology, 86,* 170–174.

Vale, W., Spiess, J., Rivier, C., & Rivier, J. (1981). Characterization of a 41-residue ovine hypothalamic peptide that stimulates the secretion of corticotropin and B-endorphin. *Science, 213,* 1394–1397.

Weiss, J. M., McEwen, B. S., Silva, M. T. A., & Kalkut, M. F. (1969). Pituitary adrenal influences on fear responding. *Science, 163,* 197–199.

4

Brain and Pituitary Cyclic Nucleotide Response to Stress*

JAMES L. MEYERHOFF, G. JEAN KANT,
G. RUFUS SESSIONS, EDWARD H. MOUGEY,
LEE L. PENNINGTON, AND ROBERT H. LENOX

Introduction

Endocrine responses to stress have been extensively studied, and several brain neurochemical systems have been shown to be responsive to stress. We have been interested in assessing *in vivo* brain and pituitary biochemical responses concurrently with plasma hormonal responses in order to elucidate the mechanisms by which the brain regulates the pituitary response to stress. Stress has been shown to activate central noradrenergic, dopaminergic, and serotonergic neurons (Barchas & Freedman, 1963; Bliss, Ailion, & Zwanziger, 1968; Cassens, Roffman, Kuruc, Orsulak, & Schildkraut, 1980; Corrodi, Fuxe, & Hokfelt, 1968; Korf, Aghajanian, & Roth, 1973). Noradrenergic stimulation has been shown to be an especially potent elevator of brain cyclic adenosine 3'5' monophosphate (cyclic AMP) *in vitro* (Daly, 1977). Cyclic nucleotides in brain are generally believed to function as "second messengers," mediating cellular responses to neurotransmitters by activating enzymes which phosphorylate specific membrane proteins (Bloom, 1976; Greengard & Kebabian, 1974). Brain cyclic AMP has been reported to increase

*This material has been reviewed by the Walter Reed Army Institute of Research, and there is no objection to its presentation or publication. The opinions or assertions contained herein are the private views of the authors and are not to be construed as official or as reflecting the views of the Department of the Army or the Department of Defense.

PERSPECTIVES ON BEHAVIORAL MEDICINE, Vol. 2
Neuroendocrine Control and Behavior

following stress (Delapaz, Dickman, & Grosser, 1975), and cyclic AMP has been reported to mediate pituitary responses to humoral stimulation *in vitro* (Ahn, Gardner, & Makman, 1979; Kaneko, Saito, Oka, Oda, & Yanaihara, 1973; Steiner, Peake, Utiger, Karl, & Kipnis, 1970). We have accordingly been particularly interested in measuring *in vivo* pituitary as well as brain cyclic AMP responses to stress.

Cold exposure, forced swimming in cold water, exposure to hot plate, and fighting have all been shown to elevate cyclic guanosine 3'5' monophosphate (cyclic GMP) in rat and mouse brain (Dinnendahl, 1975; Mao, Guidotti, & Costa, 1974). Although concurrent hormonal indices of stress were not provided, such cyclic GMP elevations have been attributed to the effects of stress (Dinnendahl, 1975). Data from our own laboratory led us to speculate that increases in brain cyclic GMP levels might be due to stressful environmental factors (Lenox, Wray, Kant, Hawkins, & Meyerhoff, 1979), suggesting that this compound might be a sensitive and specific CNS marker for the stress response.

Since forced immobilization has often been used as a stressor in the rat and has produced both hormonal and neurochemical responses (Euker, Meites, & Riegel, 1973; Keim & Sigg, 1976; Lamprecht, Williams, & Kopin, 1973), we compared the brain regional cyclic nucleotide responses to immobilization versus cold exposure, with concurrent measurement of plasma corticosterone, prolactin, and growth hormone. These hormones have shown a consistent pattern of response to stress (Brown & Martin, 1974; Dunn, Scheving, & Millet, 1972; Friedman, Ader, Grota, & Larson, 1967; Henkin & Knigge, 1963; Kokka, Garcia, George, & Elliott, 1972; Takahashi, Daughaday, & Kipnis, 1971) and were therefore assayed to provide an independent index of the stressfulness of the experimental conditions as well as to permit comparison with the established stress literature.

Experiment I: Comparison of Responses to
Forced Immobilization versus Cold Exposure

All experiments were performed on Wistar-derived, random-bred, male rats from the Walter Reed colony. The rats were housed in individual cages in a temperature controlled chamber ($23° \pm 1°C$) with fixed lighting schedule (lights on from 0700 to 1900 hours), and they were given food and water *ad libitum*.[1] For one week prior to the day of the

---

[1] In conducting the research described in this report, the investigators adhered to the *Guide for Laboratory Animal Facilities and Care*, as promulgated by the Committee of the Guide for Laboratory Animal Resources, National Academy of Sciences, National Research Council.

experiment, animals were individually brought by the same handler into the experimental room in the home cage. They were briefly handled and allowed to traverse an open-ended lucite cylinder, which closely resembled the lucite holder required to briefly immobilize the animals for sacrifice by microwave irradiation (Lenox, Gandhi, Meyerhoff, & Grove, 1976).

On the experimental day, 18 habituated animals were randomly allocated into groups, individually brought to the experimental room in their home cage by the same handler, and treated as follows:

1. Cold stress group: A 5-min duration of cold exposure included wetting of the fur with cold water for 15 sec, placement into a chamber at 4°C for 4.5 min, then placement into a lucite cylinder, insertion of a restraining plunger, and sacrifice by microwave irradiation. Less than 15 sec elapsed from the termination of the cold exposure to sacrifice.

2. Immobilization stress group: The rat was placed into the lucite cylinder by the handler. A 5-min exposure to the immobilization stress was timed from the moment the restraining plunger was inserted. The rats did not struggle or manifest other signs of stress until the plunger was inserted to immobilize them. After 5 min the animal was sacrificed by microwave irradiation in the same cylinder.

3. Control group: Animals were brought into the experimental room as noted above. The handler then placed the rat into a lucite cylinder as was done twice daily for the week prior to the experimental day. The plunger was rapidly placed behind the animal to block its exit and within 15 sec the animal was sacrificed by microwave irradiation. In all experiments rats from different treatment groups were alternated in order to distribute any circadian effects.

Animals were sacrificed by a 5-sec exposure to high-intensity microwave irradiation (Lenox, Meyerhoff, Gandhi, & Wray, 1977), using a modified Varian Model PPS-2.5 power generator with an output of 2.5 kW at a frequency of 2450 ± 20 MHz. Stavinoha, Pepelko, and Smith (1970) originally described the technique of using high-intensity microwave irradiation to simultaneously achieve sacrifice of the animal and inactivation of brain enzymes. This technique eliminates postmortem changes in many heat-stable substrates subject to such change. Investigators planning to use this technique should be aware of its limitations as well as its potential applications (Lenox, Brown, & Meyerhoff, 1979; Meyerhoff, Lenox, Brown, & Gandhi, 1980). Since immobilization is required during the sacrifice period (Meyerhoff, Gandhi, Jacobi, & Lenox, 1979), the animal was placed into a 5.7 cm diameter closed-end lucite cylinder and positioned in the waveguide applicator such that the longitudinal axis of the body was perpendicular to the microwave electric field and parallel to the direction of propagation. Precise exposure parameters were monitored, and modified electronic timing and power-leveling circuitry were incorporated (Brown, Lenox, & Meyerhoff, 1978). After sacrifice the rats were decapitated, and for ease of handling, the heads were cooled to room temperature on dry ice. Trunk blood was collected in heparinized containers, centrifuged, and the plasma stored at $-20°C$ for subsequent radioimmunoassay for corticosterone (CS) (Gross, Ruder, Brown, & Lipsett, 1972), growth hormone (GH) and prolactin (Prl).[2] The brain was dissected into 17 regions, including the pituitary (Balcom, Lenox, & Meyerhoff, 1975). The tissue samples were then weighed and sonicated in $0.05M$ sodium acetate buffer, pH 6.2. The sonicates were centrifuged at 12,000 g at 4°C and the supernatants stored at $-70°C$ until assayed for cyclic AMP and cyclic GMP (Harper & Brooker, 1975; Steiner, Parker, & Kipnis, 1972). The use of a non-parametric statistical analysis (Mann-Whitney U) for GH and Prl has been suggested by Krulich *et al.* (Krulich, Hefco, Illner, & Read, 1974), who showed that the values for these hormones are not normally distributed.

Plasma hormone data for this experiment are shown in Figure 4.1. Compared to controls, plasma CS levels were significantly elevated in animals exposed to 5 min of cold ($U = 4$, $p < .01$), as well as in animals exposed to immobilization stress ($U = 4$, $p < .05$). The plasma CS level in the control group was quite low (approximately 2 μg/100 ml) with relatively low variability, reflecting the degree of habituation of the animals to the handling procedure. Plasma GH tended to decrease in both groups exposed to the stressors, but this decrease was not statistically significant. GH levels in the control group were extremely variable, while the levels in the experimental group were much less so. Plasma Prl levels doubled in animals exposed to cold stress ($U = 4$, $p < .05$), while they increased more than tenfold in animals exposed to immobilization ($U = 0$, $p < .01$).

We found no statistically significant cyclic AMP responses to either cold or immobilization. We did see, however, a trend toward elevated levels of cyclic AMP in the pituitary in the group exposed to 5 min of immobilization (Figure 4.2). Levels of cyclic GMP were significantly elevated only in animals exposed to cold stress (Figure 4.3). The cyclic GMP increase in the cerebellum was approximately threefold, with significant increases also noted in 10 other regions including the pituitary. By con-

---

[2]Assays of growth hormone and prolactin were by radioimmunoassay using reagents and antibody supplied by the Rat Pituitary Hormone Distribution Program, NIAMD. Data are reported in terms of NIAMD standards.

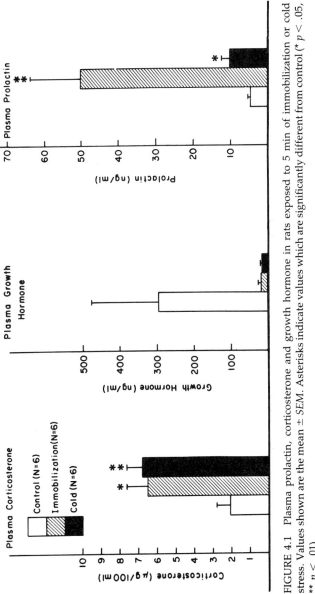

FIGURE 4.1 Plasma prolactin, corticosterone and growth hormone in rats exposed to 5 min of immobilization or cold stress. Values shown are the mean ± *SEM*. Asterisks indicate values which are significantly different from control (* $p < .05$, ** $p < .01$).

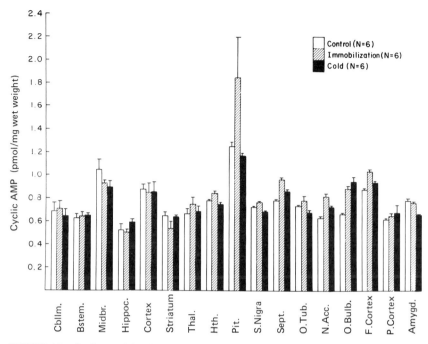

FIGURE 4.2   Cyclic AMP levels in brain regions in rats exposed to 5 min of immobilization or cold stress. Values shown are mean ± *SEM*. See Figure 4.3 for region abbreviations.

trast, levels of cyclic GMP in rats exposed to immobilization stress actually tended to be lower than control values in some regions, particularly the cerebellum. Our studies confirm and extend the reported findings of increased brain cyclic GMP following exposure to cold (Figure 4.3).

Experiment II: 15-Minute Immobilization

We were intrigued by the failure of immobilization to elevate brain cyclic GMP. The robust increases in both Prl and CS confirmed that immobilization was in fact a potent stressor, and yet levels in the cerebellum were actually slightly decreased. Although this decrease was not statistically significant, we decided to pursue the issue by examining the effect of more prolonged immobilization. Following habituation to handling and to traversing the lucite tube, we subjected rats to forced immobilization lasting 15 sec, 5 min, or 15 min ($N = 5$ per group). The 15-sec immobilization is the minimum required for sacrifice by the microwave technique. Once again we saw robust hormonal responses (Figure 4.4).

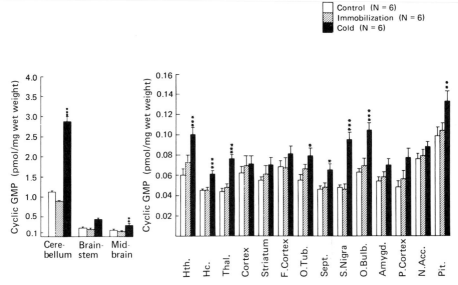

FIGURE 4.3   Cyclic GMP levels in brain regions in rats exposed to 5 min of immobilization or cold stress. (Hth) Hypothalamus, (Hc) Hippocampus, (Thal) Thalamus, (F. Cortex) Frontal Cortex, (O. Tub) Olfactory Tubercle, (Sept.) Septal Region, (S. Nigra) Substantia Nigra, (O. Bulb) Olfactory Bulb, (Amygd) Amygdala, (P. Cortex) Pyriform Cortex, (N. Acc) Nucleus Accumbens, (Pit) Pituitary. Values shown are the mean ± *SEM*. Asterisks indicate values which are significantly different from control (*p < .05, **p < .01, ***p < .001).

The low levels of CS in our well-habituated 15-sec group permitted us to again see a marked increase in CS to 5 μg/100 ml after only 5 min of immobilization (U = 0, p < .01). The levels reached 14 μg/100 ml after 15 min of immobilization (U = 0, p < .005). Plasma Prl also showed a marked response, increasing over tenfold after 5 min of immobilization and remaining at those levels at 15 min (U = 0, p < .005). We saw an increase in pituitary cyclic AMP in response to forced immobilization, which was statistically significant in the 15-min group (control: 1.19 ± 0.05 pmol/mg wet weight versus 15-min immobilized: 2.26 ± 0.56 pmol/mg wet weight, p < .05, Student's t test).

Despite hormonal indices clearly showing that the animals were stressed (Figure 4.4), cerebellar cyclic GMP was significantly decreased over 50% at 15 min (p < .005, Student's t test). Thus, although immobilization was a potent stressor, the effects on cerebellar cyclic GMP were opposite to those produced by cold or other environmental stimuli viewed as stressful.

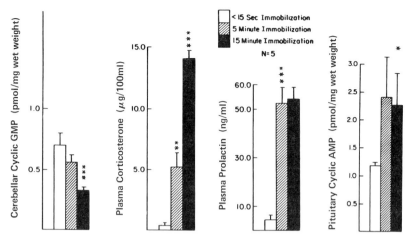

FIGURE 4.4   Effect of forced immobilization on cyclic GMP levels in cerebellum, plasma corticosterone, plasma prolactin, and cyclic AMP in pituitary (*$p < .05$, **$p < .10$, ***$p < .005$).

Experiment III: Effect of Locomotor Activity on Brain Regional Cyclic Nucleotides

In reexamining reports of brain cyclic GMP elevation following stressful manipulations (such as forced swimming in cold water, subjection to a painful stimulus, or fighting), it occurred to us that increased locomotor activity was a factor common to all of the conditions. It seemed to us that cerebellar cyclic GMP levels might be reflecting degree of locomotor activity rather than stress *per se.* Therefore, the next experiment was designed to determine whether locomotor activity increased cyclic GMP. We allowed a group of rats daily access to an activity wheel over an 8-day shaping period, and by gradually restricting their access to 5 min per day, we produced moderately consistent running (Meyerhoff *et al.,* 1978). The animals were divided into experimental ($N = 6$) and control ($N = 6$) groups balanced with respect to tendency to run in the wheel, based on averages of the preceding 2-days' running scores. Animals in the experimental group were then allowed access to the activity wheel for 5 min a day for 3 consecutive days. After the animal spontaneously entered the wheel, the sliding panel was closed, preventing the animal from leaving the wheel during the 5-min period. After the daily 5-min activity session, the rats were allowed to run through a short lucite tube.The rats rapidly learned to enter and traverse the lucite tube, which closely resembled the lucite holder required to immobilize the animals for sacrifice by microwave irradiation. The control rats were also allowed to enter the activity wheel on these 3 days, but the wheel was not permitted to turn. With the access door shut they merely explored the immobile wheel for 5 min. Following this their treatment was identical to that of the experimental rats: They traversed the lucite tube, were weighed, and returned to their home cages. On the fourth day, the animals were treated in a manner identical to the preceding 3 days except that following 5 min in the movable or fixed wheel, the animals were placed in the lucite holder, an immobilizing plunger was immediately inserted, and the rats were rapidly sacrificed by exposure to microwave irradiation. The rats did not struggle or manifest other signs of stress until the plunger was inserted to immobilize them. Following sacrifice, plasma was collected, brains were dissected, and samples were assayed for cyclic AMP, cyclic GMP, and plasma hormone levels.

The experimental group averaged 52 revolutions (range 30–76) for the entire 5-min period in the activity wheel. As seen in Figure 4.5, this group had cerebellar cyclic GMP levels more than twice as high as levels in control rats, which merely explored the wheel while it was prevented from revolving (2.00 ± 0.10 versus 0.92 ± 0.10 pmol per mg wet weight, $p < .0005$ Student's t test). The cerebellar cyclic GMP levels in the controls were similar to levels we find in animals sacrificed immediately upon removal from their home cages (Lenox *et al.*, 1980). The levels of

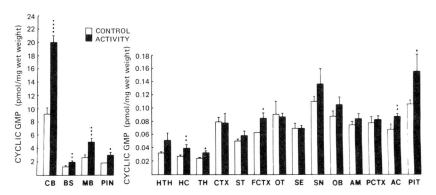

FIGURE 4.5   Levels of cyclic GMP in brain regions of rats in control versus activity group. The data shown represent mean ± SEM values for the six animals in each group. (CB) Cerebellum, (BS) Brainstem, (MB) Midbrain, (PIN) Pineal, (HTH) Hypothalamus, (HC) Hippocampus, (TH) Thalamus, (CTX) Cortex, (ST) Corpus Striatum, (FCTX) Frontal Cortex, (OT) Olfactory Tubercle, (SE) Septal Region, (SN) Substantia Nigra, (OB) Olfactory Bulb, (AM) Amygdala, (PCTX) Piriform Cortex, (AC) Nucleus Accumbens, and (PIT) Pituitary (*$p < .05$, **$p < .025$, ***$p < .001$, ****$p < .0005$).

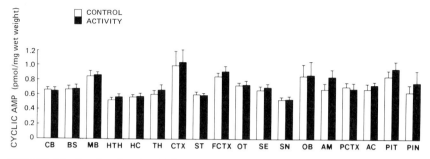

FIGURE 4.6   Levels of cyclic AMP in brain regions in rats in control versus activity groups. Abbreviations are as in Figure 4.5.

cyclic GMP were elevated in 8 other brain regions in the activity group. Levels of cyclic AMP (Figure 4.6) were not affected in any of the 18 regions examined. As shown in Figure 4.7, experimental and control groups both had slightly elevated plasma CS, suggesting they were somewhat aroused compared to "gentled" animals, habituated to handling, sacrificed immediately upon removal from their home cages. As the CS levels were not significantly different between activity (6.93 ± 0.99 μg/100 ml) versus control (7.67 ± 1.36 μg/100 ml) groups ($p < .05$,

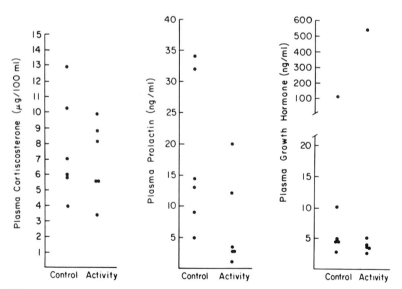

FIGURE 4.7   Plasma levels of corticosterone, prolactin, and growth hormone of rats in control versus activity groups.

Student's t test), we suggest that locomotor activity, rather than environmental stress, may have been associated with the elevations in cerebellar cyclic GMP. Plasma Prl levels following locomotor activity were 6.93 ng/ml, while levels in the 5-min exploratory control group were 17.86 ng/ml; the difference between groups was not statistically significant ($.10 > p > .05$, Mann-Whitney U). These levels, while elevated compared to levels in gentled animals sacrificed immediately upon removal from their home cages, were similar to levels previously seen following 5-min exposure to cold, and far below the 50 ng/ml levels seen following 5 min of forced immobilization. Plasma GH levels also were not significantly different between activity and control groups.

Thus, we found that cerebellar cyclic GMP levels were twice as high in animals allowed 5 min of running in activity wheels compared to animals merely allowed to explore the immobilized wheel for 5 min (Meyerhoff & Lenox *et al.*, 1979). Elevations in cyclic GMP levels were seen in many of the brain regions examined, and comparison of Figures 4.3 and 4.5 reveals that the regional pattern of elevation following locomotor activity resembles that following cold exposure. In both experiments, the magnitude of the effect was greatest in the cerebellum.

Experiment IV: The Time Course of Cerebellar Cyclic GMP Response to Locomotor Activity

Having confirmed our hypothesis that locomotor activity could elevate brain cyclic GMP levels independent of stress effects, we felt that design of future experiments and interpretation of data would require an understanding of the dynamics of this response. Therefore, we sought to determine whether the increases were proportional to the duration of locomotor activity. We obtained a set of six activity wheels driven by a single motor. We found that rats could run at 5 RPM for up to 5 min without apparent difficulty, and we required groups of rats to run at this rate for 0, 0.25, 0.5, 1, 2, and 5 min. Following activity of these various durations, the animals were sacrificed by microwave irradiation and the cerebellum dissected into vermis and lateral cerebellum. We found that the response to locomotor activity, although present in both portions, was more pronounced in the vermis, where a fourfold increase was seen after running at 5 RPM for 5 min (Figure 4.8). The increases in both vermis and lateral cerebellum reached statistical significance at 1.0 min ($p < .05$, Student's t test).

We have also examined the rate of decrease in cerebellar cyclic GMP levels over time following termination of locomotor activity. Rats were

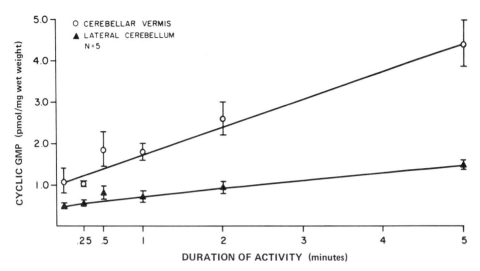

FIGURE 4.8   Cerebellar cyclic GMP-increases proportional to duration of locomotor activity.

required to run for a 5-min period at 5 RPM in the motorized activity wheels, then allowed to rest for varying periods of time in the wheels (which would not move with the motor turned off). All rats remained in the wheels for a total of 30 min. The 5-min running condition was imposed at various times so that animals were subjected to 5 min of running followed by 0, 5, 10, 15, 20, or 25 min of rest and then were immediately sacrificed by exposure to microwave irradiation. Control animals were placed in the wheel for 30 min with the motor off. The levels of cyclic GMP were elevated 250% in whole cerebellum after 5 min of running. As seen in Figure 4.9, the levels decreased rapidly after 5 min of inactivity and approached control levels after 10 min.

Discussion

Seeking to determine whether cyclic nucleotides were valid indicators of stress, we confirmed the report (Mao *et al.*, 1974) that cold exposure elevates cerebellar cyclic GMP but found that forced immobilization failed to produce this effect. Our hormonal data indicate that the immobilized animals were indeed stressed (Lenox *et al.*, 1980). Moreover, prolonged immobilization actually lowered cyclic GMP. We then dem-

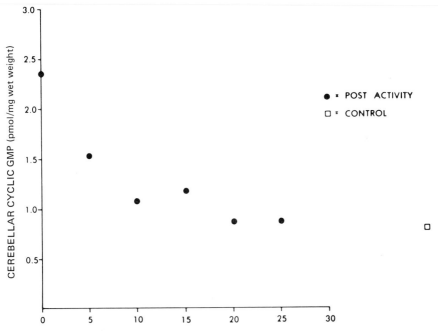

MINUTES OF REST FOLLOWING TERMINATION OF 5-MINUTE RUNNING PERIOD

FIGURE 4.9 Return of cerebellar cyclic GMP levels to baseline with rest following activity.

onstrated that locomotor activity in the absence of stress produced robust elevations of cyclic GMP (Meyerhoff & Lenox et al., 1979), and that the increases are proportional to the duration of the locomotor activity. We have also shown that forced immobilization produces marked elevations in pituitary cyclic AMP.

The in vivo, pituitary cyclic AMP-increases are particularly interesting in view of the reports of cyclic AMP mediation of pituitary responses to humoral stimulation in vitro (Ahn et al., 1979; Kaneko et al., 1973; Steiner et al., 1970). We were not able to replicate the pituitary cyclic AMP-increase reported following a 5-min cold exposure (Mao et al., 1974) but are presently studying the effects of more prolonged cold exposure. We have demonstrated that the pituitary cyclic AMP response to 15-min immobilization occurs in female as well as male rats (Kant, Sessions, Lenox, & Meyerhoff, 1981). We are presently comparing the effects of a variety of stressors on the pituitary cyclic AMP response.

Studies of cyclic AMP in brain regions have demonstrated no significant response under a variety of stressors (Dinnendahl, 1975; Mao *et al.*, 1974). Delapaz *et al.* (1975) reported an increase of cyclic AMP in several regions after prolonged electric foot shock, but their method of tissue fixation and preparation render comparison difficult. Although we have not found significant increases in cyclic AMP in any brain region following brief stress, we may find increases following more prolonged stress.

The findings in Experiment I of an elevation of plasma CS, coupled with reduction in plasma GH in animals exposed to either cold or immobilization stress, are consistent with the reported hormonal response to a variety of stressors. The relatively low plasma CS values in the stressed animals (6–7 μg/100 ml) reflect the fact that animals were sacrificed after only 5 min of exposure to the stressor. In fact, detection of this early rise in plasma CS levels was possible, in part, due to the very low levels found in the control animals. GH has been shown to decrease markedly in rats following exposure to various arousing stimuli. Both cold and immobilization dramatically reduced GH levels. The large variability in GH levels seen in the control rats reflects spontaneous surges of GH release (Martin *et al.*, 1978). The response of the Prl system to the two stressors differed significantly. It has been well documented that plasma Prl increases in rats exposed to immobilization stress (Euker *et al.*, 1973; Keim & Sigg, 1976). In this experiment Prl levels rose tenfold after 5 min of immobilization. Reports differ as to the effect of cold on plasma Prl (Jobin, Ferland, Cote, & Labrie, 1975; Mueller, Chin, Dibit, Chin, & Meites, 1974). After a 5-min exposure, we found the magnitude of Prl response to immobilization was much greater than the response to cold. In general, the differences we observed between pituitary response to cold versus immobilization are consistent with the concept of selective responses to various environmental stimuli proposed by Mason (1971).

It is possible that many environmental or drug-associated changes in brain cyclic GMP are mediated via changes in locomotor activity. We have reported that immobilization attenuates the elevation in cerebellar cyclic GMP induced by cold exposure or apomorphine (Meyerhoff *et al.*, 1978). The latter effect has also been demonstrated in animals paralyzed with d-tubocurarine (Breese, Mueller, & Mailman, 1979). Although locomotor activity or its suppression may contribute to the changes in cerebellar cyclic GMP in many cases, it cannot be assumed that locomotor activity is the only relevant factor. Any number of drugs might produce their effects on cyclic GMP independent of any effects on activity. For example, RO 20-1724, a phosphodiesterase inhibitor which elevates cyclic GMP (Kant, Lenox, & Meyerhoff, 1980), has marked sedative properties.

Conclusions

Our data suggest that cyclic GMP levels in the cerebellum and in a number of other brain regions are not influenced by stress *per se*, but rather by the amount of locomotor activity elicited by the experimental situation. Hence, we feel that there is a clear requirement to consider locomotor activity in designing and interpreting experiments involving measurement of cyclic GMP in brain regions. The use of plasma hormonal data was essential to establish that the nature of the cyclic GMP response to immobilization stress was, indeed, anomalous and demonstrates the importance of using hormonal indices concurrently in exploring neurochemical responses to environmental stressors.

Pituitary cyclic AMP responses seem a very promising variable to explore in linking neuronal and hormonal responses to stress. As noted, we found that 15 min of forced immobilization produced a significant elevation of pituitary cyclic AMP, as well as increases in plasma corticosterone and prolactin. This may represent a highly useful model for assessment of *in vivo* biochemical responses to stress at the pituitary level. We are presently using this model to compare pituitary responses to a variety of acute and chronic stressors and to elucidate mechanisms of neuronal and neurotransmitter regulation of pituitary response.

Acknowledgments

The authors wish to thank Rosa Thorpe, Clifton Johnson, Clyde Kenion, Golden Driver, Frances Farrow, Mike Vrabec, Clinton Wormley, and Kathy Rice for their excellent technical assistance, Frederick J. Manning, Timothy F. Elsmore, and C. Fred Tyner for their helpful comments, and Pat Conners for her diligent help in typing the manuscript.

References

Ahn, H. S., Gardner, E., & Makman, M. H. (1979). Anterior pituitary adenylate cyclase: Stimulation by dopamine and other monoamines. *European Journal of Pharmacology, 53,* 313–317.

Balcom, G. J., Lenox, R. H., & Meyerhoff, J. L. (1975). Regional gammaaminobutyric acid levels in rat brain determined after microwave fixation. *Journal of Neurochemistry, 24,* 609–613.

Barchas, J. D., & Freedman, D. X. (1963). Brain amines: response to physiological stress. *Biochemical Pharmacology, 12,* 1225–1238.

Biggio, G., Costa, E., & Guidotti, A. (1977). Pharmacologically induced changes in the

3':5'-cyclic guanosine monophosphate content of rat cerebellar cortex: Difference between apomorphine, haloperidol and harmaline. *Journal of Pharmacology and Experimental Therapeutics, 200,* 207–215.

Bliss, E. L., Ailion, J., & Zwanziger, J. (1968). Metabolism of norepinephrine, serotonin and dopamine in rat brain with stress. *Journal of Pharmacology and Experimental Therapeutics, 164,* 122–135.

Bloom, F. E. (1976). The role of cyclic nucleotides in central synaptic function. In E. Costa & P. Greengard (Eds.), *Advances in biochemical pharmacology,* (Vol. 15, pp. 273–282). New York: Raven Press.

Breese, G. R., Mueller, R. A., & Mailman, R. B. (1979). Effect of dopaminergic agonists and antagonists on *in vivo* cyclic nucleotide content: Relation of guanosine 3':5'-monophosphate (cGMP) changes in cerebellum to behavior. *Journal of Pharmacology and Experimental Therapeutics, 209*(2), 262–270.

Brown, G. M., & Martin, J. B. (1974). Corticosterone, prolactin, growth hormone response to handling and new environment in the rat. *Psychosomatic Medicine, 36*(3), 241–247.

Brown, P. V., Lenox, R. H., & Meyerhoff, J. L. (1978). Microwave enzyme inactivation system: Electronic control to reduce dose variability. *IEEE Transactions on Biomedical Engineering, 25*(2), 205–208.

Cassens, G., Roffman, M., Kuruc, A., Orsulak, P. J., & Schildkraut, J. J. (1980). Alterations in brain norepinephrine metabolism induced by environmental stimuli previously paired with inescapable shock. *Science, 209,* 1138–1140.

Corrodi, H., Fuxe, K., & Hokfelt, T. (1968). The effect of immobilization stress on the activity of central monoamine neurons. *Life Sciences, 7,* 107–112.

Daly, J. W. (1977). *Cyclic nucleotides in the nervous system.* New York: Plenum.

Delapaz, R. L., Dickman, S. R., & Grosser, B. I. (1975). Effects of stress on rat brain adenosine 3'5' monophosphate *in vivo. Brain Research, 85,* 171–175.

Dinnendahl, V. (1975). Effects of stress on mouse brain cyclic nucleotide levels *in vivo. Brain Research, 100,* 716–719.

Dunn, J., Scheving, L., & Millet, P. (1972). Circadian variation in stress-evoked increases in plasma corticosterone. *American Journal of Physiology, 222*(2), 402–406.

Eddy, N. B., Touchberry, C. F., & Lieberman, J. E. (1949). Synthetic analgesics. *Journal of Pharmacology and Experimental Therapeutics, 98,* 121–130.

Euker, J., Meites, J., & Riegle, G. (1973). Serum LH and prolactin following restraint stress in the rat. *Physiologist, 16,* 307.

Friedman, S. B., Ader, R., Grota, L. J., & Larson, T. (1967). The plasma corticosterone response to parameters of electric shock stimulation in the rat. *Psychosomatic Medicine, 29*(4), 323–328.

Greengard, P., & Kebabian, J. W. (1974). Role of cyclic AMP in synaptic transmission in the mammalian peripheral nervous system. *Federation Proceedings, 33,* 1059–1067.

Gross, H. A., Ruder, J. J., Brown, K. S., & Lipsett, M. B. (1972). A radioimmunoassay for plasma corticosterone. *Steroids, 20*(6), 681.

Hamilton, C. L., & Brobeck, J. R. (1966). Food intake and activity of rats with rostral hypothalamic lesions. *Proceedings of the Society for Experimental Biology and Medicine, 122,* 270–272.

Harper, J. F., & Brooker, G. (1975). Femtomole sensitive radioimmunoassay for cyclic AMP and cyclic GMP after 2'0 acetylation by acetic anhydride aqueous solution. *Journal of Cyclic Nucleotide Research, 1,* 207–218.

Henkin, R. I., & Knigge, K. (1963). Effect of sound on hypothalamic pituitary adrenal axis. *American Journal of Physiology, 204,* 710–714.

Jobin, M., Ferland, L., Cote, J., & Labrie, F. (1975). Effect of exposure to cold on hypothalamic TRH activity and plasma levels of TSH and prolactin in the rat. *Neuroendocrinology, 18,* 204–212.

Kaneko, T., Saito, S., Oka, H., Oda, T., & Yanaihara, N. (1973). Effects of synthetic LH-RH and its analogs on rat anterior pituitary cyclic AMP and LH and FSH release. *Metabolism, 22*(1), 77–80.

Kant, G. J., Lenox, R. H., & Meyerhoff, J. L. (1980). *In vivo* effects of apomorphine and 4-(3-butoxy-4-methoxybenzyl)-2-imidazolidinone (RO 20-1724) on cyclic nucleotides in rat brain and pituitary. *Biochemical Pharmacology, 29,* 369–373.

Kant, G. J., Sessions, G. R., Lenox, R. H., & Meyerhoff, J. L. (1981). The effects of hormonal and circadian cycles, stress and activity on levels of cyclic AMP and cyclic GMP in pituitary, hypothalamus, pineal and cerebellum of female rats during the estrus cycle. *Life Sciences, 29,* 2491–2499.

Keim, K. L., & Sigg, E. B. (1976). Physiological and biochemical concomitants of restraint stress in rats. *Pharmacology, Biochemistry and Behavior, 4,* 289–297.

Kokka, N., Garcia, J. F., George, R., & Elliott, H. W. (1972). Growth hormone and ACTH secretion: Evidence for an inverse relationship in rats. *Endocrinology, 90*(3), 735–743.

Korf, J., Aghajanian, G. J., & Roth, R. M. (1973). Increased turnover of norepinephrine in the rat cerebral cortex during stress: Role of the locus coeruleus. *Neuropharmacology, 12,* 933–938.

Krulich, L., Hefco, E., Illner, P., & Read, C. B. (1974). The effects of acute stress on the secretion of LH, FSH, prolactin and GH in the normal male rat, with comments on their statistical evaluation. *Neuroendocrinology, 16,* 293–311.

Lamprecht, L., Williams, R. B., & Kopin, I. J. (1973). Serum dopamine-betahydroxylase during development of immobilization-induced hypertension. *Endocrinology, 92*(3), 953–956.

Lenox, R. H., Gandhi, O. P., Meyerhoff, J. L., & Grove, H. M. (1976). A microwave applicator for *in vivo* rapid inactivation of enzymes in the central nervous system. *IEEE Microwave Theory and Technique, 24,* 58–61.

Lenox, R. H., Meyerhoff, J. L., Gandhi, O. P., & Wray, H. L. (1977). Microwave inactivation: Pitfalls in determination of regional levels of cyclic AMP in rat brain. *Journal of Cyclic Nucleotide Research, 3,* 367–379.

Lenox, R. H., Brown, P. V., & Meyerhoff, J. L. (1979). Microwave inactivation: A technique with promise and pitfalls. *Trends in Neuroscience, 2*(4), 106–109.

Lenox, R. H., Wray, H. L., Kant, G. J., Hawkins, T. D., & Meyerhoff, J. L. (1979). Changes in brain levels of cyclic nucleotides and γ-aminobutyric acid in barbiturate dependence and withdrawal. *European Journal of Pharmacology, 55,* 159–169.

Lenox, R. H., Kant, G. J., Sessions, G. R., Pennington, L. L., Mougey, E. H., & Meyerhoff, J. L. (1980). Specific hormonal and neurochemical responses to different stressors. *Neuroendocrinology, 30,* 300–308.

Mao, C. C., Guidotti, A., & Costa, E. (1974). Interactions between gamma aminobutyric acid and guanosine cyclic 3'5' monophosphate in rat cerebellum. *Molecular Pharmacology, 10,* 735–745.

Martin, J. B., Brazeau, P., Tannenbaum, G. S., Willoughby, J. O., Epelbaum, J., Terry, L. C., & Durand, D. (1978). Neuroendocrine organization of growth hormone secretion. In S. Reichlin, R. J. Baldessarini, & J. B. Martin (Eds.), *The hypothalamus,* (Vol. 56, pp. 329–357). New York: Raven Press.

Mason, J. W. (1971). A re-evaluation of the concept of "non-specificity" in stress theory. *Journal of Psychiatric Research, 8,* 323–333.

Meyerhoff, J. L., Lenox, R. H., Kant, G. J., Sessions, G. R., Mougey, E. H., & Pennington, L. L. (1978). The effects of locomotor activity on cerebellar levels of cyclic GMP. *Society for Neuroscience Abstracts, 4,* 111.

Meyerhoff, J. L., Gandhi, O. P., Jacobi, J. H., & Lenox, R. H. (1979). Comparison of microwave irradiation at 986 verses 2450 MHz for *In Vivo* inactivation of brain enzymes in rats. *IEEE Transactions on Microwave Theory and Techniques, 27,* 267–270.

Meyerhoff, J. L., Lenox, R. H., Kant, G. J., Sessions, G. R., Mougey, E. H., & Pennington, L. L. (1979). The effect of locomotor activity on cerebellar levels of cGMP. *Life Sciences, 24,* 1125–1130.

Meyerhoff, J. L., Lenox, R. H., Brown, P. V., & Gandhi, O. P. (1980). The inactivation of rodent brain enzymes in-vivo using high-intensity microwave irradiation. *IEEE Transactions on Microwave Theory and Techniques. Proceedings of the IEEE, 68*(1), 155–159.

Mueller, G. P., Chin, H. T., Dibit, J. A., Chin, J. J., & Meites, J. (1974). Effects of warm and cold temperatures on release of TSH, GH, and prolactin in rats. *Proceedings of the Society for Experimental Biology and Medicine, 147,* 698–700.

Rubin, E. H., & Ferrendelli, J. A. (1977). Distribution and regulation of cyclic nucleotide levels in cerebellum, *in vivo. Journal of Neurochemistry, 29,* 43–51.

Stavinoha, W., Pepelko, B., & Smith, P. (1970). Microwave irradiation to inactivate cholinesterase in the rat brain prior to analysis for acetylcholine. *Pharmacologist, 12,* 257.

Steiner, A. L., Peake, G. T., Utiger, R. D., Karl, I. E., & Kipnis, D. M. (1970). Hypothalamic stimulation of growth hormone and thyrotropin release *in vitro* and pituitary 3'5'-adenosine cyclic monophosphate. *Endocrinology, 86,* 1354–1360.

Steiner, A. L., Parker, C. W., & Kipnis, D. M. (1972). Radioimmunoassay for cyclic nucleotides. *Journal of Biological Chemistry, 247,* 1106–1113.

Takahashi, K., Daughaday, W. M., & Kipnis, D. M. (1971). Regulation of immunoreactive growth hormone secretion in male rats. *Endocrinology, 88,* 909–917.

Volicer, L., & Hurter, B. P. (1977). Effects of acute and chronic ethanol administration and withdrawal on adenosine 3':5'-monophosphate and guanosine 3':5'-monophosphate levels in the rat brain. *Journal of Pharmacology and Experimental Therapeutics, 200*(2), 298–305.

Wei, E., Loh, H. H., & Way, E. L. (1973). Quantitative aspects of precipitated abstinence in morphine-dependent rats. *Journal of Pharmacology and Experimental Therapeutics, 184*(2), 398–403.

5
Neuroendocrine Response Patterns and Stress: Biobehavioral Mechanisms of Disease*

REDFORD B. WILLIAMS, JR.

Introduction

Early theorizing about the role of stress in disease postulated a non-specific increase in any of several parameters used to measure arousal when "stress" was applied, and the greater the stress, the larger the increase in arousal level (Duffy, 1962). Perhaps the most widely known example of this kind of thinking is to be found in the writing of Selye (1950) on the "general adaptation syndrome." Selye proposed that a wide variety of stimuli, such as cold, heat, exercise, trauma, fasting, emotional stimuli, and many others, all elicit nonspecific reactions in the body, including, particularly, stimulation of the pituitary–adrenocortical axis. A great deal of more recent thinking and laboratory experimenta-tion has resulted in what can only be considered a radical reorientation of the earlier view of stress as having unidimensional, nonspecific ef-fects on bodily function. This recent work has led to the realization that stress is a far more complex phenomenon than was earlier thought, and this has led many to wish to discard the concept of stress altogether in favor of more accurate descriptors. Rather than follow this trend, I pre-

*Preparation of this paper was supported by research grants, HL-18589 and HL-22740, from the National Heart, Lung and Blood Institute, and by a Research Scientist Develop-ment Award, MH-70482 to the author.

fer to retain the venerable term and address the problems by refining its definition so as to take into account the new knowledge.

A modern definition of stress must recognize that stress does not have across-the-board, nonspecific, unidimensional effects on bodily functions. Rather, the occurrence of stress depends not just on the environmental stimuli to which the organism is subjected, but also on a wide variety of the organism's characteristics—both innate and acquired—which determine, along with the characteristics of the particular environmental stimuli, the organism's interpretation of those stimuli. Stress, then, results from the *interaction* between a particular organism and a particular environmental situation. Furthermore, depending upon the specific type of interaction which results, qualitatively different *patterns of response*—extending across many response systems, including the somatomotor, the autonomic nervous system, and the neuroendocrine system—are integrated by the brain to enable the organism to adapt most effectively to its environment.

Advances in the understanding of CNS regulation of cardiovascular function led the English physiologist S. M. Hilton to propose a modification of the earlier conceptualization of brain stem "centers," each of which regulates a single cardiovascular function (e.g., a vasomotor center). Hilton suggests

> that a new approach may be made by starting from the view that the central nervous system is organized to produce not single, isolated variables, but integrated patterns of response. Any variable which can be described or measured independently is actually a component of several such patterns. . . . In this system, the repertoire of patterned responses [may be] very small. (Hilton, 1975, p. 214)

Another major contributor to modern thinking about stress is John Mason. Based upon his extensive research of multiple hormonal responses to a wide variety of laboratory stressors, Mason (1975a) has concluded that the neuroendocrine system does not show a nonspecific response to stress, and that "a fundamental task in biology is to determine how the many separate bodily parts or processes are integrated into the organism as a whole" (p. 144). Recognizing that the brain has three "motor effector systems" (the skeletal musculature, the autonomic nervous system and the neuroendocrine system) upon which to call in adapting to varying environmental demands, Mason rightly notes "that we must take into consideration a broadening array of multiple, interdependent variables, from both a psychosocial and endocrine viewpoint, if we are eventually to understand the organization of psychoendocrine relationships" (Mason, 1975a, p. 143). Rather than reacting to this increasing complexity by reducing problems in the study of stress to "comfortably manageable units," Mason concludes that we must design our experiments so as "to deal with complexity itself" (p. 145). Based upon an elegant series of studies in which he showed that in the absence of psychological distress, neither exercise, fasting, nor heat was associated with increased adrenal cortical responses, Mason concluded that our understanding of the stimuli used in psychoendocrine research must be extended

> with particular attention to isolating the input stimuli, whether psychological or physical, in as "pure" a form as possible. . . . Once the pattern of hormonal responses to the "elemental" natural stimuli are known, then the patterns of response to various natural combinations of stimuli should become more interpretable, and such intriguing questions as how adaptive priorities are handled by the integrative machinery when diverse stimuli coexist may be more readily examined. (1977a, p. 177)

While a great deal of research effort has been devoted to the study of the responses of single hormones to a wide variety of naturalistic as well as experimental laboratory stressors (see Rose, 1980, and Mason, 1975b, for reviews of this research), a consideration of the thinking of both Hilton and Mason leads to the conclusion that a more appropriate strategy is to evaluate the effects of relatively "pure" environmental stimuli on responses tapping a broad array of bodily systems.

In addition to such a strategic consideration, it is also important to recognize that there is by no means universal agreement as to what constitutes a pure stimulus for any given single hormonal response, not to mention a specific pattern of hormonal response. Regarding the nature of the psychological stimuli which specifically stimulate the pituitary–adrenocortical system as compared to the adrenal medullary system, Henry (1983) has reviewed much of the literature in this area— particularly the work of Frankenhaeuser and her group (Frankenhaeuser, Landberg, & Forsman, 1980)—and concludes that "under appropriate conditions the adrenal medullary and the adrenal cortical responses represent behavioral patterns that move in different directions" (p. 47). More specifically, Henry (1983) proposes that under conditions where the classic "fight or flight" response is activated (e.g., as when Frankenhaeuser, et al., 1980, found "effort with distress" in their subjects) both catecholamine, particularly epinephrine, and cortisol excretion rates increased; when there was only effort without distress only catecholamine excretion increased. In addition to fight or flight, Henry (1983) posits an association between helplessness and depression and increased cortisol release.

While it is difficult to deny that intense emotional states—anger, fear, anxiety, depression, and the like—are associated with increases in a wide variety of autonomically and neuroendocrinologically mediated functions, these emotional states are notoriously difficult to study, whether one is attempting to assess or to induce them in either naturalistic or laboratory settings. Some individuals will respond to a given laboratory manipulation with anger, others with fear, and still others with indifference. Moreover, while perhaps even most people can give accurate reports of their emotional state, there is still a significant proportion who may not be consciously aware of their emotional state. It is the latter group who are undoubtedly responsible for the paucity of experimental laboratory studies in which reliable increases in any given hormone or pattern of hormones have been found to be related to reports of affects across a group of subjects. Rather than attempt to either induce or measure *emotional states* in human experimental studies, an alternative and by no means contradictory strategy would be to require subjects to engage in specific behaviors, the performance of which can be measured, and to evaluate the autonomic and neuroendocrine responses which are engendered. Once reliable autonomic and neuroendocrine response patterns can be linked to specific *behavioral states*, then it may be possible with greater confidence to explore the affective correlates of such response patterns. It is this latter strategy which has guided my own research into the cardiovascular and neuroendocrine correlates of stress and which forms the framework for the discussion to follow in this chapter regarding the participation of stress-induced neuroendocrine response patterns in biobehavioral mechanisms of disease. To introduce that discussion, however, I first present a model which attempts to organize for the reader the points that have been made thus far.

As shown in Figure 5.1, it is the behavior of target organs which is ultimately responsible for the initiation and progression of disease processes across the life span. The study of such changes in the structure and function of the bodily organs constitutes the field of pathophysiology. As alluded to in the preceding discussion, and illustrated by the model, the behavior of the target organs is complexly determined. First, of course, the genetic makeup of the individual directly influences target organ behavior; for example, levels in the blood of the enzyme dopamine-beta-hydroxylase (DBH) appear to reflect the level of activity in the sympathetic nervous system, and studies have shown that DBH levels are genetically determined (Lamprecht, Eichelman, Williams, Wooten, & Kopin, 1974). To the extent that such genetic influences play a role in the responsivity of target organs to the mes-

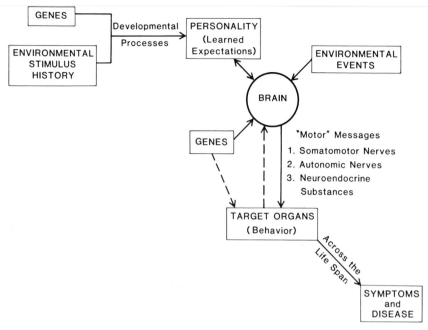

FIGURE 5.1 Conceptual model showing how the brain might transduce the interplay between personality and environmental events into bodily effects that could lead to disease.

sages sent to them via the brain's three motor effector systems, it would be a mistake to neglect them in any study of physiological responses to any specific environmental stimulus. The model also makes the point, as emphasized by both Hilton and Mason, that bodily adjustments to any environmental stimulus situation are transduced by the brain via a coordinated, integrated pattern of motor messages in all three effector systems. The nature of such integrated patterns is almost certainly the outcome of adaptive evolutionary responses to forces of natural selection.

More pertinent to the present discussion, we must look to the brain as the locus where the transduction of environmental events into bodily processes takes place. As illustrated in the model, the nature of this transduction will depend on characteristics of the person and of the environmental stimulus situation. For example, as is illustrated below, the observation of a growling tiger on an isolated jungle trail in northeast India will be interpreted far differently from the observation of such a beast within the confines of the National Zoo. Similarly, persons with different expectations of the world and the people in it (i.e., with different personalities) will also interpret the same environmental situations differently. For example, one type of person will become impatient and angry with those ahead of him in a bank line that is moving slowly, while another type of person will not be bothered in the least in the same situation. As is also illustrated in the model, the nature of the personality which we carry with us thoughout life is the result of developmental processes involving the interplay between our genetic predispositions and our environmental stimulus history.

While the model shown in Figure 5.1 is not intended as either a complete or final, it does represent an attempt, taking into account the best information currently available, to highlight critical classes of variables which determine who will develop which disease, as well as how and when. That is, the development of a given disease at a given time is the result of changes in target organ behaviors which are themselves determined by how the brain transduces experience into motor messages to the organs. This transduction process is a function of the interplay between the characteristics of the environment, the individual's genetic makeup and the individual's expectations of the world, or personality. With these principles in mind, it is now appropriate to consider in more detail the data showing how certain types of behavioral challenges lead reliably to specific patterns of autonomic and neuroendocrine response, as well as how persons with different personalities might express these characteristic patterns differently

Physiological Response Patterns and Behavioral Challenge

The Emotional Motor–Mental Work and Sensory Intake
Response Patterns

As noted above, intense emotions clearly lead to increased levels of autonomic and neuroendocrine function. However, emotions are hard to induce and measure, and, perhaps as a result, we do not as yet have broad agreement as to the specific patterns of response which correlate with which emotions. Taking an alternative approach to this problem, my colleagues and I over the past several years have attempted to induce specific behavioral states in human subjects and to characterize the patterns of cardiovascular and, more recently, neuroendocrine response exhibited in association with the behavioral states. Our perspective derives primarily from the work of the Laceys (see Lacey & Lacey, 1974), who noted some time ago that experimental tasks requiring mental work (e.g., mental arithmetic) result in a specific pattern of physiological response characterized by an *increase* in heart rate in association with increased skin sudomotor activity; in contrast, they found that when the experimental task involved primarily attentive observation of sensory stimuli with little or no requirements for internal cognitive elaboration, the response pattern was one of *decreased* heart rate and increased sudomotor activity. This "directional fractionation" of heart rate responses to mental work as compared to sensory intake tasks led to Laceys (Lacey, 1967) to question the unidimensional conception of arousal contained in classical arousal theory (Duffy, 1962) and to propose that different patterns of arousal occur in association with differing environmental demands—particularly those involving mental work as compared to sensory intake behaviors.

Based on observations of diastolic blood pressure increases in association with interpersonal interaction (McKegney & Williams, 1967; Williams, Kimball, & Willard, 1973), we employed the technique of venous occlusion plethysmography (Whitney, 1930) to measure forearm blood flow (FBF), an index of skeletal muscle blood flow, among healthy young males and females during varying behavioral tasks (Bittker, Buchsbaum, Williams, & Wynne, 1975; Williams, Bittker, Buchsbaum, & Wynne, 1975), including the performance of mental arithmetic (serial subtractions), sensory intake (reading words projected backwards and out of focus on a screen), and interpersonal interaction (an interview about the subject's current life situation). The findings of this study indicated that in addition to the divergence of heart rate response with demands for mental work versus sensory intake, the pattern of active skeletal muscle vasomotor response differs as well. During mental work, there was observed, in addition to a marked heart rate increase, an increase in FBF and a decrease in forearm vascular resistance (FVR). The latter indicated that the vasomotor response was an active vasodilatation, since the associated increase in cardiac output could alone be responsible for a passive increase in FBF. During sensory intake on the other hand, there was an active vasoconstriction in the forearm, as indexed by a significant increase in FVR. The vasodilatation and vasoconstriction responses were not limited to the situations in which the explicit demands of the tasks required mental work and sensory intake behavior, respectively. During interpersonal interaction, when the subjects could either attend to the interviewer or not, those who were blindly rated as being attentive showed a different vasomotor response than did those who were rated as inattentive to the interviewer. As shown in Figure 5.2, prior to the interview, those who were subsequently rated as attentive were already in a more vasoconstricted state than the nonattenders; nevertheless, during the interview the attenders

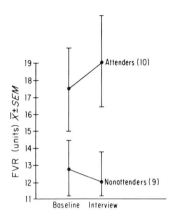

FIGURE 5.2   Changes in forearm vascular resistance (FVR) during a personal interview in those judged to be attention (Attenders) or inattentive (Nonattenders) to the interviewer.

increased their FVR even more, while the nonattenders decreased their FVR. In an earlier study (Williams, Frankel, Gillen, & Weiss, 1973) we had found that FBF increased during another mental work task (subjects were asked to say three words in association to each of a series of words called out to them).

Thus, it appears that when subjects are required to engage in tasks involving mental work (such as serial subtractions or word association testing) with little demand for sensory intake, they exhibit a characteristic pattern of vasomotor response, a key feature of which is skeletal muscle vasodilatation; in contrast, when the task demands are for sensory intake the cardiovascular response pattern is characterized primarily by an active vasoconstriction in skeletal muscle. Supportive of this formulation is a considerable body of research employing animal models. During a period when their observed behavior consisted of closely watching another cat who was behaving in a very aggressive manner (due to brain stimulation), hemodynamically monitored cats showed a decrease in heart rate and cardiac output in combination with a vasoconstriction in the artery supplying the hind limb muscles. In contrast, when the monitored cat either fought or fled from the other cat, the cardiac output and heart rate increased in association with vasodilatation of the hind limb artery. Anderson and Brady (1979) extended these findings in a series of studies in dogs, in which they found increased total peripheral resistance despite decreased cardiac output when dogs were trained to inhibit skeletal motor activity.

Based on such observations as these, Zanchetti (1976) has suggested that there appears to be a dual cardiovascular response pattern subserving emotional behavior, "one type [skeletal muscle vasoconstriction] being the usual companion of immobile confrontation of the preparatory stage, the other type [skeletal muscle vasodilatation] being characteristic of emotional movement (the classical 'defense pattern')" (p. 145). Based on an extensive body of research, Obrist (1976) has proposed that the critical elements of those behavioral states in which peripheral vasodilatation and vasoconstriction are found involve "active coping" and "passive coping," respectively. That is, when the subject is required to produce an active motor response in order to cope with the demands of the situation, there would be produced an increase in cardiac output and a skeletal muscle vasodilatation—the classical defense reaction. In contrast, where no motor response is available and the subject can only passively experience the situation, then the characteristic response is a peripheral vasoconstriction. While such an interpretation is in agreement with much of the available data cited above, particularly that of Anderson and Brady (1979), it is not in agreement with all the data, and, moreover, may not be the most parsimonious explanation for the observed effects.

In the Williams *et al.* (1975) study, subjects were engaged in active coping behavior during both the mental work (producing numbers out loud as they serially subtracted 13 from 1179) and the sensory intake tasks producing words—at about the same rate as the subtractions—as each new slide was projected on the screen in front of them). Nevertheless, when that active coping behavior involved mental work "inside the head," with little or no requirement for sensory intake, the cardiovascular response was clearly one of skeletal muscle *vasodilation;* and when the active coping behavior involved close attention to visual stimuli, with only a minimum of internal cognitive elaboration, the response was clearly one of active skeletal muscle *vasoconstriction.* It would appear more correct, as well as more parsimonious to conclude—in line with the principle outlined in the model shown in Figure 5.1 of three motor effector systems—that the decrease in ongoing skeletal motor activity and the skeletal muscle vasoconstriction which appear to be so reliably linked are both part of an integrated pattern of responses which is being transduced by the brain in an attempt to adapt to some environmental demands.

What might be the likely nature of the decision-making process whereby the brain decides to produce this characteristic response of decreased motor activity and skeletal muscle vasoconstriction? Is the decision reached that "I must get very still," with the result that skeletal muscle activity diminishes and the skeletal muscle vasculature vasoconstricts? Or is it more likely that a different, perhaps more goal-

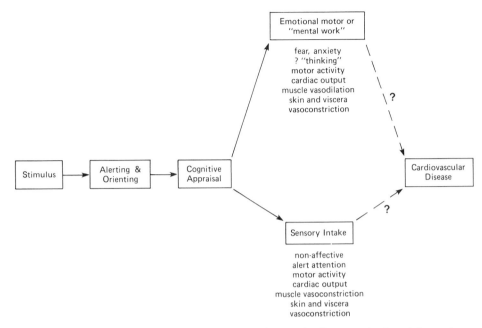

FIGURE 5.3   Conceptual schema of sequence of events leading to activation of "mental work" and "sensory intake" response systems.

related decision is reached, such as "There is something out there which may be of significance to me and I should pay close attention"? Since a still body provides a better platform for the sense organs, the skeletal musculature quiets, and since a quiet musculature needs less blood there is also a vasoconstriction. Figure 5.3 illustrates the likely sequence of events whereby both the defense (emotional motor)–mental work and the sensory intake response patterns might be activated.

Let us return to the situation in which one encounters a growling tiger. First of all, the perception of the tiger leads to an alerting and orienting of the organism to the tiger. Then begins a cognitive appraisal process wherein one evaluates the environmental context and one's past history of experience with growling tigers. If the context is an isolated jungle trail in northeast India, one likely reaches the conclusion that an emergency exists and the emotional motor–mental work response pattern is activated—a very adaptive response, since it prepares the body for intense physical exertion by increasing the cardiac output and shunting that blood away from the skin and viscera to the skeletal musculature. It might be asked why does mental work alone, without any fear arousal or emergency aspects—as occurs during serial subtractions or word association testing without any harassment—lead to the same response of increased cardiac output and muscle vasodilatation. While a full discussion of this issue would be beyond the scope of this chapter, it is interesting to speculate that the capacity to think—that is, to engage in mental as opposed to physical work—evolved as a function of that part of the brain which controls motor activity.

If the growling tiger is encountered while one is strolling through the National Zoo in Washington, D.C., on the other hand, rather than the cognitive appraisal process leading to the decision that an emergency exists, it is far more likely that the decision will be reached that "something out there is interesting and I wish to learn more about it," resulting in activation of the sensory intake response system with its characteristic decrease in skeletal muscle activity and active skeletal muscle vasoconstriction.

If these two response patterns, the emotional motor–mental work pattern with its active muscle vasodilatation and the sensory intake pattern with its active muscle vasoconstriction, are really expressions of two of the body's fundamental response systems (Hilton, 1975), then the principle of the three motor effector systems outlined in Figure 5.1 suggests that there should also be characteristic neuroendocrine response patterns associated with each (and, though I do not dwell on it extensively in this chapter, the evolutionary perspective would require that the neuroendocrine responses associated with each pattern should have some selection advantage).

We tested this hypothesis in a recent study, a preliminary report of which has been published (Williams *et al.*, 1982). The results support the hypothesis that tasks requiring sensory intake as compared to mental work behavior will, in addition to different skeletal muscle vasomotor responses, also be associated with qualitatively different patterns of neuroendocrine response. Furthermore, they illustrate the relationships outlined in the model shown in Figure 5.1 in that genetic and personality factors appear to modulate the expression of the different response patterns.

Several aspects of this study deserve emphasis as illustrative of both the principles already described and new technological advances in the study of neuroendocrine function. Using a counterbalanced design, we brought 31 young male undergraduates into the lab on two separate occasions, at the same time of day each time and one week apart. Following a baseline period of 20 min, half the subjects performed a mental work task (serial subtractions) on the first occasion, while the other half performed a 20-min sensory intake task (signaled choice reaction time), with crossover to the other task in the second lab session. For the mental arithmetic task, subjects were offered a small prize for good performance, though it is important to note that no harassment or punishment for poor performance was imposed. No incentives, positive or negative, were imposed for the reaction-time task (pilot testing had shown that any incentive appeared to attenuate the expected skeletal muscle vasoconstriction). All subjects were evaluated for presence of the Type A behavior pattern using both the structured interview (SI) and the Jenkins Activity Survey (JAS). With respect to technological advances, to obtain blood samples for subsequent neuroendocrine assays we used a Cormed continuous exfusion pump. This device utilizes a peristaltic pump and special heparin-impregnated catheters to obtain a continuous, integrated blood sample at the rate of 0.6 cc/min. This ensures that all of the neuroendocrine secretory activity during the experimental periods, including that occurring in episodic secretory "bursts," is assessed; with episodic blood sampling, for example, every 5 min, it is possible to miss such secretory bursts. In addition, with the advent of new and sensitive radioimmunoassay techniques, we were able to measure a broader array of hormones in the same blood sample than has been possible until very recently. With these new assay techniques the situation is not unlike that confronting scientists just after the invention of the microscope: Wherever one looks something new and interesting is likely to be found. In addition to the frequently measured heart rate and blood pressure responses, we also assessed FBF, a critical index of hemodynamic adjustments in skeletal muscle.

The overall findings are shown in Table 5.1. It is evident that characteristics related both to the nature of the tasks (mental work versus sensory intake) and to the nature of the subjects (Type A versus Type B—using only those subjects who were A or B on both the SI and the JAS) were important in determining not only quantitative but qualitative aspects of the responses observed in cardiovascular and neuroendocrine function. Focusing first on cardiovascular response, mental arithmetic performance was associated with clear vasodilatation in the forearm, as indexed by an increase in FBF and a decrease in FVR; in contrast, during reaction time performance, there was no significant change overall in either FBF or FVR, although the Type B subjects did show the predicted increase in FVR ($p < .05$, one-tailed). The vasodilatation during mental arithmetic was significantly greater in the Type A subjects. It is worth noting that the heart rate and blood pressure responses of the Type A's and B's did not differ significantly, although there was a trend ($p = .10$) toward greater heart rate response in the Type A subjects. Most prior studies (e.g., Dembroski, MacDougall, Herd, & Shields, 1979; Manuck & Garland, 1979) have found larger heart rate and systolic blood pres-

TABLE 5.1
Cardiovascular and Neuroendocrine Responses (Change from Baseline) during Performance of Mental Arithmetic and Reaction Time Tasks among A and B Subjects[a]

Response	Mental arithmetic			Reaction time		
	A (N = 11)	B (N = 10)	p	A (N = 11)	B (N = 10)	p
Cardiovascular						
Heart rate (beat/min)	+18 ± 2	+13 ± 2	N.S.	+4 ± 2	+2 ± 1	N.S.
Systolic blood pressure (mm Hg)	+20 ± 4	+19 ± 4	N.S.	+7 ± 2	+6 ± 2	N.S.
Diastolic blood pressure (mm Hg)	+14 ± 2	+11 ± 2	N.S.	+6 ± 2	+7 ± 2	N.S.
FBF (ml per 100 ml per minute)	+1.5 ± 0.3	+0.7 ± 0.1	.02	+0.3 ± 0.2	−0.1 ± 0.1	N.S.
FVR (100 ml/min)	−14.0 ± 2.2	−4.8 ± 2.3	.01	−1.9 ± 3.1	+6.1 ± 3.2	N.S.
Neuroendocrine						
Norepinephrine (pg/ml)	+188 ± 35	+103 ± 24	.05	+76 ± 22	+37 ± 20	N.S.
Epinephrine (pg/ml)	+47 ± 15	+12 ± 6	.05	+4 ± 3	+15 ± 19	N.S.
Cortisol (µg per 100 ml)	+8.3 ± 2.3	+0.2 ± 0.9	.006	−1.1 ± 2.0	−0.6 ± 1.0	N.S.
Prolactin (ng/ml)	+2.9 ± 0.9	+0.8 ± 0.9	N.S.	−0.7 ± 0.8	+1.2 ± 0.7	N.S.
Testosterone (ng/ml)	+0.5 ± 0.5	+0.3 ± 0.5	N.S.	+2.1 ± 0.5	−0.2 ± 0.9	.05

[a]From Williams *et al.*, 1982. Two-tailed *t* test or analysis of covariance with baseline as covariate; criterion α = .05. Each value represents the mean ± SEM. N.S., not significant.

sure responses in Type A as compared to Type B subjects during experimental tasks in which various forms of harassment were used. In our study without the use of harassment, the skeletal muscle vasomotor response of the Type A subjects was clearly greater than that of the Type B subjects; yet the blood pressure response was identical. It may well be that the tendency of Type A subjects to show a greater heart rate response with attendant increase in cardiac output and systolic blood pressure was counterbalanced, with respect to the blood pressure response, by the decreased peripheral resistance associated with the greater skeletal muscle vasodilatation. Unless the skeletal muscle hemodynamics are studied, such relationships cannot be detected.

The picture becomes even more interesting when we turn to the neuroendocrine responses. First, there were quantitative differences. Overall, the norepinephrine response to the reaction-time task, while significant, was smaller than to the mental arithmetic task. Of even greater interest, however, are the qualitative differences—both between the tasks and between the Type A and B subjects. Overall (i.e., considering all 31 subjects) there was a significant increase in epinephrine, prolactin, and cortisol and no change in testosterone during mental arithmetic performance. In contrast, during reaction-time performance there was no increase in epinephrine, cortisol, and prolactin, but a significant increase in testosterone. Compared to Type B, the Type A subjects showed significantly larger epinephrine and cortisol responses (the prolactin difference narrowly missed the .05 significance level) to mental arithmetic and a significantly larger testosterone response to reaction-time performance. Thus, mental work led to a qualitatively different neuroendocrine–cardiovascular response pattern from that of sensory intake, and both these response patterns were expressed to a quantitatively greater degree in the Type A as compared to the Type B subjects.

In addition to individual differences in response related to personality (presumably Type A behavior is a manifestation of certain underlying personality traits), there were also differences in response that may be attributable to genetic influences (though learning cannot be ruled out with the data at hand). As shown in Figure 5.4, among those subjects with a positive family history for hypertension in one or both parents, those with higher JAS Type A scores showed a larger cortisol response to the reaction-time task, while among those without a positive family history, Type A subjects were, if anything, hyporesponsive. The Type A by family history interaction was highly significant for cortisol ($p = .008$) and marginally ($p = .10$) so for diastolic blood pressure. In contrast to these interactions during reaction-time performance, during mental

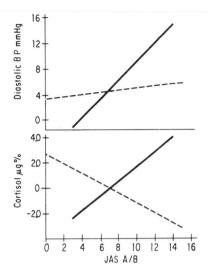

FIGURE 5.4   Diastolic blood pressure and cortisol responses to reaction-time task as a function of Type A score on the Jenkins Activity Survey, among subjects with (solid line) and without (broken line) a family history of hypertension (reprinted with permission from *Science, 218:* 483–485, 1982).

arithmetic performance no significant Type A by family history interactions were found.

To put these complex findings into what will hopefully be a more comprehensible perspective, let us refer again to the model outlined in Figure 5.1. We have found that when ENVIRONMENTAL EVENTS are such that mental work behavior (*internal cognitive elaboration,* to use the Laceys', 1974, term) is required, a qualitatively as well as quantitatively different pattern of autonomic and neuroendocrine responses is observed in comparison to when sensory intake behavior is required. When we assess characteristics which reflect different PERSONALITY TRAITS, we find that reliable differences are observed in the expression of both the mental work and sensory intake response patterns. Moreover, when a characteristic which may be related to differences in the GENES carried by the subjects is considered, we find an intriguing interaction with respect to certain responses to the sensory intake but not the mental work task. Thus, all of the core classes of influences (personality, environmental events, and genes) postulated to be important determinants of how the brain transduces experience into patterns of physiological response were found in this study to be meaningfully and reliably related to the response patterns which were observed under varying demands for mental work or sensory intake behavior.

Although the details of the specific neuroanatomical and neuro-chemical mechanisms whereby the brain accomplishes this transduction remain to be fully characterized, there is considerable evidence for the existence of brain mechanisms which could fulfill such a role. Using immunohistochemical and axonal transport methods, Sawchenko and Swanson (1981) have identified noradrenergic pathways arising in the dorsal vagal complex, the ventrolateral medulla, and the locus ceruleus which end in specific subdivisions of the paraventricular and supraoptic nuclei which are involved in the regulation of responses from the pituitary gland and from both divisions of the autonomic nervous system. They conclude that such circuitry may be involved in "the neural mechanisms that underlie integrated visceral responses" Natelson, Smith, Stokes, and Root (1974) found that stimulation of the hypothalamic "defense" area in monkeys resulted in significant increases in plasma corticosteroid levels. Williams, Richardson, and Eichelman (1978) reported that noradrenergic neurons originating in the locus ceruleus were responsible for mediating the peripheral sympathetic nerve response of two rats to shock-induced fighting, but not the response to foot shocks administered to a single rat.

Given that we find the different neuroendocrine response patterns as described above when subjects are required to engage in sensory intake versus mental work behavior, it is now appropriate to consider how our findings relate to the work of others who have attempted to identify the critical psychological stimuli for increased secretion of specific hormones, as well as how the response patterns we have observed might serve some adaptive function.

Relation of the Emotional Motor–Mental Work and
Sensory Intake Patterns to Previous Research and Their
Possible Functional Significance

As cited earlier, both Henry and Frankenhaeuser link effort with distress to increased levels of both cortisol and catecholamines (particularly epinephrine), while they feel effort without distress is associated with elevations only of catecholamines. Our finding of increases in norepinephrine, epinephrine, and cortisol during mental arithmetic, along with significant positive correlations among the increases of these three hormones during mental arithmetic in our whole sample of 31 men, suggests that during mental work both adrenal cortical and adrenal medullary activation occurs. It certainly calls into question the generality of Henry's (1983) assertion that these two response systems "represent behavioral patterns that move in different directions" Since most of

Frankenhaeuser's work in this area has involved the urinary excretion of cortisol and catecholamines, it is possible that some of the differences may be related to effects related to renal clearance of these substances. On the other hand, it could well be the case that the two sets of findings are not in disagreement. A task in which not only effort is required but in which distress is also generated would certainly be expected to generate more "mental work," in terms of trying to figure out what is going on or ruminating about it, than would a task in which everything is predictable and all one needs to do is carry it out without having to think much about it. Thus, increased mental work, with its attendant increased release of both epinephrine and cortisol, could be the underlying mechanism for the increased levels of these substances which Lundberg and Frankenhaeuser (1980) observe during a more distressing task. Our findings are harder to reconcile, however, with their finding of epinephrine but not cortisol increases during a less distressing self-paced reaction-time task. Again, since they found this in urine, it will be important to show the same effect when plasma levels are evaluated. Williams *et al.* (1982) found virtually no change in plasma epinephrine during reaction-time performance.

Our finding of increases in both epinephrine and cortisol during mental arithmetic is also in accord with the observation by Brandenberger, Follenius and Wittersheim (1980) of increases in both these hormones during a memorization task in humans. While it is logical to infer that both of these studies used tasks that have in common the requirement that subjects engage in mental work, it is harder to see why either task should be distressing, either in general or because it is less controllable, the latter characteristic being the one Frankenhaeuser has proposed as critical for cortisol responses. While tasks requiring mental work are not by necessity uncontrollable, it does appear reasonable to suppose that tasks which contain elements of uncontrollability will require more mental work than controllable tasks. Thus, the element common to all tasks that have been found to stimulate cortisol secretion appears more likely to be the requirement for mental work, rather than uncontrollability or distress; although tasks that are uncontrollable or that engender distress are clearly capable of stimulating cortisol release. Among such tasks as mental arithmetic, memorization tests, tasks that are uncontrollable, tasks that engender concerns about personal danger, and the like, the most plausible common element—perhaps Mason's (1975a) "pure" psychological input stimulus—may be, I suggest, the need for subjects to engage in mental work.

To my knowledge, our findings of significant prolactin and testosterone responses to mental arithmetic and reaction-time tasks, respec-

tively, represent the first reports of reliable responses of these substances to an experimental laboartory stressor in humans. In his
excellent review, Rose (1980) notes a paucity of studies of prolactin
response to psychologically disturbing stimuli and concludes that "it is
not yet known whether there are particular psychological stimuli which
are specifically provocative of prolactin secretion which are not at the
same time associated with increased cortisol, catecholamine, or growth
hormone secretion" (p. 257). In our study we found that prolactin secretion was stimulated by mental arithmetic performance, though the prolactin increase was itself uncorrelated with either the epinephrine or
cortisol responses, which, as noted above, were themselves positively
correlated with each other. We did note, however, an interesting pattern
of correlations among prolactin, cortisol and epinephrine responses to
the reaction-time task, when only the Typa A subjects were considered.
Among these subjects, the prolactin response to the reaction-time task
was negatively correlated with both the epinephrine ($r = -.75$) and
cortisol ($r = -.66$) responses, which were positively correlated with each
other ($r = +.73$). Although replication will be essential for this possibly
accidental finding, it does suggest that, at least among some individuals
who can be identified by their Type A behavior, brain mechanisms
which inhibit prolactin secretion are activated and also involved in stimulating epinephrine and cortisol secretion. One such mechanism which
is known to inhibit prolactin release, although its effect on the other
hormones is less clear, is dopamine. Thus, the association of a fall in
prolactin levels with increases in epinephrine and cortisol levels amont
Type A's during sensory intake behavior may be reflective of activation
of CNS dopaminergic mechanisms during sensory intake behavior.

Possibly reflective of a similar phenomenon to that described above
for Type A subjects only is the finding by Miyabo, Asato, and Mizushima (1977) that only in neurotics (and not in non-neurotic controls) the
growth hormone and cortisol responses to mirror drawing were negatively correlated. Although admittedly speculative, such interpretations
of brain mechanisms as advanced above are at least supported by some
evidence, and they attest to the wisdom of Mason's (1975a) suggestion
that by measuring a broader range of hormones we can learn more about
the control mechanisms for their secretion in association with psychological stimuli.

With respect to testosterone secretion, levels of this hormone have
been most often reported to decrease in association with any manipulation considered to be stressful (Rose, 1980). The only known report of
increases in testosterone have been in association with victory in male–
male dominance confrontations in animal studies (Bernstein, Gordon, &

Rose, 1978). It is possible that our finding of increased testosterone during the reaction time task may represent a clue to the underlying pure psychological stimulus for testosterone secretion. Surely, whatever else they may be doing during a dominance confrontation, the two male animals are paying very close attention to each other. Supportive of this hypothesized link between sensory intake and testosterone secretion is evidence presented by Thompson and Wright (1979) that testosterone administration results in increased "persistence" as well as a focusing and narrowing of attention in animals. Such behavioral effects of testosterone could have obvious survival values. First, they might directly influence which animal survives the confrontation, and, secondly, they would obviously influence which genes survive.

Also possibly related is the suggestion by Maxur and Lamb (1980) that among human males testosterone increases with the achievement or defense of a dominant position. In our study it would be logical to assume that the Type A's were trying to achieve a dominant position during mental arithmetic performance just as much as during reaction-time performance. Indeed, evidence of their striving during mental arithmetic can be seen in their serveralfold increases in both cortisol and epinephrine. However, the Type A's in our study did not change testosterone levels at all during mental arithmetic testing. During reaction-time testing, however, when they showed no epinephrine or cortisol responses, they increased their plasma testosterone levels by nearly 50%. This suggests that there is something about engaging in sensory intake behavior that is specifically stimulative of testosterone secretion. As with the possible mediation by mental work of cortisol increases during performance of uncontrollable tasks, it may be that activation of the sensory intake response system is responsible for the stimulation of testosterone secretion by dominance confrontations.

Often, interpretations of findings in scientific experiments are determined by the hypotheses with which we undertake the studies. When Lundberg and Frankenhaeuser (1980) expose their subjects to a task which they design to be uncontrollable and find that the subjects report more distress than during a more controllable task and also excrete more cortisol, they conclude that it is the uncontrollability of the task which is responsible. This is an entirely reasonable inference on their part. On the other hand, when Williams et al. (1982) design a task to require mental work without any sensory intake demands and find cortisol secretion to increase, they conclude that it is the mental work which is responsible, particularly since it is hard to see how this task is any less controllable than a reaction-time task during which no cortisol response is found. It may not be possible to reach a conclusion at present as to which interpretation is the correct one, or even the truer one. Rather than fall back on the old saw, "more research will be needed to resolve these issues," I will stick my neck out and assert that it will ultimately prove to be truer that the more basic, fundamental behaviors of mental work (with its occasional but not invariable link to the defense reaction) and sensory intake are responsible for the characteristic autonomic and neuroendocrine response patterns which occur in association with various affective states. Such an interpretation has a certain appeal in relying as it does on the general design in nature where as more complex functions (e.g., the emotions of fear, anger, and depression) evolve, they are often grafted onto simpler, earlier functions. One interesting example of this phenomenon is the use of certain biochemical compounds which happen to already be around, such as vasopressin and oxytocin, as neurotransmitters in the CNS.

Pathophysiological Consequences of Neuroendocrine Responses to Stress

Whatever the ultimate resolution of the debates as to the nature of the pure psychological stimulus for any given hormone or hormonal pattern, it is not so difficult to accept the proposition that excessive cardiovascular and neuroendocrine responses, particularly to laboratory stressors that mimic in some respects the situations and behaviors of everyday life, could be playing an important role in the pathogenesis of a wide variety of physical and emotional disorders. I do not dwell in any detail here on the extensive body of evidence linking hyperactivity of the pituitary–adrenolcortical axis with clinical depression (for an excellent review, see Carroll, 1978), but focus instead on the possible implications of excessive physiological responses for physical disorder, with particular emphasis on coronary heart disease.

Coronary Heart Disease

It is now generally accepted that persons displaying the Type A behavior pattern are at greater risk to develop clinical coronary heart disease (CHD), and there is also evidence for increased coronary atherosclerosis (CAD) among Type A men and women (see Surwit, Williams, and Shapiro, 1982, for a review of the role of Type A behavior in both CHD and CAD). The question now arises, can we explain the increased CHD risk and levels of CAD among Type A individuals through a consideration of their autonomic and neuroendocrine responses to the stresses of everyday life? Elsewhere in this volume, Glass (Chapter 10), reviews his own and others' work in which Type A men have been found to show larger increases in plasma catecholamines and in various parameters of cardiovascular function when exposed to a wide variety of laboratory stressors, most often involving some form of harassment with the goal of differentially arousing the Type A as compared to the Type B subjects.

Williams *et al.* (1982) obtained similar findings with respect to both norepinephrine and epinephrine responses to mental arithmetic among young Type A males. In addition, we found that when a relatively pure mental work stimulus was employed, Type A's showed hyper-responsivity in that function which we felt to be most specific for mental work—skeletal muscle vasodilatation. Utilizing our own design of both mental work and sensory intake tasks and with continuous blood samples obtained for assay of a wide range of hormones, we were able to extend the earlier findings of cardiovascular and catecholamine hyperresponsivity among Type A's to include responses of both cortisol and testosterone as well. Furthermore, we were able to show that this cortisol and testosterone hyper-responsivity among young Type A males was not general but selective: Cortisol excess occurred only during mental work, while testosterone excess occurred only during sensory intake. Moreover, although the larger prolactin response to mental arithmetic among our Type A subjects did not reach statistical significance ($p = .10$, two-tailed), it was close, and with a larger sample might become significant. In addition to the widely postulated role of catecholamines and the cardiovascular and metabolic responses they might cause, how might excessive levels of the other hormones we found among the Type A's play a role in the pathogenesis of CHD?

There is extensive evidence that cortisol and related compounds have a wide range of effects that could play a role in atherogenesis, not the least of which is the potentiation of the metabolic and cardiovascular effects of catecholamines. Cortisol has been shown to increase the activity of catecholamine-synthesizing enzymes in the adrenal medulla, as well as to inhibit the activity of enzymes which break down catecholamines (Kopin, 1980). Henry (1983) reviews an extensive literature documenting the following effects of glucocorticoids: (1) increased serum lipids, (2) increased atherosclerosis in dogs fed an atherogenic diet, and (3) increased numbers of dead or injured cells in arterial endothelium. It has also been shown that corticosteroids potentiate alpha-adrenergic vascular responses to catecholamines (Schmid, Eckstein, & Abboud, 1966), an effect which is likely mediated by inhibition of extraneuronal clearance pathways for catecholamines by corticosteroids (Goldie, 1976).

Hydrocortisone administration to humans has been shown to acutely reduce beta-receptor density in lymphocytes and increase beta-receptor density in granulocytes, while the long-term effect was to increase receptor density in both types of cells (Davies & Lefkowitz, 1980).

All of the above effects of corticosteroids could be logically expected to potentiate processes involved in endothelial injury, the most widely accepted model of atherogenesis (Ross & Glomset, 1976). The administration of corticosteroids has been associated with the acceleration of arteriosclerosis in patients with rheumatoid arthritis (Kalbak, 1972). Most directly implicating corticosteroids in atherogenesis was the observation of increased cortisol levels during a stressful, morning medical test among patients with more severe coronary atherosclerosis compared to patients with minimal or no disease (Troxler, Sprague, Albanese, Fuchs, & Thompson, 1977).

In the light of the above observations, our finding of a severalfold increase in plasma cortisol levels among our young Type A males during mental arithmetic performance takes on added significance. If, in addition to what they demonstrate during mental work performance in the laboratory, they also show cortisol hyper-responsivity when carrying out mental work tasks in real-life situations (which are by no means rare), then the excessive cortisol responses of Type A males might be playing an important role in the increased coronary atherosclerosis which the weight of evidence (Surwit *et al.*, 1982) suggests they have. Supportive of such an interpretation is the observation that despite increased plasma ACTH levels relative to middle-aged Type B men, middle-aged Type A men exhibit the same levels of cortisol, and a reduced cortisol repsonse to ACTH administration, suggesting that excessive ACTH secretion during earlier years may have resulted in reduced adrenal cortical responsivity (Friedman, Byers, & Rosenman, 1972). Such "down regulation" of adrenal cortical responsivity would not be expected in young adulthood, the age at which the Type A subjects in the Williams *et al.* (1982) study showed dramatic cortisol hyper-responsivity. Further support for this hypothesized role of excessive cortisol in the increased CAD levels among Type A's could be forthcoming if planned studies show relative cortisol response excess among patients with more severe CAD by angiography.

In addition to their cortisol hyper-responsivity during mental work performance, it is also possible that the increased plasma testosterone response of Type A's during sensory intake behavior could contribute to atherogenic processes. First, however, it should be noted that although providing the first evidence of increased plasma testosterone responses to exogenous stressors, our study was not the first to find evidence of increased testosterone production among Type A individuals. Zumoff *et al.* (1977) found that while Type A and B men did not differ in terms of nocturnal excretion of testosterone in the urine, the Type A men did show significant increases in testosterone excretion during the working hours—a time when, if real, their tendency to secrete more testosterone during sensory intake behavior would most likely be expressed. This confirmatory evidence gives us considerably more confidence in our finding of increased testosterone levels during sensory intake behavior among Type A males. The potential role of testosterone excess in atherogenesis is supported by the observation in animal models of atherosclerosis (catheter stress) that atheroma formation is increased with exogenous testosterone administration (Uzunova, Ramy, & Ramwell, 1978.

Another mechanism whereby the increased testosterone response we observe in Type A men might play a role in CHD pathogenesis is suggested by three reports (Klaiber *et al.*, 1982; Luria *et al.*, 1982; Phillips, Castelli, Abbott, & McNamara, 1983) of increased plasma estradiol levels among men with, as compared to men without, CHD. In none of these studies did plasma testosterone levels differentiate CHD from non-CHD groups, though a tendency toward higher testosterone levels in CHD patients was noted. Based on these three independent reports of elevated estradiol levels among men with CHD, it appears that estradiol, or something associated with estradiol, may be playing a role in CHD. Along with the other groups, Klaiber *et al.* (1982) note that the major source of estradiol in males is via aromatization of testosterone in adipose and muscle tissues. Our finding of both testosterone and norepinephrine hyper-responsivity among Type A men could provide an explanation of this surprising association between hyperestrogenemia and CHD in men, since, as Klaiber *et al.* (1982) note, it has been shown that addition of norepinephrine to Sertoli-cell–enriched cultures induces an increase in aromatization of testosterone to estradiol. Thus, as Type A men secrete increased amounts of testosterone, their concommitant increased secretion of norepinephrine speeds the conversion of the testosterone to estradiol. This could result in elevated estradiol levels while, unless sampled at the time of the excessive secretion, testosterone levels might not be found elevated. While known effects of estradiol to increase adrenergic activity could be playing a role in pathogenesis as suggested by Klaiber *et al.* (1982), it is also possible that even the transient metabolic and other effects of testosterone postulated above to enhance atherogenesis could be the primary pathogenic mechanism. In the latter case, the correlation of elevated estradiol levels with CHD could be an artifactual one caused by the fact that a major pathway for clearance of testosterone is via aromatization to estradiol. In either event, the essential factor underlying the association between estradiol and CHD would be the increased secretion of testosterone. In this light, our finding of increased testosterone secretion during sensory intake tasks among Type A men becomes an even more plausible candidate for playing at least a partial role in their increased CHD risk.

Although the possible role in atherogenesis of prolactin excesses is less obvious, this hormone does have effects which suggest a possible role. Prolactin has been shown to increase mobilization of calcium into serum independently of the vitamin D system (Pachuga & DeLuca, 1981). Since calcium plays an important role in vascular responsivity to catecholamines (e.g., as documented by the use of calcium channel blockers in the treatment of coronary vasospasm), this effect of prolactin could be involved in processes which promote endothelial injury. Based on the finding of decreased blood pressure in neonatal rats given anti-serum to prolactin, it has been suggested that endogenous prolactin is involved in blood pressure regulation (Mills, Buckman, & Peake, 1982).

Though circumstantial, the striking confluence documented above of evidence of significant or nearly significant excesses among Type A subjects in a wide array of hormones which have been hypothesized or shown to play either a direct or indirect role in atherogenesis provides a rather convincing picture, given the present state of knowledge concerning atherogenesis, that the increased risk of CHD and CAD among Type A individuals may be mediated by such hormonal excesses. Siegrist (1980) has suggested that a tendency of Type A individuals to unrealistically appraise challenging situations as more demanding than they actually are could be responsible for their increased risk of disease. Our data are consistent with such a hypothesis, but suggest that, more specifically, the nature of Type A individuals' excessive responsivity will be determined by the kind of behavior—mental work versus sensory intake—required by the characteristics of any given situation.

Other Diseases

While the evidence is most convincing for the participation of neuroendocrine hyper-responsivity in the pathogenesis of CHD, it is quite possible that with further research a role for such hyper-responsivity will emerge with respect to a wide variety of other disorders. For example, D. E. Anderson (personal communication, 1982) has shown that while neither increased salt intake nor increased peripheral resistance associated with motor inhibition results in sustained hypertension, dogs trained to inhibit motor activity *and* given excess salt do develop sustained hypertension. He postulates that in addition to sympathetic nervous system influences, it is likely that other hormonal responses (vasopressin?) may be important in mediating this hypertensive effect. In addition, the work of Riley (1981) suggests that adrenal cortical excesses in association with stress may influence immunocompetence in such a way as to promote the development and progression of cancer. Finally, Dilman (1981) suggests that hormonal excesses may play an important role in accelerating the aging process in general.

Whatever the ultimate outcomes, it is very likely that the kinds of excessive neuroendocrine and autonomic responses to stress which have been described in this chapter will ultimately contribute to our understanding of the nature of a wide range of pathological processes.

Neuroendocrine and Autonomic Responses as Determinants of Behavior

If we refer once more to the model outlined in Figure 5.1, we see that it is possible for both the genes and the effects of the brain's motor messages, either directly or via feedback effects, to influence the working of the brain to transduce experience into motor functions. It is intriguing, therefore, to speculate that rather than personality structure causing some persons to behave in a Type A way, the biologically determined characteristics of their motor messages may be the primary cause of their Type A behavior and of the personality structure which they have.

There is some evidence, for example, that the adrenergic hyperresponsivity which several investigators have found among Type A individuals could be responsible for at least some of their Type A behavioral stylistics. Krantz (1985) has reported that administration of the nonspecific beta-blocker propranolol results in decreased intensity of Type A speech stylistics, but not of the hostile content expressed during the structured interview. Schmieder, Friedrich, Neus, and Ruddel (1982) reported that a cardioselective beta-blocker which by virtue of its limited lipid solubility has limited access to the brain has similar effects on Type A speech stylistics, while administration of a diuretic, which probably stimulates via reflex mechanisms increasing sympathetic activity, results in increased Type A speech stylistics. Thus, it appears that at least some of the motoric components of Type A behavior are determined by peripheral adrenergic hyper-responsivity. Since there is evidence from animal studies that catecholamine responses to stress are under genetic control (Kopin, 1980), it could well be that a genetically determined tendency to more intense sympathetic discharge, for example, during both mental work and sensory intake behaviors, could be responsible for Type A individuals' typical rapid and plosive speech characteristics.

It is also possible that testosterone hyper-responsivity during sensory intake behaviors may be similarly "hard-wired" and responsible for some of the other behaviors exhibited by Type A persons. We have already noted the effect of testosterone to increase persistence, focus attention, and to be associated with efforts to achieve a dominant position—all characteristics of the Type A person. In addition, plasma testosterone levels have been found to be correlated with increased aggressive behavior in man (Ehrenkranz, Bliss, & Sheard, 1974).

Increased corticosteroid levels are also known to have behavioral effects which could predispose to Type A behavior. Corticosterone administration has been shown to be a necessary factor for the development of stress-induced analgesia in the rat (MacLennan *et al.*, 1982). It is intriguing to speculate that in addition to the effects of increased testosterone levels on persistence, the effect of cortisol excess in Type A's could act in them to potentiate a similar form of stress-induced analgesia and enable (cause?) them to persist longer in stressful tasks than their Type B counterparts, who lack the extra cortisol in response to stressors. It is known that CNS noradrenergic systems are involved in many aspects of the body's response to stress (Kopin, 1980). Since corticosteroids have been shown to affect the function of noradrenergic systems in the brain (Maas & Mednieks, 1971; Mobley & Sulser, 1980), it is quite possible that their adrenal cortical hyper-responsivity to stress could exert profound influences upon the way in which the brain of Type A's transduces environmental events into motor messages to the body.

While most of us working in the Type A field have made the assumption that it is something about the psychological makeup of the Type A person that is responsible for his (and probably her as well) increased autonomic and neuroendocrine responses to a wide variety of stressors, the known effects of the hormones which have been found to respond excessively among Type A's could just as well be themselves the cause of the psychological makeup of the Type A person. Recall that in Figure 5.1 the personality results from developmental processes involving the interplay between the genes and the environment. If studies of these developmental processes show that the kinds of autonomic and neuroendocrine hyper-responsivity which have been found in older Type A's, ranging from age 8 to 65, are also present from birth, then it will prove necessary to adopt the view that Type A behavior results from, rather than causes, excessive bodily responses. Krantz (1983) has advanced similar speculations regarding the biological basis of Type A behavior.

Implications for Treatment

While it is always a laudable goal to push back the boundaries of our knowledge of the workings of nature, the subject matter of this chapter—the influence of the stresses of life upon the functioning of the body—also has exceedingly important implications for the practical task of increasing our understanding of disease processes so as ultimately to devise better means of prevention and treatment. In the absence of detailed knowledge concerning pathogenic mechanisms, our efforts at prevention and treatment must be not only cumbersome and of small effect but also inefficient. For example, until the polio virus was identified as the pathogenic agent in infantile paralysis, the expensive and labor intensive Sister Kenny treatment method was all we had to offer the victims of this dread disease. With the identification of the polio virus as the causative agent it became possible to devise a vaccine which is not only far more effective in controlling the disease but is also strikingly less expensive. An even more extreme example of this phenomenon of inefficient technology in the control of a disease is provided by the fact that in the seventeenth century the only effective means of controlling the plague epidemic in London was to burn down (accidentally, of course) the whole city!

In the absence of more detailed knowledge concerning the pathogenic mechanisms underlying the relationship between Type A behavior and CHD, for example, we can only try to change Type A's into Type B's. While preliminary efforts to apply such an approach to the problem of secondary prevention in Type A's following a myocardial infarction appear to have a beneficial effect (Friedman *et al.*, 1982), to undertake such a task in that half of the healthy population which is Type A, numbering the United States alone over 100 million, would likely prove to be an inefficient approach, even if effective. It seems reasonable to assume that if we could identify those aspects of the bodily functioning of the Type A persons which are involved in pathogenesis, it should prove possible to narrow greatly the size of the population in whom preventive efforts, even inefficient ones, are warranted. Even more important, identification of pathogenic mechanisms could also serve to provide far sharper targets for intervention efforts. For example, the now well-known effect of beta-blockade to reduce the recurrence rate in myocardial infarction victims may well be acting via reductions in the adverse cardiovascular effects of adrenergic hyper-responsivity among Type A persons.

To illustrate how detailed knowledge of pathogenic mechanisms might be employed, let us presume that the cortisol and testosterone hyper-responsivity among Type A's during mental work and sensory intake, respectively, ultimately can be shown to be the critical pathogens relating Type A behavior to increased CHD. If we could be sure of that, then we could set about the task of devising means to attenuate that hyper-responsivity with the goal of interdicting the atherogenic process. The search for such means could lead to unexpected areas. For example, the new, oral antifungal drug, ketoconozole (Nizoral), has been found to have some very interesting side effects—it inhibits the trophic hormone-stimulated synthesis of both testosterone and adrenal steroids (Pont, 1983)! While I by no means intend to imply that the day is near when all Type A persons with excessive cortisol and testosterone responses to mental work and sensory intake should be placed on prophylactic ketoconozole, if we could be reasonably confident of the pathogenic role of those hormones in CHD, then studies to evaluate the effectiveness of that durg in the prevention of CHD would be easy to justify. The point to retain from this speculative digression is that with identification of specific pathogenic mechanisms it becomes possible to devise preventive and treatment measures that will be far more effective and efficient than those available in the absence of such knowledge.

Summary and Conclusions

Humans enter the world with a particular complement of genetic material. Based upon the interplay between that material and the things that happen to them as they grow, they come to have particular learned expectations of the world and the people and things in it, which may be described as their personality. Depending upon the nature of that personality, the continuing expression of their genes and the things that continue to happen in their environment, their brain sends motor messages to their bodily organs which in most cases aid them in adapting to the vicissitudes of life. When the motor messages sent by the brain are too intense or continue for too long, then various pathogenic processes are set in motion and, eventually, disease develops. In this chapter I have reviewed research findings more specifically illustrative of these various processes. It is to be hoped that future research to clarify further the mechanisms touched upon herein will lead to better understanding of health and disease and, ultimately, to the identification of better means to reduce the pain and suffering associated with it.

References

Anderson, D. E. & Brady, J. V. (1979). Experimental analysis of psychosomatic interactions: Behavioral influence upon physiological regulations. In R. S. Davidson (Ed.), *Modification of pathological regulations* (pp. 189–231). New York: Gardner Press.

Bernstein, I. S., Gordon, T. P., & Rose, R. M. (1978). Influences of sexual and social stimuli upon circulating levels of testosterone in male pigtail macaques. *Behavioral Biology, 24,* 400–404.
Bittker, T. E., Buchsbaum, M. S., Williams, R. B., & Wynne, L. C. (1975). Cardiovascular and neurophysiologic correlates of sensory intake and rejection: II. Interview behavior. *Psychophysiology, 12,* 434–438.
Brandenberger, G., Follenius, M., Wittersheim, G., & Metz, B. (1980). Communications. *Journal of Physiology* (Paris) 76, 29A–34A.
Carroll, B. J. (1978). Neuroendocrine function in psychiatric disorders. In M. Lipton, A. D. Miscio, & K. F. Killom (Eds.), *Pharmacology. A generation of progress* (p. 487). New York: Raven Press.
Davies, A. O. & Lefkowitz, R. J. (1980). Corticosteroid-induced differential regulation of adrenergic receptors in circulating human lymorphonuclear leukocytes and mononuclear leukocytes. *Clinical Endocrinology and Metabolism, 51*(3), 599–605.
Dembroski, T. M., MacDougall, J. M., Herd, J. A., & Shields, J. L. (1979). Effects of level of challenge on pressor and heart rate responses in Type A and Type B subjects. *Journal of Applied Social Psychology, 9,* 209–228.
Dilman, V. M. (1981). *The law of deviation of homeostasis and diseases of aging.* New York: John Wright, PSG Inc.
Duffy, E. (1962). *Activation and behavior.* New York: Wiley.
Ehrenbranz, J., Bliss, E., & Sheard, M. H. (1974). Plasma testosterone: Correlation with aggressive behavior and social dominance in man. *Psychosomatic Medicine, 36*(6), 469–475.
Frankenhaeuser, M., Lundberg, U., & Forsman, L. (1980). Note on arousing Type A persons by depriving them of work. *Journal of Psychosomatic Research, 24,* 45–47.
Friedman, M., Byers, S. O., & Rosenman, R. H. (1972). Plasma ACTH and cortisol concentration of coronary-prone subjects[1] (36530). *Proceedings of the Society for Experimental Biology and Medicine 140:* 681–684.
Friedman, M., Thoresen, C. E., Gill, J. J., Ulmer, D., Thompson, L., Powell, L., Price, V., Elek, S. R., Rabin, D. D., Breel, W. S., & Pigget, G. (1982). Feasibility of altering Type A behavior pattern after myocardial infarction: Recurrent coronary prevention project study: Methods, baseline results, and preliminary findings. *Circulation, 66,* 83–92.
Goldie, R. G. (1976). The effects of hydrocortisone on responses to and extraneuronal uptake of (−) isoprenalin in cat and guinea-pig atria. *Clinical and Experimental Pharmacology and Physiology, 3,* 225–233.
Henry, J. P. (1983). Coronary heart disease and arousal of the adrenal cortical axis. In T. M. Dembroski & T. Schmidt (Eds.), *Biobehavioral bases of coronary heart disease* (pp. 1–29). Basel: Karger.
Hilton, S. M. (1975). Ways of reviewing the central nervous control of the circulation—old and new. *Brain Research, 87,* 213–219.
Kalbak, K. (1972). Incidence of arteriosclerosis in patients with rheumatoid arthritis receiving long-term corticosteroid therapy. *Annals of Rheumatic Disease, 31,* 196–200.
Klaiber, E. L., Broverman, D. M., Haffajee, C. I., Hochman, J. S., Sacks, G. M., & Dalen, J. E. (1982). Serum estrogen levels in men with acute myocardial infarction. *American Journal of Medicine, 73,* 872–881.
Kopin, I. J. (1980). Catecholamines, adrenal hormones, and stress. In D. J. Krieger & J. C. Hughes (Eds.), *Neuroendocrinology* (pp. 159–166). New York: Hospital Practice Publishing.
Krantz, D. (1985). Psychobiological substrates of the Type A behavior pattern. *Health Psychology,* In Press.
Lacey, J. I. (1967). Somatic response patterning and stress. Some revisions of activation

theory. In M. H. Appley & R. Turnball (Eds.). *Psychological stress: Issues in research,* 1967, New York: Appleton.

Lacey, J. I. & Lacey, B. C. (1974). On heart rate responses and behavior: A reply to Elliott. *Journal of Personality and Social Psychology, 30,* 1–18.

Lamprecht, F., Eichelman, B. S., Williams, R. B., Wooten, G. F., & Kopin, I. J. (1974). Serum dopamine-beta-hydroxylase (DBH) activity and blood pressure response of rat strains to shock-induced fighting. *Psychosomatic Medicine, 36:* 298–303.

Lundberg, U. & Frankenhaeuser, M. (1980). Pituitary-adrenal and sympathetic-adrenal correlates of distress and effort. *Journal of Psychosomatic Research, 24,* 125–130.

Luria, M. H., Johnson, M. W., Pego, R., Seuc, C. A., Manubens, S. J., Wieland, M. R., & Wieland, R. G. (1982). Relationship between sex hormones, myocardial infarction, and occlusive coronary disease. *Archives of Internal Medicine, 142,* 42–44.

Maas, J. W. & Mednieks, M. (1971). Hydrocortisone-mediated increase of norepinephrine uptake by brain slices. *Science, 171,* 178–179.

MacLennan, A. J., Drugan, R. C., Hyson, R. L., Maier, S. F., Madden, J., IV, & Barchas, J. D. (1982). Corticosterone: A critical factor in an opioid form of stress-induced analgesia. *Science, 215,* 1530–1532.

Manuck, S. B. & Garland, F. N. (1979). Coronary-prone behavior pattern, task incentive and cardiovascular response. *Psychophysiology, 2,* 136–142.

Mason, J. W. (1975a). Emotion as reflected in patterns of endocrine integration. I. Some theoretical aspects of psychoendocrine studies of emotion. In L. Levi (Ed.), *Emotions— their parameters and measurement* (pp. 143–181). New York: Raven Press.

Mason, J. W. (1975b). Psychologic stress and endocrine function. In E. Sachar (Ed.), *Topics with psychoendocrinology* (pp. 1–18). New York: Grune & Stratton.

Mazur, A. & Lamb, T. A. (1980). Testosterone, status, and mood in human males. *Hormones and Behavior, 14,* 236–246.

McKegney, F. P. & Williams, R. B. (1967). Psychological aspects of hypertension: II. The differential influence of interview variables on blood pressure. *American Journal of Psychiatry, 123,* 1539–1543.

Mobley, P. L. & Sulser, F. (1980). Rapid communication: Adrenal steroids affect the norepinephrine-sensitive adenylate cyclose system in the rat limbic forebrain. *European Journal of Pharmacology, 65,* 321–323.

Mills, D. E., Buckman, M. T., & Peake, G. T. (1982). Neonate treatment with antiserum to prolactin lowers blood pressure in rats. *Science, 217,* 162–164.

Miyabo, S., Asato, T., & Mizushima, N. (1977). Prolactin and growth hormone responses to psychological stress in normal and neurotic subjects. *Journal of Clinical Endocrinology and Metabolism, 44*(5), 947–951.

Natelson, B. H., Smith, G. P., Stokes, P. E., & Root, A. W. (1974). Plasma 17-hydroxycorticosteroids and growth hormone during defense reactions. *American Journal of Physiology, 226,* 560–568.

Obrist, P. A. (1976). The cardiovascular–behavioral interaction—as it appears today. *Psychophysiology, 13,* 95–107.

Pachuga, D. N. & DeLuca, H. F. (1981). Stimulation of intestinal calcium transport and bone calcium mobilization by prolactin in vitamin D-deficient rats. *Science, 214,* 1038–1039.

Phillips, G. B., Castelli, W. P., Abbott, R. D., & McNamara, P. M. (1983). Association of hyperestrogenemia and coronary heart disease in men in the Framingham cohort. *American Journal of Medicine, 74,* 863–869.

Pont, A. (March, 1983). Paper presented at Western Society for Clinical Investigation, Carmel, Cal.

Rose, R. M. (1980). Endocrine responses to stressful psychological events. Psychology of psychoendocrinology of stress. In E. J. Sachar (Ed.), *Advances in psychoneuroendocrinology* (pp. 251–276). Philadelphia: Saunders.

Ross, R. & Glomset, J. A. (1976). The pathogenesis of atherosclerosis (Parts 1 and 2). *New England Journal of Medicine, 295:* 369–377, 420–425.

Riley, V. (1981). Biobehavioral factors in animal work on tumorigenesis. In S. M. Weiss, J. A. Herd, & B. H. Fox (Eds.), *Perspectives on behavioral medicine* (pp. 183–214). New York: Academic Press.

Sawchenko, P. E. & Swanson, L. W. (1981). Central noradrenergic pathways for the integration of hypothalamic neuroendocrine and autonomic responses. *Science, 214,* 685–687.

Schmid, P. G., Eckstein, J. W., & Abboud, F. M. (1966). Effects of 9-a-flurohydrocortisone on forearm vascular responses to norepinephrine. *Circulation, 34,* 620–626.

Schmieder, R., Friedrich, G., Neus, H., & Ruddel, H. (March, 1982). Effects of beta-blockers on Type A coronary-prone behavior. Paper presented at American Psychosomatic Society Meeting, Denver.

Selye, H. (1950). *Stress.* Montreal: ACTA.

Siegrist, J. (1980). Psychosocial coronary risk constellation in the work setting. In J. Siegrist, K. Dittmann, & I. Weber (Eds.), *Soziale Belastungen und Herginfarkt* (pp. 85–96). Stuttgart: Enke.

Surwit, R. S., Williams, R. B., & Shapiro, D. (1982). *Behavioral approaches to cardiovascular disease.* New York: Academic Press.

Thompson, W. R. & Wright, J. S. "Persistence" in rats: Effects of testosterone. *Physiological Psychology, 7,* 291–294.

Troxler, R. G., Sprague, E. A., Albanese, R. A., Fuchs, R., & Thompson, A. J. (1977). The association of elevated plasma cortisol and early atherosclerosis as demonstrated by coronary angiography. *Atherosclerosis, 26,* 151–162.

Uzunova, A. D., Ramey, E. R., & Ramwell, P. W. (1978). Gonadal hormones and pathogenesis of occlusive arterial thrombosis. *American Journal of Physiology, 234,* 454–459.

Whitney, R. J. (1953). The measurement of volume changes in human limbs. *Journal of Physiology, 121,* 1–27.

Williams, R. B., Bittker, T. E., Buchsbaum, M. S., & Wynne, L. C. (1975). Cardiovascular and neurophysiologic correlates of sensory intake and rejection: I. Effects of cognitive tasks. *Psychophysiology, 12,* 427–432.

Williams, R. B., Frankel, B. L., Gillin, J. C., & Weiss, J. (1973). Cardiovascular response during a work association test and interview. *Psychophysiology, 10,* 571–577.

Williams, R. B., Kimball, C. P., & Willard, H. N. (1973). The influence of interpersonal interaction upon diastolic blood pressure. *Psychosomatic Medicine 34,* 194–198.

Williams, R. B., Lane, J. D., Kuhn, C. M., Melosh, W., White, A. D., & Schanberg, S. M. (1982). Type A behavior and elevated physiological and neuroendocrine responses to cognitive tasks. *Science, 218,* 483–485.

Williams, R. B., Richardson, J. S., & Eichelman, B. S. (1978). Location of central nervous system neurones mediating blood pressure response of rats to shock-induced fighting. *Journal of Behavioral Medicine, 1,* 177–185.

Zanchetti, A. (1976). Hypothalamic control of circulation. In S. Julius & M. D. Esler (Eds.), *The Nervous system in arterial hypertension* (pp. 136–148). Springfield, IL: Thomas.

Zumoff, B., Rosenfeld, R. S., Friedman, M., Byers, S. O., Roseman, R. H., & Hellman, L. (1977). Comparison of plasma and urinary steroids in men with Type A and Type A behavior patterns. Advisory group for Aerospace Research and Development, Conference proceedings No. 231, Prospective medicine opportunities in aerospace medicine (London), A12-1–A12–8

6

Brain Mechanisms in Effects of Social Support on Viability

EVERETT W. BOVARD

Effects of Social Relationships

A number of studies, reviewed below, have shown the critical effect of the presence or absence of social relationship on disease outcome and on growth and development of the individual. What is needed now is a physiological mechanism to account for these results, and that is our concern here. First, the studies.

Berkman and Syme (1979) found that persons who were married, had friends, or belonged to community or religious groups had a significantly lower age-adjusted mortality rate from the leading causes of death than those who were isolated or alone. The relationship held not only with overall mortality rate, but separately with four leading causes of death: ischemic heart disease, cancer, cerebrovascular and circulatory disorders, and a category including all other causes of death, such as diseases of the digestive and respiratory systems, accidents and suicide.

The mortality risk for those with the least social ties was about twice that for those with the most ties. These effects were independent of health habits or socioeconomic status. The results were based on a random sample of 6928 adults in Alameda County, California, followed for 9 years.

This study suggests the possibility that social circumstances alter the susceptibility of humans to a wide range of diseases. Any physiological mechanism hypothesized to account for the overall connection between social support and reduced mortality must, in addition, specifically ac-

PERSPECTIVES ON BEHAVIORAL MEDICINE, Vol. 2
Neuroendocrine Control and Behavior

count for the effects of social relationship on each disease process or environmental insult involved.

In developing such an hypothesis, however, it may prove fruitful to begin by considering the relationship of social support to one specific disease alone.

Bruhn and Wolf's (1979) study of the small, close-knit Italian–American community of Roseto, Pennsylvania, during the 1960s, shows the effects of social support on the incidence of heart disease. Family and interfamily relationships were extremely close and mutually supportive in this community, where traditional Italian family-centered values obtained. The people of Roseto were relatively obese compared to the people of two neighboring communities, but they did not differ essentially in levels of animal fat in their diets, serum cholesterol, hypertension, or smoking and exercise habits from the people in these communities. Yet their mortality rate from myocardial infarction was substantially lower than that of their neighbors, and well below the national average. There were also lower rates of incidence of senile dementia and peptic ulcer in Roseto. To understand in more precise physiological detail what happened in Roseto, it may prove useful to consider two experimental studies on effects of social relationship—one on humans and one on rabbits.

In an experimental study with humans, Back and Bogdanoff (1964) showed that, under the stress of venipuncture, reduced free fatty acid (FFA) mobilization occurs in the bloodstream as a result of sympathetic autonomic activation when this stress takes place in the presence of friends, compared to strangers. This study suggests that the mechanism involved in the Roseto study is inhibition of sympathetic autonomic activity under social support, thus reducing FFA mobilization and also reducing sympathetic output to the sinoatrial node of the heart and to the coronary arteries. This could very well be the major mechanism in the effects of social interaction in reducing mortality due to ischemic heart disease, cerebrovascular disease, and circulatory disorders found in the Berkman and Syme studies.

The work of Henry, Ely *et al.* (1971) and Henry, Stephens, Axelrod, and Mueller (1971) has shown that in mice, activation of the sympathetic autonomic system and consequent adrenal medullary activation under emotional stress are associated with development of arteriosclerosis, diseases of the coronary arteries, myocardial fibrosis, degeneration of the aorta, and nephritis. Further, direct stimulation at regular intervals of the lower splanchnic nerve, which provides sympathetic input to the aorta, has been shown to lead to arteriosclerosis in experimental rats in a study by Gutstein and Lataillade (1962).

Thus, these studies suggest that inhibition of sympathetic autonomic reactivity to stress, as a result of social support, should have protective consequences for the cardiovascular system. This conclusion is supported by studies of ventricular fibrillation, a leading cause of sudden cardiac death, in humans and animals. A retrospective study by Reich, Murawski, DeSilva, and Lown (1979) has shown that such abnormally rapid, chaotic beating of the heart ventricles can be triggered by acute emotional states such as anger, depression, fear, anticipated excitement, and grief, even in patients relatively free from heart disease. Experimental work on animals by Verrier and Lown (1981), their colleagues, and others has shown that emotional stress can precipitate such fibrillation in the ischemic heart, and that these effects are mediated by the sympathetic limb of the autonomic nervous system. In respect to emotional stress, Verrier and Lown found that under ischemia induced by occlusion of a coronary artery, dogs were three times as susceptible to ventricular fibrillation in an environment in which they had been previously shocked, as they were in an nonaversive environment. Along these same lines, Skinner, Lie, and Entman (1974) showed that coronary occlusion in a pig in an unfamiliar environment produced ventricular fibrillation in a few minutes; when this procedure was carried out in a familiar environment, however, onset of the fibrillary episode was delayed and even prevented.

Direct evidence of sympathetic autonomic mediation of the effects of emotional stress on fibrillation has been provided by Satinsky, Kosowsky, Lown, and Kerzner (1971), reviewed by Verrier and Lown (1981). Electrical stimulation of cardiac acceleration and vasomotor centers in the posterior hypothalamus following experimentally induced acute myocardial ischemia in anesthetized dogs increased the incidence of ventricular fibrillation tenfold (from 6.3 to 62.5%), compared to ligation of the coronary artery in the absence of such hypothalamic stimulation.

Further, as Verrier and Lown note in their review, direct stimulation of the sympathetic efferent pathway to the heart, by stimulation of the stellate ganglion itself, has been found to increase the incidence of ventricular fibrillation during myocardial ischemia. They note further that the pro-fibrillatory influence of CNS stimulation is abolished either by cardiac sympathectomy or by administration of sympatholytic drugs. Their conclusion that the sympathetic nervous system mediates the effect of emotional stress on vulnerability of the heart to ventricular fibrillation appears to be amply warranted by the experimental data. It would follow, therefore, that inhibition of sympathetic autonomic input to the heart under emotional support from family and friends could reduce vulnerability to ventricular fibrillation under severe emotional stress, and thereby protect the individual with social support from sudden cardiac death.

Finally, Verrier and Lown (1981) note that vagal stimulation has been found to raise the threshold for ventricular fibrillation in dogs. This protective effect of parasympathetic input to the heart depends, however, on the existing level of sympathetic activity. At a low level, no effect of vagal stimulation is observed; but when sympathetic tone is raised, for example, by stimulation of sympathetic input to the heart, then vagal stimulation is effective in blocking fibrillation. These considerations suggest that parasympathetic input to the heart could be the final common pathway for the protective effects of social support on ischemic heart disease.

To put this another way, the Back and Bogdanoff (1964) study suggests that the presence of family and friends (i.e., social support) raises the threshold for sympathetic autonomic response to stress. This could easily be tested by comparing cardiac acceleration in response to the cold pressor test in subjects in the presence and absence of emotional support (or even imagined emotional support as induced under hypnosis). What this would mean is that, under the supportive influence of their dense social networks, the people of Roseto would show minimal or reduced reactivity to the stresses of everyday life. It should be again noted here that their cholesterol levels and fat intake were at the same levels as those in nearby towns where the incidence of heart disease was much higher. The key difference, therefore, would be the threshold for stress.

Related to the Back and Bogdanoff study is an experimental study with rabbits by Nerem, Levesque, and Cornhill (1980). They showed that establishment of a social relationship between experimenter and rabbit, involving petting, talking to, and playing with the animal, reduced diet-induced atherosclerotic lesions by 60% (in area) in three independent studies. Notable in this study was the fact that, as in the Roseto study, there was no significant difference in cholesterol levels or diet between experimental and control animals, nor was there any difference in resting heart rate. If our hypothesis is correct, however, there should be a difference between experimental and control rabbits in respect to threshold for stress, as measured by FFA mobilization or cardiac acceleration in response to a mild stressor. Again, this could easily be tested.

These two experimental studies therefore suggest, but do not conclusively demonstrate, that the key factor in protection against heart disease under emotional support in the Bruhn and Wolf (1979) and Berkman and Syme (1979) studies is reduced physiological response to environmental stress, in particular, a higher threshold for sympathetic autonomic reactivity.

A secondary factor, however, may be a higher threshold for the pituitary–adrenocortical response to stress under social support. As Williams *et al.* (1982) note, hydrocortisone has been found to potentiate the sympathetic–adrenal medullary response by stimulating catechol-synthesizing enzymes, inhibiting a catecholamine-degrading enzyme, and increasing activity of adrenergic receptors. Elevated plasma hydrocortisone levels during an oral glucose tolerance test among U.S. Air Force personnel have been found to be correlated with increased arteriographically demonstrated coronary atherosclerosis (Troxler, Sprague, Albanese, Fuchs, & Thompson, 1977).

Therefore it would follow that the enhanced catecholamine and hydrocortisone responsivity of Type A (coronary-prone) young men to mental work, in contrast to the responsivity of Type B, as found by Williams *et al.* (1982), would put the Type A personality under special risk for coronary atherosclerosis, with the elevated sympathetic–adrenal medullary response potentiated by the elevated pituitary–adrenocortical response. Thus, social support may turn out to be a key factor in alleviating the risk of ischemic heart disease in Type A personality, if we can show that it inhibits both arms of the response to stress.

Further light may be shed on the hypothesis that social support may also inhibit the pituitary–adrenocortical response to stress when we consider what happens to children who are raised in what can only be called an emotionally stressful atmosphere, where social support is conspicuous by its absence. These circumstances have been shown to produce severe retardation of bone growth and weight gain, termed *psychosocial* or *deprivation dwarfism*.

Powell, Brasel, Raiti, and Blizzard (1967) found that severely growth-retarded children, from emotionally disturbed home atmospheres, whose height in each case was equal to that of children half their age, showed evidence of abnormally low growth hormone levels in the blood. When these children were removed from their families and placed in a convalescent home, they rapidly grew up to the normal height for their respective ages without any special hormonal treatment or psychotherapy, presumably because of a more adequate supply of growth hormone in these circumstances.

Gardner (1972) reports one instructive case of such psychosocial dwarfism in which a child who had spent 2 years in a disordered home situation showed a bone maturation age 3 years younger than his chronological age and was severely underweight. Further, this child showed an abnormally low reserve of adrenocorticotropic hormone (ACTH) in the anterior pituitary. After hospital treatment and placement in a foster home with an emotionally supportive atmosphere, however, the child was examined again 18 months later and found to have near normal pituitary ACTH reserves, above average weight, and close to normal bone maturation.

These studies of Powell *et al.* (1967) and Gardner (1972) suggest, therefore, that an emotionally disturbed home atmosphere inhibits the release of growth hormone from the anterior pituitary and stimulates release of ACTH from the anterior pituitary to such an extent that normal ACTH reserves may be depleted. This suggests, then, that social relationships, in addition to affecting sympathetic autonomic activity, have a critical influence on human growth hormone and ACTH output from the anterior pituitary, and therefore on blood plasma levels of human growth hormone, on the one hand, and of hydrocortisone, released from the adrenal cortex under ACTH stimulation, on the other.

But human growth hormone has been shown to increase the size and number of cells cultured in a test tube (Moon & St. Vincent, 1957), while hydrocortisone has the opposite effect of inhibiting their growth and multiplication (Wellington & Moon, 1960). On the assumption that these two hormones can cross over from maternal to fetal blood in the placenta, it would follow that the predominance of one or the other would have a critical effect on development of brain cells (proceeding at the rate of about 40,000 cells per min) and body cells in the fetus. Thus, emotional support of a pregnant woman could well affect brain development of her fetus. In this connection, Nuckolls, Cassel, and Kaplan (1972) have shown that women with psychosocial assets have one-third the complications during pregnancy compared to women without such assets.

One component of the social relationship with rabbits in the Nerem *et al.* (1980) study, namely handling or tactile stimulation, has been shown to have pronounced consequences for the physical development of the premature infant and also of the laboratory rat. Rice (1977) found that 60 min per day of tactile stimulation and cuddling by the mothers of premature infants for one month after birth, led to significantly increased weight gain, accelerated development of neurological reflexes, and increased cognitive development in the form of socializing and vocalizing. Previous studies reviewed by Bovard (1958), in particular the pioneering study of Weininger (1954), showed that early handling of the laboratory rat had significant effects on internal metabolism, including increased skeletal growth, improved weight gain resulting from better food assim-

·ilation (but not from eating more), decreased emotionality, and increased resistance to extreme stress (immobilization), in the form of reduced apparent heart damage and fewer gastrointestinal bleeding points.

Schanberg and Kuhn (see Chapter 7, this volume) have shown that the biochemical effect of tactile stimulation on laboratory rats, and, presumably, on human infants as well, is an increase in an enzyme closely related to protein synthesis and cell growth, along with a related rise in growth hormone levels. This enzyme, ornithine decarboxylase (ODC), falls rapidly, along with growth hormone, on separation of rat pups from their mothers. Stroking of the pups with a wet brush by the experimenter prevents the fall of ODC and growth hormone following maternal separation. In addition, ODC and growth hormone are closely related in that suppression of growth hormone decreases ODC activity, while stimulation of growth hormone levels increases ODC.

These biochemical consequences of tactile stimulation could account for the increased weight gain seen in handled rats—produced by better assimilation of food but not by eating more—as well as their increased skeletal growth (Bovard, 1958). The latter could be effected by somatomedin, which, as Schanberg and Kuhn point out, mediates the stimulation of skeletal growth caused by growth hormone, and which appears depressed in maternally deprived children (D'Ercole, Underwood, & Van Wyk, 1977). Further, this biochemical mechanism could account for the increased weight gain found to result in premature infants cuddled and stroked by their mothers for 60 min a day for one month (Rice, 1977), and even from the use of lamb's wool in incubators.

Scott and Richards (1979) found that when low birth-weight babies aged 27 days were bedded alternatively each 24 hours in lamb's wool and cotton in their incubators, they gained significantly more weight, 10 g per 24 hours, under the lamb's wool condition compared to the cotton. This result clearly suggests that the extra tactile stimulation provided by lamb's wool compared to cotton was instrumental in the observed weight gain, which also could be accounted for in terms of the increased growth hormone output and ODC activity related to protein synthesis found to result from tactile stimulation, by Schanberg and Kuhn.

The finding that tactile stimulation increases ODC levels in the heart and liver of rat pups suggests that the ability of handled rats to survive total food and water deprivation 53.8 hours longer than controls of the same weight (Long, 1954) may be due to increased deposition of glycogen reserves in both heart and liver of handled animals, resulting from higher growth hormone levels in blood plasma and resultant increased ODC activity in these organs.

The studies of Schanberg and Kuhn on biochemical effects of maternal deprivation in rat pups do not, however, completely support the hypothesis on human psychosocial dwarfism offered above, namely that an emotionally stressful home atmosphere would have the effects of (1) inhibiting growth hormone output, and (2) stimulating ACTH output from the anterior pituitary. The findings of their study and a previous one by Kuhn, Butler, and Schanberg (1978) show no effects of maternal deprivation on serum corticosterone levels of rat pups, which should have been elevated under the hypothesis put forward here. Further, complete adrenalectomy did not abolish the effect of deprivation in lowering ODC levels. Therefore the pituitary–adrenocortical axis does not appear to be involved in their results.

In the case of children suffering from psychosocial dwarfism, while the absence of tactile stimulation may be a factor, the chief element in their home relationships appears to be emotional stress. This is demonstrated by depletion of ACTH reserves as reported by Gardner (1972). In this case, severe emotional stress may operate through hypothalamic mechansims (discussed below) to produce the abnormally low growth hormone levels found in psychosocial dwarfism by Powell et al. (1967). Thus, it may be possible that the low growth hormone levels found in both maternally deprived rat pups and in growth-retarded children living in disturbed family atmospheres arise through separate and distinct mechanisms.

Hypothalamic Mechanism

A single hypothesis to account for the results of the above studies is that of reciprocal inhibition between the anterolateral and posteromedial hypothalamic zones (Bovard, 1961).

On the basis of stimulation and lesion studies, the hypothalamus may be roughly divided into two functional zones. The tear-shaped zone to the right in Figure 6.1 is the posterior hypothalamic zone, extending from the mammillary bodies and in an anterior and medial direction to the median eminence of the tuber cinereum, just above the pituitary. Stimulation of this posterior zone has been found by Hess (1957) and others to elicit sympathetic autonomic reactions, such as a rise in blood pressure and dilatation of the pupils, and to increase general excitability of the motor system. Further, stimulation and lesion studies together

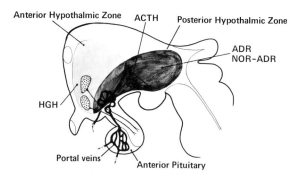

FIGURE 6.1   The hypothalamus and pituitary in median sagittal section (the right hypothalamus is shown). The hypothalamus, on each wall of the third ventricle, is about the size of one's little finger nail, but it controls internal metabolism of the entire body. This it does by means of two systems: the release of hormones into the bloodstream, and activation of the autonomic nervous system.

The posterior hypothalamic zone is associated with the response to stress and expenditure of energy. Under stress, it uses a chemical signal (releasing factor) transported by the portal veins to trigger the release of adrenocorticotrophic hormone (ACTH) from the anterior pituitary into the bloodstream. The area of the posterior zone involved in ACTH release is indicated. In turn, ACTH triggers the release of hydrocortisone (cortisol) from the adrenal cortex. This hormone elevates blood pressure and blood glucose, thus being protective under shock, but it also inhibits cell growth. Further, the posterior zone under emotional or physical stress also activates the sympathetic division of the autonomic nervous system, which elevates heart rate, inhibits digestion, and stimulates release of adrenaline and noradrenaline from the adrenal medulla. The area involved in activation of the sympathetic system is indicated by ADR, NOR-ADR. Activation of the posterior zone therefore has protein catabolic consequences, whether one is running a marathon or involved in a family argument.

In contrast, activation of the anterior hypothalamic zone appears to have protein anabolic consequences and results in conservation of energy. This zone is associated with the release of human growth hormone (HGH) from the anterior pituitary by means of a releasing factor traveling through the portal veins. The area related to HGH release is indicated above. In turn, HGH promotes cell multiplication and growth throughout the body and is therefore associated with healing of wounds and fractures. Further, the anterior zone is associated with activity of the parasympathetic division of the autonomic system, which slows heart rate and promotes digestion, assimilation of food, and the elimination of waste products.

In summary, the hypothalamus regulates internal metabolism through these two zones of opposite function. Evidence from stimulation and lesion studies suggests these two zones are reciprocally inhibitory (see p. 115). The view proposed here is that a socially supportive environment activates the anterior zone, thereby inhibiting the posterior zone and thus conserving the metabolic resources of the individual who has been subjected to disease, injury, or emotional stress. This diagram was prepared by Dr. and Mrs. Peter Gloor of Montreal Neurological Institute.

with recording of electrical activity under stress (Harris, 1960; Porter, 1952, 1953; Slusher, 1958) have suggested that the posterior zone of the hypothalamus mediates the pituitary–adrenocortical response to stress. Taken together, these and other studies suggest that the posterior hypothalamus mediates both arms of the response to stress, the sympathetic–adrenal medullary and the pituitary–adrenocortical (see Figure 6.1). The end effects of activation of this zone are, therefore, protein catabolic, since these conjoint responses involve the breakdown of protein reserves into glucose for immediate energy expenditure.

But the response to stress obviously includes behavioral and experiential components as well. Available evidence suggests that these reactions, including (1) the defense reaction of flight or attack (Hess, 1957), (2) a state of anxiety and terror in monkeys more unpleasant than extreme pain (Lilly, 1957), and (3) even a directed attack on the experimenter in a study by Bovard and Gloor (1961a), are also elicited by posterior hypothalamic stimulation. Abrahams, Hilton, and Zbrozyna (1960) showed that the points in the conscious cat's brain where electrical stimulation resulted in coordinated defensive behavior were also the same points in the anesthetized cat's brain where stimulation resulted in increased cardiac output, vasodilation of skeletal muscle and vasoconstriction in skin and viscera. These responses are apparently mediated by beta-adrenergic receptors. Such cardiovascular responses, therefore, must be included in the defense reaction of Hess.

The evidence suggests, then, that the hypothalamus is only one sector of a well-defined subcortical system for elaboration of defensive responses such as fear and rage (de Molina & Hunsperger, 1959), extending from the amygdala to the hypothalamus and perhaps to the mesencephalon below as well. What is involved in these highly organized defensive reactions, as well as in the response to stress, that are elicited from posterior hypothalamic stimulation, are fiber patterns and relative concentrations of cell bodies, rather than clearly defined cell nuclei or centers, as the work of Hess (1957) in brain stimulation and the work of Metuzals (1959) in neuroanatomy of the hypothalamus so clearly suggests. An interesting point is that Endroczi and Lissak (1964) found that emotional reactivity resulting from medial hypothalamic stimulation was not correlated with increased corticosteroid output, and they conclude that separate neural controls exist for defensive responses and for the pituitary–adrenocortical response.

The anterior hypothalamic zone, oval-shaped and lighter, is to the left in Figure 6.1. It extends from the preoptic region and anterior commissure caudally and laterally to the infundibular region. A horizontal cross section of the hypothalamus would show the anterior zone extending laterally in the posterior direction, while the posterior zone extends like a peninsula medially in the anterior direction, on either side of the third ventricle.

Experimental stimulation and lesion studies of the anterior and lateral hypothalamus have shown that activation of this region has parasympathetic autonomic effects, including lowering of blood pressure, constriction of the pupil, and reduction of pulse rate, and that it decreases motor excitability of the animal (Hess, 1957). There is some suggestion from stimulation and lesion experiments that the anterior zone mediates release of growth hormone from the anterior pituitary (Del Vecchio, Genovese, & Martini 1958; Hinton & Stevenson, 1959). In particular, O'Brien, Happel, and Bach (1964) found that direct stimulation of the paraventricular nucleus in the anteromedial hypothalamus, adjacent to the supraoptic nucleus, by means of telemetry produced a marked acceleration of growth in infant kittens. Another study, however, has also implicated the posteromedial hypothalamus in areas mediating growth hormone release (Bernhardis, Box, & Stevenson, 1963).

In the general case, then, activation of the anterior and lateral hypothalamic zone has protein anabolic consequences involving conservation and storage of energy. These would include parasympathetic stimulation of assimilation and digestion of food as well as slowing of the heart rate, and stimulation of protein synthesis at the cellular level by growth hormone (Moon & Jentoft, 1960), as well as growth hormone mediation of glycogen storage in the liver under fasting conditions.

The metabolic consequences of activation of each of these two zones are, therefore, functionally incompatible. It does not come as any surprise, therefore, that activation of each zone appears also to inhibit the other; the two zones are, in fact, reciprocally inhibitory (Bovard, 1961). In particular, reciprocal inhibition of the posterior and anterior zone in respect to autonomic function has been shown in cat by Gellhorn, Nakao, and Redgate (1956). Further, Redgate and Gellhorn (1955) showed that the balance of excitability between anterior and posterior hypothalamus determines blood pressure and pulse rate levels, as well as drug-induced reflex changes in blood pressure. This reciprocal inhibition of the sympathetic and parasympathetic divisions of the autonomic system is reflected at the level of autonomic input to the stomach (Koizumi & Suda, 1963).

In respect to pituitary–adrenocortical function, Suzuki, Romanoff, Koella, and Levy (1960) found that electrical stimulation of the anterior and dorsal hypothalamus inhibits release of hydrocortisone from the adrenal cortex of dogs, while stimulation of the ventral posterior hypothalamus increases output of this hormone from the adrenal cortex.

Endroczi and Lissak (1964) found that stimulation of the septal and of the anterior and lateral hypothalamic areas inhibited corticosteroid secretion, while stimulation of the posterior tuber cinereum, median eminence, and premammillary regions of the hypothalamus increased such secretion. Stimulation of the dorsal tegmentum of the mesencephalon decreased, but stimulation of the ventral tegmentum increased, corticosteroid output.

To sum up, stimulation of the anterior hypothalamic zone has been shown, therefore, to inhibit both arms of the response to stress, the sympathetic autonomic and the pituitary–adrenocortical. On the other hand, activation of the posterior hypothalamic zone inhibits anterior zone mediation of parasympathetic activity, as the studies of Gellhorn and his colleagues (1957) have shown. While there is no direct evidence as yet to suggest that posterior hypothalamic stimulation under stress would also inhibit endocrine functions mediated by the anterior zone, such as release of growth hormone, indirect evidence does support this view.

It was noted above that severely growth-retarded children, living in emotionally stressful home atmospheres, show abnormally low growth hormone levels (Powell *et al.*, 1967) and, in a case reported by Gardner (1972), depletion of pituitary ACTH reserves. This suggests that in these situations, such chronic emotional stress activates the posterior hypothalamic zone, thus, at one and the same time depleting ACTH stores in the anterior pituitary and inhibiting anterior hypothalamic mediation of growth hormone release into the bloodstream.

Under acute stress, however, such as capture or ether anesthesia in monkeys, growth hormone output may be increased (Brown, Schalch, & Reichlin, 1967). Other factors increasing growth hormone release are a fall in blood glucose, sleep, exercise, a rise in amino acids, and alpha-adrenergic stimuli such as L-dopa. On the other hand, a rise in plasma glucose and beta-adrenergic stimuli inhibit growth hormone output, through the mediation of somatostatin (Federman, 1983).

Since the sensory intake reaction described by Williams (1981), in which the organism is primarily attending to environmental stimuli, apparently involves increased peripheral resistance through vasoconstriction in skeletal muscle mediated by alpha-adrenergic receptors (Surwit, Williams, & Shapiro, 1981), it is possible that this response also involves an increase in growth hormone secretion from the anterior pituitary.

The defensive reaction elicited by posterior hypothalamic stimulation and mediated by beta-adrenergic receptors therefore should involve inhibition of growth hormone output, but this is not congruent with the findings of Brown *et al.* (1967) and others that, at least acute stress elevates plasma growth hormone levels. Only further experimental work can resolve this apparent discrepancy.

What this evidence suggests overall, therefore, is that two systems concerned with autonomic and endocrine functions, respectively, each reciprocally inhibitory, coexist in the brain. These systems are represented in, but cannot be too specifically localized within, the hypothalamus. The reciprocally inhibitory system involved in pituitary–adrenocortical response appears to be represented more caudally in the midbrain, as noted above, and there is evidence that it is represented rostrally in the amygdala as well (Bovard & Gloor, 1961b).

The threshold for stress, that is, the probability that a neutral stimulus will trigger the physiological response to stress considered above, can be considered inversely related to activity of the posterior and medial hypothalamic zone that mediates this response. The more active the zone, the lower the threshold. One consequence of this would be that as one stress piles on top of the other, each succeeding stressor would encounter a lower threshold for activation of the posterior zone, and therefore would induce greater depletion of protein reserves.

What reciprocal inhibition of the anterior and posterior hypothalamic zones implies, therefore, is that the threshold for stress is determined by the relative balance of activity between them. Relatively predominant anterior zone activity would mean a higher threshold for stress, while predominant posterior activity would mean a low threshold for stress, with the organism over-reacting to environmental change and thereby dribbling away its protein reserves.

If interaction with significant others (family, friends), as well as tactile stimulation, can be shown to activate the anterior hypothalamic zone, then two consequences should follow on the basis of the above considerations:

1. *Promotion of protein anabolism,* including increased conversion of glucose to glycogen and storage in the liver (and heart), mediated by growth hormone; improved digestion and assimilation of food, due to parasympathetic activation; and accelerated bone growth, wound healing, and increased antibody production, from increased growth hormone output.

2. *Inhibition of protein catabolism,* through inhibition of the posterior hypothalamic zone mediating the response to stress and, therefore, (as one result) a higher threshold for both the sympathetic autonomic and anterior pituitary–adrenocortical responses to stress.

In terms of the reciprocal inhibition hypothesis, then, the underlying reason that density of social ties protects the individual against a wide range of diseases (Berkman & Syme, 1979), would be that it alters the balance of internal metabolism from the protein catabolic to the protein anabolic side, from energy expenditure to energy conservation. This is most clearly shown by the effects of absence and presence of social support on bone maturation of the child suffering from psychosocial dwarfism (Gardner, 1972). In practical terms, a handled rat (or baby) should survive starvation longer because of increased reserves of glycogen in the heart and liver (Bovard, 1958). Whatever the physical disease or injury sustained by the organism under anterior hypothalamic dominance, it should be able to maintain its organization (negentropy) more effectively against the disorganization and randomness (entropy) resulting from the disease or injury simply because, under this or previous environmental assaults, it expends less and conserves more of its vital metabolic reserves. It can thus bring greater reserves to bear against a life-threatening disease or injury.

The outward manifestation of this inward metabolic change therefore would be an increased threshold for response to stress, reflecting relative dominance of the anterior hypothalamic zone over the posterior. Thus, under the stressful procedure of venipuncture (Back & Bogdanoff, 1964), the presence of social support reduces sympathetic autonomic reactivity and thereby reduces FFA mobilization with possible ameliorative consequences for atherosclerosis; and similiarly, under the natural stresses of the life cycle, the presence of close inter- and intrafamily ties (Bruhn & Wolf, 1979), reduces sympathetic autonomic input to the sinoatrial node and coronary arteries, protecting the heart against stress. Propranolol (Inderal) and other beta-blocking agents pharmacologically mimic, so to speak, the effect of social support in inhibiting sympathetic autonomic input to the cardiovascular system.

Further, relative dominance of the anterior zone should result in inhibition of the emotional reactivity, fear, anger, and anxiety associated with physical illness or injury that has been shown in animal brain lesion and stimulation studies to be mediated by the posterior hypothalamus. A number of studies suggest such inhibition of the emotional stress component of illness could have survival value.

Bartlett, Helmendach, and Inman (1954) have shown that cats subjected to emotional stress (restraint) and extreme cold were unable to maintain body temperature, which fell almost as rapidly as that of dead animals, whereas cats subjected to cold alone could maintain their body temperature reasonably well. It would appear emotional stress has an additive effect, accelerating depletion of the body's vital protein and carbohydrate stores when the organism is already under physical stress. Other animal studies (Ross & Herczeg, 1956) have shown the protective effects of sympathetic blocking agents under such lethal stress as tumbling.

The psychological disorganization in the life of an unmarried, pregnant high school girl may be reflected in her higher blood plasma hydrocortisone levels, which in turn could inhibit brain and body cell development in the fetus. So in a sense, outward entropy, the impaired density of social relationship, may be reflected in inward entropy, the breakdown of protein reserves and consequent energy expenditure under hydrocortisone and sympathetic autonomic activity.

The holding and touching of the human infant by mother or nurse—the more physical expression of a social relationship—may not only produce a bond between them (Klaus & Kennell, 1976), but also alter the baby's metabolism as seen in weight gain (Rice, 1977). Even skin stimulation from lamb's wool (Scott & Richards, 1979), or from gel foam mattresses has been found to improve weight gain in premature infants.

Some of this is new, some not. Anesthetists have found that visiting the patient the night before an operation and establishing a personal relationship with him or her has value in inducing quick and easy anesthesia on the operating table the next day. In general, it has been found that the more frightened and upset the patient is, the more difficult it is to induce anesthesia; that is to say, the more active the sympathetic system, the more resistance the anesthetic drug has to overcome in quietening the patient (P. Gloor, personal communication, 1959).

The key point to consider here is that social relationships, at first physical and then more symbolic, can alter internal metabolism of the individual and increase his or her viability.

The specific mechanism hypothesized to account for the protective effects of social support in ischemic heart disease (Berkman & Syme, 1979; Bruhn & Wolf, 1979) is inhibition of sympathetic autonomic input to the heart, coronary arteries, and adrenal medulla. This could be effected by activation of the anterior hypothalamic zone under social support, by pathways discussed below, and consequent inhibition of the posterior zone mediating sympathetic activity.

Such inhibition of sympathetic input to the cardiovascular system and adrenal medulla would (1) protect the heart from the effects of sympathetic activation on arteriosclerosis and coronary disease shown in the Henry, Ely, et al. (1971) and Henry, Stephens, et al. (1971) studies and the Gutstein and Lataillade study (1962) noted above; (2) protect the cardiovascular system from the widespread effects of catecholamines by reducing their circulating levels; and (3) thereby reduce mobilization of FFAs, a precursor of arteriosclerosis; and (4) protect the ischemic heart from ventricular fibrillation and sudden failure resulting from sympathetic input under emotional stress (Verrier & Lown, 1981).

The effect of social and tactile stimulation in reducing diet-induced atherosclerosis in the rabbit (Nerem et al., 1980), can be accounted for under the reciprocal inhibition hypothesis in similar fashion by assuming that these two kinds of input activate the anterior hypothalamus, thereby dampening posterior hypothalamic activity and, thus, inhibiting sympathetic autonomic input to the cardiovascular system and adrenal medulla.

The effect of tactile stimulation in increasing weight gain in the premature infant (Rice, 1977; Scott & Richards, 1979) and in the laboratory rat (Bovard, 1958; Weininger, 1954) can be accounted for in terms of improved food assimilation under parasympathetic activation resulting from input of tactile stimulation to the anterior zone. In the case of early handling of the laboratory rat, greater skeletal length and greater resistance to starvation can be accounted for in terms of increased growth hormone output and, hence, increased protein synthesis, resulting from anterior hypothalamic activation.

Decreased cardiovascular and gastrointestinal damage under severe stress in the early handled rat, and decreased emotional reactivity, could be ascribed to inhibition of the posterior hypothalamus under anterior hypothalamic activation.

In the case of psychosocial dwarfism, the mechanism involved would be dominance of the pituitary–adrenocortical response to stress and the consequent dominance of its end product, hydrocrotisone, over growth hormone in the bloodstream, in an adverse emotional climate. This would involve posterior hypothalamic mediation of this stress and, therefore, inhibition of anterior hypothalamic mediation of the release of growth hormone from the anterior pituitary. Recovery from this condition would appear to involve an opposite relation between these two hormones in the blood, with growth hormone now dominant in a supportive emotional climate mediated by the anterior hypothalamus.

In the case of cancer, the protective mechanism hypothesized is inhibition of the pituitary–adrenocortical response to stress and, hence, lower levels of plasma hydrocortisone. Under the reciprocal inhibition hypothesis, this could be brought about by activation of the anterior hypothalamic zone under social support, through pathways discussed below, and consequent inhibition of the posterior hypothalamic zone. Keller, Weiss, Schleifer, Miller, and Stein (1981) have shown that a graded series of stressors produces progressively greater suppression of lymphocyte function, as measured by number of circulating lymphocytes and other means. Riley (1981) found that rotation-induced anxiety stress in mice enhanced growth of tumors that were under control of cell-mediated defenses such as T-lymphocytes and thymocytes. Direct injection into mice of corticosterone or synthetic corticosteroids had the same effect. The presumed mechanism here would be reduced immunological competence of lymphocytes and thymus elements and reduced surveillance capacity of NK (natural killer) cells effected by the high plasma corticosterone levels induced by the emotional stress.

Riley (1975) had shown previously that when mice were carefully shielded from everyday laboratory stress—light change, capture and handling by caretakers, laboratory noise and so on—tumor incidence dropped far below that of controls. In one experiment (Riley, 1981) mammary tumor incidence from an injected virus in female mice at 400 days of age was 92 and 68% for two groups housed under stressful conditions compared to less than 10% for mice housed under low-stress conditions.

Taken together, these considerations suggest that the increased survival rate under cancer for persons with social support found by Berkman and Syme (1979) may be due in part to a nonspecific reduction in stress induced by presence of family and friends. This would mean, therefore, that belonging to a social network would be reflected in lower plasma hydrocortisone levels under the stress of daily life (an hypothesis that could be easily disconfirmed) and, further, that persons without such support, and with higher hydrocortisone levels, would suffer reduced immunocompetence.

The real challenge here is to determine the specific biochemical mechanisms in the presumed impairment of lymphocyte and NK cell function under high plasma corticosteroid levels.

One difficulty in applying the results of experimentation with virally induced tumors (such as mammary tumors) in mice to humans is that such viral origin is involved in only about 6% of human cancers, such as in some leukemias (B. H. Fox, personal communication, 1981). Further, while cell-mediated immunological defenses may be important for mice, they may be only the third line of defense against cancer in man and, hence, not so critical in human cancer, in which the first line of defense is liver metabolism of potentially carcinogenic chemicals, and the second is self-repair of mutagenic errors by the DNA molecule, according to Fox.

In general, as Fox points out, the greatly increased life span and number of cells in humans compared to mice results in a greatly increased risk that any one of these cells will go cancerous in a lifetime from other than viral causes, such as, for example, transforming genes from tumor cells that can cause normal cells to become cancerous (Marx, 1982) and that may be the final common pathway by means of which many carcinogens act (Bishop, 1982).

Thus, the hypothesis put forward here, at best, could account for only a small proportion of the variance in increased survival of cancer patients with social support found by Berkman and Syme.

In the case of accidents and suicide (Berkman & Syme, 1979), it is

conceivable that inhibition of posterior hypothalamic-mediated emotionality (such as in suicide, rage reactions turned against the self) under
social support could have survival value. Warheit (1979) found that a
person's support structure (spouse, friends) is critical to his or her susceptibility to depression.

Eluding explanation (at least to this writer) are the specific physiological mechanisms that may be involved in reduced mortality under social
support in digestive and respiratory illnesses (Berkman & Syme, 1979)
and the accelerated development of neurological reflexes and cognitive
competence found to result from tactile stimulation of premature infants
(Rice, 1977).

A possible hypothesis to account for the effects of early handling on
mental development of premature infants, however, would be increased
synaptic connections between cortical cells as evidenced by increased
dendritic spines. This result was found in neonatal rats as a result of
early stimulation, including handling, by Schapiro and Vukovich (1970).
They hypothesize that increased afferent input from such stimulation
increases regional blood flow to maturing cortical neurons, thus providing them with a nutritionally rich environment.

In any case, the hypothesis that social support alters internal metabolism by influencing the balance of hypothalamic activity does require
elucidation of the precise mechanisms involved in the case of each lethal
factor. This task obviously has only just begun.

Amygdaloid Mediation

What we have not yet considered, however, is the pathway by means
of which social support or tactile stimulation could influence the balance
of hypothalamic activity and thereby alter internal metabolism.

The most suitable candidate for such mediation of the influence of
social interaction on the hypothalamus is the amygdala, a small gray
nucleus deep in the anterior temporal lobe. By means of two projection
pathways, the stria terminalis and the ventral amygdalofugal tract, the
amygdala brings just about all of hypothalamic activity under its management and control (Egger, 1972), with the possible exception of home-
ostatic regulation of temperature, electrolyte and water balance, and
autonomic control over the cardiovascular and digestive systems (Gloor,
1972).

On the basis of its input from the olfactory, visual, and temporal
cortex (and from the frontal lobe in man), the amygdala can be considered to make a "decision"—which, after all, has to be made at some

point in the brain—as to what internal metabolic state would be most appropriate for the situation the person or animal finds himself in. For example, the presence of food would lead through mediation of olfactory and visual input by the amygdala to anterior and lateral hypothalamic activity and, hence, to parasympathetic autonomic promotion of digestion and assimilation of food. Conversely, presence of a predator would lead to posterior hypothalamic activation and, hence, to expenditure of energy in an emergency situation, rather than conservation of energy.

According to the pioneer studies of Klüver and Bucy (1939), in the absence of the amygdala bilaterally, due to bilateral temporal lobe removal, the monkey appears unable to differentiate between motivationally relevant or irrelevant stimuli (e.g., edible and inedible objects). He seems unable to differentiate positive from negative reinforcing stimuli. For these reasons, after bilateral amygdalectomy, the affective meaning of a social situation cannot be determined by the monkey, and in the natural state, his social bonds are disrupted (Kling, 1972). The monkey becomes a social isolate, appears fearful, and withdraws from any form of close contact with group members.

These considerations strongly suggest that, in the absence of amygdaloid mediation, neither maternal–infant bonding (Klaus & Kennell, 1976), nor pair-bonding (Money, 1980), would take place. In fact, observations of bilaterally amygdalectomized monkey mothers show that even rudimentary elements of maternal behavior fail to appear, and that the normally intense maternal–infant bond in nonhuman primates is "shattered" in these circumstances (Kling, 1972). The amygdala and probably the frontal cortex as well appear to be essential for maintenance of social bonds in the monkey.

The amygdala thus appears to transmit to the rest of the brain what Gloor (1978) has termed the "subtle tuning of mood" appropriate to a given social situation, which would include familiar faces, gestures and posture, and vocalizations appropriate to approach or avoidance (Altman, 1962, reviewed by Gloor, 1978). The evidence available thus suggests that the function of the amygdala is to monitor input of information about the environment, and translate its significance for the individual (in terms of positive or negative consequences) into internal metabolic dispositions, carried out by the hypothalamus.

Moods can be considered the brain's overall readout, after millions of computations, of what life situation one is facing. The mood is therefore a reflection in consciousness of the amygdala's split-millisecond decision as to what one's environment means—possible death, food, or a mate— and its physiological consequences. In short, the amygdala, on the basis of comparison of past experience with present, imposes its affective interpretation of the environment upon the brain in general, and the hypothalamus in particular, as Gloor suggests (1972, 1978).

An example of this is provided by a remarkable experiment by Downer (1961), reviewed by Gloor (1972). The amygdala was removed on one side in a monkey in which all visual communication from each eye to the opposite hemisphere had been cut. Each eye could only, therefore, process visual information to the lateral geniculate nucleus and the visual cortex on the same side of the brain. When the eye on the same side as the amygdalectomy was blocked, so that visual information from the other eye was processed by the intact hemisphere, the monkey demonstrated his usual fear and aggressiveness towards humans. But when visual information was processed through the eye on the same side as the amygdalectomy only, and the hemisphere on the same side, with no input from the amygdala, then the monkey approached humans and ate out of their hands with no compunction. The amygdala, therefore, contributes affective meaning to visual and other sensory input.

But how could the mere presence of social stimuli (e.g., friends, as in the Back and Bogdanoff study), in the absence of tactile stimulation, alter hypothalamic function? It is certainly conceivable that tactile stimulation, involved in the Rice (1977) study and in the studies reviewed by Bovard (1958) is mediated by the amygdala through skin receptors, and available evidence suggests this view. Machne and Segundo (1956) found touching any portion of the skin most effective in arousing electrical activity of the amygdala. That amygdaloid mediation is indeed essential for the effects of early handling is suggested by the observation that the usual effect of handling in reducing emotional reactivity of the laboratory rat is not obtained when carbachol has been injected into the amygdala (Belluzzi, 1972).

But how is "pure" social support mediated by the amygdala?

It can be suggested that, in the lifetime of the individual, the presence of members of the same species (i.e., social stimuli) ordinarily would have become correlated with powerful positive reinforcements, such as food, physical affection (tactile stimulation), and relief of discomfort.

These primary positive reinforcements or unconditioned stimuli can be presumed to have built-in access to the anterior hypothalamic zone through amygdaloid mediation, and thereby to have protein anabolic consequences, such as the effects of early handling on weight gain in premature infants (Rice, 1977) and laboratory rats (Bovard, 1958).

Feedback to the amygdala from the hypothalamus would relate satisfaction of basic needs at the hypothalamic level (e.g., elevation of blood glucose levels through food assimilation and consequent inhibition of the medial "start" eating center) to initially neutral environmental stimuli, such as the voice and odor of one's mother, activating the amygdala from the cortex (Gloor, 1978). Just as the hypothalamus monitors blood content of glucose and blood temperature, so at a higher level the amygdala can be thought of as monitoring hypothalamic activity. Thus, correlation of sensory input with basic need satisfaction would take place in the amygdala.

Social stimuli therefore would become secondary (learned) reinforcers or conditioned stimuli that because of their association with such powerful primary (built-in) positive reinforcers as physical comfort and affection, would themselves acquire the power to activate the anterior hypothalamic zone through amygdaloid mediation.

This mechanism can best be elucidated with reference to early work on dogs at Johns Hopkins (Lynch, 1977). Human petting of dogs produces sudden marked decrease from the usual resting pulse rate, resulting in a drop of as much as 10–60 beats per min. The handling or petting can be considered an unconditioned, or built-in, stimulus for cardiac deceleration, presumably mediated through parasympathetic autonomic input to the heart. Even the mere presence of a person who had previously petted the dog resulted in reduced heart rate. This is analogous to the effect of friends in reducing stress of venipuncture found by Back and Bogdanoff (1964), and can be considered a conditioned stimulus for cardiac deceleration.

But in the Johns Hopkins studies, the effect of the presence of a human on the dog's heart rate was shown to be strictly dependent on the dog's past experience with that person. When the entrance of a person to the laboratory was followed by electric shock rather than by petting, the dog responded to future entrance of that person by relatively greater acceleration of heart rate.

Thus, presence of a person elicited "cardiac, respiratory, and motor responses from the dog which were dependent on the reinforcement associated with that individual" (Lynch, 1977, p. 174). This key observation suggests, therefore, that one's social network or other social support is a conditioned stimulus that—through its association with physical affection, feeding, or relief of discomfort, or with other unconditioned stimuli that have in common the built-in response of inhibiting posterior hypothalamic activity—has acquired the power of inhibiting both the sympathetic autonomic and the pituitary–adrenocortical responses to stress.

But as Gloor points out (1978), olfactory memories are relatively permanent compared to memories associated with other sensory modalities. This may be related to the fact that in mammals below primates, olfactory input to the amygdala predominates and signals the nature of the environment. It may be that in humans, because of this evolutionary heritage, laid down in neural networks, olfactory stimuli are either pleasant or unpleasant, and virtually never neutral in affective response (P. Gloor, personal communication, 1959), and that some odors, like decaying human flesh, seem to have built-in emotional significance.

The relative permanence of olfactory memories therefore could be related to their mediation by the amygdala (often termed "the olfactory thalamus"), to their emotional significance, and to their possible storage in long-term memory through nearby hippocampal circuits. Hence, if correlation of social stimuli with need satisfaction takes place in the amygdala, as the evidence from monkeys clearly suggests (Kling, 1972), then social stimuli as secondary reinforcers may be relatively immune from extinction.

As Gloor put the matter,

> Furthermore, the sets of signals eliciting particular affective states, especially in a social situation, must be deeply ingrained and relatively immune to short-term interruption by occasional stimuli which may be incongruous with the usually prevailing affective bias pertaining to a particular situation. For instance, the occasional sudden outburst of anger, or even violence in a parent directed against its offspring does not fundamentally alter the positive affective bond between the two, provided such outbursts are not the prevailing and frequent interaction. (1978, p. 205)

It would seem logical to suggest, therefore, that the effects of social networks to which we belong (home, neighborhood, work) are primarily mediated by the amygdala. In turn, the amygdala excites or inhibits hypothalamic neurons governing internal metabolism, that is, conservation or expenditure of energy. Thus, the social network affects internal metabolism through amygdalo–hypothalamic mediation.

Presumably, the amygdala has to assess the environment in terms of the law of the excluded middle from Aristotelian logic, that is, as being either positively or negatively reinforcing, but not both simultaneously. Any ambiguities would have to be resolved at least eventually, one way or another.

Environmental stimuli could result in an internal state of either protein anabolism or catabolism, but not both at the same time, because the mutually antagonistic relationship between the anterior and posterior hypothalamic zones governing internal metabolism would preclude this.

In this connection, a simple count of the number of arguments a married couple has compared to the number of times the couple has intercourse over a given period of time, provides a surprisingly accurate prediction of the future course of their relationship. When emotional hassles tend to outnumber acts of lovemaking, then a split-up becomes more probable (Howard & Dawes, 1976). Thus, the brain has a tendency to resolve affective ambiguities one way or another, in either a positive or negative direction.

The presence of social stimuli, therefore, could color the amygdala's interpretation of an otherwise threatening environment on the positively reinforcing side. This in turn would lead to a reduced posterior hypothalamic response and, hence, lower the metabolic cost of psychological or emotional stress.

For example, the pain from a compound fracture would still be there, but the presence of an understanding doctor or nurse would reduce the emotional stress component—the worry, anxiety, and fear attendant on the injury—thus keeping to a minimum the overall protein catabolic consequences of the injury. Specifically, activation of the anterior hypothalamic zone through social support would inhibit the posterior zone and thereby reduce blood plasma content of hydrocortisone, which has been shown to inhibit growth and multiplication of cultured human cells (Wellington & Moon, 1960).

Further, such support through activation of the anterior hypothalamus could also facilitate release of growth hormone from the anterior pituitary, thereby facilitating knitting of the bone fracture.

In summary, then, it is the conservation of metabolic resources effected by social support through amygdalo–hypothalamic mechanisms that could explain how a social network of family and friends can protect the individual against the ravages of disease and death.

References

Abrahams, V. C., Hilton, S. M., & Zbrozyna, A. (1960). Active muscle vasodilatation produced by stimulation of the brain stem: Its significance in the defense reaction. *Journal of Physiology* (London), *154*, 491–513.

Altman, S. A. (1962). A field study of the sociobiology of rhesus monkeys, *Macaca mulatta. Annals of the New York Academy of Sciences, 102*, 338–435.

Back, K. W., & Bogdanoff, M. D. (1964). Plasma lipid response to leadership, conformity, and deviation. In P. H. Leiderman & D. Shapiro (Eds.), *Psychobiological approaches to social behavior* (pp. 36–39). Stanford: Stanford University Press.

Bartlett, R. G., Jr., Helmendach, R. H., & Inman, W. I. (1954). Effect of restraint on temperature regulation in the cat. *Proceedings of the Society for Experimental Biology and Medicine, 85*, 81–83.

Belluzzi, J. D.(1972). Long lasting effects of cholinergic stimulation of the amygdaloid complex in the rat. *Journal of Comparative and Physiological Psychology, 80*, 269–282.

Berkman, L. F., & Syme, S. L. (1979). Social networks, host resistance and mortality: a nine-year follow-up study of Alameda County residents. *American Journal of Epidemiology, 109,* 186–204.

Bernhardis, L. L., Box, B. M., & Stevenson, J. A. F. (1963). Growth following hypothalamic lesions in the weanling rat. *Endocrinology, 72,* 684–692.

Bishop, J. M. (1982). Oncogenes. *Scientific American, 246,* March, 80–92.

Bovard, E. W. (1958). The effects of early handling on viability of the albino rat. *Psychological Review, 65,* 257–271.

Bovard, E. W. (1961). A concept of hypothalamic functioning. *Perspectives in Biology and Medicine, 5,* 52–60.

Bovard, E. W., & Gloor, P. (1961a). Unpublished data, 1961.

Bovard, E. W., & Gloor, P. (1961b). Effect of amygdaloid lesions on plasma corticosterone response of the albino rat to emotional stress. *Experientia, 17,* 521–526.

Brown, G. M., Schalch, D. S., & Reichlin, S. (1967). Growth hormone response to stress in the squirrel monkey. *Federation Proceedings, 26,* 585.

Bruhn, J. G., & Wolf, S. (1979). *The Roseto story.* Norman, Okalhoma: University of Oklahoma Press.

Del Vecchio, A., Genovese, E., & Martini, L. (1958). Hypothalamus and somatotrophic hormone release. *Proceedings of the Society for Experimental Biology and Medicine, 98,* 641–644.

De Molina, A. F., & Hunsperger, R. W. (1959). Central representation of affective reactions in forebrain and brain stem: electrical stimulation of amygdala, stria terminalis, and adjacent structures. *Journal of Physiology* (London), *145,* 251–265.

D'Ercole, A. J., Underwood, L. E., & Van Wyk, J. J. (1977). Serum somatomedin-C in hypopituitarism and in other disorders of growth. *Journal of Pediatrics, 90,* 375–381.

Downer, J. L. de C. (1961). Changes in visual gnostic functions and emotional behavior following unilateral temporal pole damage in the "split brain" monkey. *Nature* (London), *191,* 50–51.

Egger, M. D. (1972). Amygdalo-hypothalamic neurophysiological relationships. In B. E. Eleftheriou (Ed.), *The neurobiology of the amygdala* (pp. 319–342). New York: Plenum.

Endroczi, E., & Lissak, K. (1964). Effect of hypothalamic and brain stem structure stimulation on pituitary-adrenocortical function. *Acta Physiologica Academiae Scientiarum Hungaricae, 24,* 67–77.

Federman, D. D. (1983). 3. Endocrinology, V. Pituitary. In E. Rubinstein & D. D. Federman (Eds.), *Scientific American Medicine* (p. 3). New York: *Scientific American.*

Gardner, L. I. (1972). Deprivation dwarfism. *Scientific American, 227,* July, 76–82.

Gellhorn, E. (1957). *Autonomic balance and the hypothalamus.* Minneapolis: University of Minnesota Press.

Gellhorn, E., Nakao, H., & Redgate, E. (1956). The influence of lesions in the anterior and posterior hypothalamus on tonic and phasic autonomic reactions. *Journal of Physiology* (London), *131,* 402–423.

Gloor, P. (1960). Unpublished data, 1960.

Gloor, P. (1972). Temporal lobe epilepsy: its possible contribution to the understanding of the functional significance of the amygdala and of its interaction with neocortical-temporal mechanisms. In B. E. Eleftheriou (Ed.), *The neurobiology of the amygdala* (pp. 423–457). New York: Plenum.

Gloor, P. (1978). Inputs and outputs of the amygdala: what the amygdala is trying to tell the rest of the brain. In K. E. Livingston and O. Hornykiewicz (Eds.), *Limbic mechanisms* (pp. 189–209). New York: Plenum.

Gutstein, W. H., & Lataillade, J. (1962). Stress hardens arteries in test. Study reported in the *New York Times,* Feb. 17, p. 21.

Harris, G. W. (1960). Central control of pituitary secretion. In J. Field (Ed.), *Handbook of physiology: Section 1 Neurophysiology* (Vol II, pp. 1007–1038). Washington, DC: American Physiological Society.

Henry, J. P., Ely, D. L., Stephens, P. M., Ratcliffe, H. L., Santisteban, G. A., & Shapiro, A. P. (1971). The role of psychosocial factors in the development of arteriosclerosis in CBA mice. *Atherosclerosis, 14,* 203–218.

Henry, J. P., Stephens, P. M., Axelrod, J., & Mueller, R. (1971). Effect of psychosocial stimulation on the enzymes involved in the biosynthesis and metabolism of noradrenaline and adrenaline. *Psychosomatic Medicine, 33,* 227–237.

Hess, W. R. (1957). *The functional organization of the diencephalon.* New York: Grune & Stratton.

Hinton, G. G., & Stevenson, J. A. F. (1959). The effect of hypothalamic lesions on the growth of young rats. *Federation Proceedings, 18,* 69.

Howard, J. W., & Dawes, R. M. (1976). Linear prediction of martial happiness. *Personality and Social Psychology Bulletin, 2,* 478–480.

Keller, S. E., Weiss, J. M., Schleifer, S. J., Miller, N. E., & Stein, M. (1981). Suppression of immunity by stress: effect of a graded series of stressors on lymphocyte stimulation in rat. *Science, 213,* 1397–1400.

Klaus, M. H., & Kennell, J. H. (1976). *Maternal-infant bonding.* St. Louis: Mosby.

Kling, A. (1972). Effects of amygdalectomy on social-affective behavior in non-human primates. In B. E. Eleftheriou (Ed.), *The neurobiology of the amygdala* (pp. 511–536). New York: Plenum.

Klüver, H., & Bucy, P. (1939). Preliminary analysis of functions of the temporal lobes in monkeys. *Archives of Neurology and Psychiatry, 42,* 979–1000.

Koizumi, K., & Suda, I. (1963). Induced modulations in autonomic efferent neuron activity. *American Journal of Physiology, 205,*738–744.

Kuhn, C. M., Butler, S. R., & Schanberg, S. M. (1978). Selective depression of serum growth hormone during maternal deprivation in rat pups. *Science, 201,* 1034–1036.

Lilly, J. C. (1957). True primary emotional state of anxiety-terror-panic in contrast to a "sham" emotion or "pseudo-affective" state evoked by stimulation of the hypothalamus. *Federation Proceedings, 16,* 81.

Long, H. G. (1954). Unpublished study, University of Toronto.

Lynch, J. J. (1977). *The broken heart.* New York: Basic Books.

Machne, X., & Segundo, J. P. (1956). Unitary response to afferent volleys in amygdaloid complex. *Journal of Neurophysiology, 19,* 232–240.

Marx, J. L. (1982). Gene transfer yields cancer clues. *Science, 215,* 955–957.

Metuzals, J. (1959). The structure of the hypothalamic final common pathway to the adenohypophysis in the cat. I. The periventricular area of the nucleus arcuatus and the eminentia mediana. *Journal of Comparative Neurology, 113,* 103–138.

Money, J. (1980). *Love and love-sickness.* Baltimore: Johns Hopkins University Press.

Moon, H. D., & Jentoft, V. L. (1960). Human somatotropin activity in tissue culture. *Federation Proceedings, 19,* 157.

Moon, H. D., & St. Vincent, L. (1957). Effect of somatotropin on cells in tissue culture. *Science, 125,* 643–644.

Nerem, R. M., Levesque, M. J., & Cornhill, J. F. (1980). Social environment as a factor in diet-induced atherosclerosis. *Science, 208,* 1475–1476.

Nuckolls, K. B., Cassel, J., & Kaplan, B. H. (1972). Psychosocial assets, life crisis, and the prognosis of pregnancy. *American Journal of Epidemiology, 95,* 431–441.

O'Brien, C. P., Happel, L., & Bach, L. M. N. (1964). Some hypothalamic effects of STH-influenced growth and insulin sensitivity in kittens. *Federation Proceedings, 23,* 205.

Porter, R. W. (1952). Alterations in electrical activity of the hypothalamus induced by stress stimuli. *American Journal of Physiology, 169,* 629–637.

Porter, R. W. (1953). Hypothalamic involvement in the pituitary-adrenocortical response to stress stimuli. *American Journal of Physiology, 172,* 515–519.

Powell, G. F., Brasel, J. A., Raiti, S., & Blizzard, R. M. (1967). Emotional deprivation and growth retardation simulating idiopathic hypopituitarism, II: Endocrinological evaluation of the syndrome. *New England Journal of Medicine, 276,* 1279–1283.

Redgate, E. S., & Gellhorn, E. (1955). Relation of anterior hypothalamic excitability to cardiovascular reflexes. *American Journal of Physiology, 183,* 654.

Reich, P., Murawski, B. J., DeSilva, R. A., & Lown, B. (1979). Psychologic studies in patients with ventricular arrhythmias. *Psychosomatic Medicine, 41,* 74–75.

Rice, R. D. (1977). Neurophysiological development in premature infants following stimulation. *Developmental Psychology, 13,* 69–76.

Riley, V. (1975). Mouse mammary tumors: Alteration of incidence as apparent function of stress. *Science, 189,* 465–467.

Riley, V. (1981). Psychoneuroendocrine influences on immunocompetence and neoplasia. *Science, 212,* 1100–1109.

Ross, C. A., & Herczeg, S. A. (1956). Protective effects of ganglionic blocking agents on traumatic shock in the rat. *Proceedings of the Society for Experimental Biology and Medicine, 91,* 196–199.

Satinsky, J., Kosowsky, B., Lown, B., & Kerzner, J. (1971). Ventricular fibrillation induced by hypothalamic stimulation during coronary occlusion. *Circulation, 40,* II–60.

Schapiro, S., & Vukovich, K. R. (1970). Early experience effects upon cortical dendrites: a proposed model for development. *Science, 167,* 292–294.

Scott, S., & Richards, M. (1979). Nursing low birthweight babies on lambswool. *Lancet, 1*(8124), 1028.

Skinner, J. E., Lie, J. T., & Entman, M. L. (1974). Modification of ventricular fibrillation latency following coronary artery occlusion in the conscious pig: the effects of psychological stress and beta-adrenergic blockade. *Circulation, 34,* 692–696.

Slusher, M. A. (1958). Disassociation of adrenal ascorbic acid and corticosterone responses to stress in rats with hypothalamic lesions. *Endocrinology, 63,* 412–419.

Surwit, R. S., Williams, R. B., & Shapiro, D. (1981). *Behavioral factors in cardiovascular disease.* New York: Academic Press.

Suzuki, T., Romanoff, E. B., Koella, W. P., & Levy, C. K. (1960). Effect of diencephalic stimuli on 17-hydroxycorticosteroid secretion in unanesthetized dogs. *American Journal of Physiology, 198,* 1312–1314.

Troxler, R. G., Sprague, E. A., Albanese, R. A., Fuchs, R., & Thompson, A. J. (1977). The association of elevated plasma cortisol and early atherosclerosis as demonstrated by coronary angiography. *Atherosclerosis, 26,* 151–162.

Verrier, R. L., & Lown, B. (1981). Autonomic nervous system and malignant cardiac arrhythmias. In H. Weiner, M. A. Hofer, & A. J. Stunkard (Eds.), *Brain, behavior, and bodily disease* (pp. 273–291). New York: Raven Press.

Warheit, G. P. (1979). Life events, coping, stress, and depressive symptomatology. *American Journal of Psychiatry, 136*(4B), 502–507.

Weininger, O. (1954). Physiological damage under emotional stress as a function of early experience. *Science, 119,* 285–286.

Wellington, J. S., & Moon, H. D. (1960). The effect of hydrocortisone on cultures of human liver cells. *Federation Proceedings, 19,* 158.

Williams, R. B. (1981). Behavioral factors in cardiovascular disease: An update. In J. W. Hurst (Ed.), *Update V: The heart* (pp. 219–230). New York: McGraw-Hill.

Williams, R. B., Jr., Lane, J. D., Kuhn, C. M., Melosh, W., White, A. D., & Schanberg, S. M. (1982). Physiological and neuroendocrine response patterns during different behavioral challenges: differential hyperresponsivity of young type A men. *Science, 218,* 483–485.

PART II

Applied
Psychoneuroendocrinology

7

The Biochemical Effects of Tactile Deprivation in Neonatal Rats

SAUL M. SCHANBERG AND CYNTHIA M. KUHN

Normal mother–infant interactions are critical for normal growth and behavioral development in most mammalian species, and disruption of this interaction elicits marked behavioral and physiological responses, including changes in body temperature, locomotor activity, heart rate, and "emotional reactivity" (Hinde & Spencer-Booth, 1971; Hofer, 1970, 1975). Some of these acute changes can be prevented by other members of the species or by external supports. However, in many species including rats, cats, dogs, monkeys, and humans, the sensory stimulation provided by physical contact between the young animal and the mother or some other adult animal is necessary for normal somatic growth and behavioral development (Hofer 1973, 1975; Plaut & Davis, 1972; Plaut, Thal, Haynes, & Wagner, 1974). In all these species, a marked retardation of both physical growth and behavioral development results when the stimulation provided by contact between the young animal and other members of the species is prevented. For example, the behavioral development of monkeys is markedly abnormal if they are restrained from physical contact with the mother, even if visual, auditory, and olfactory interactions are maintained (Harlow & Harlow, 1965; Harlow & Zimmerman, 1959; Hinde & Spencer-Booth, 1971).

The most dramatic sequelae of restricted interaction between infants and adults that have been reported are those occurring in humans.

*S. M. Schanberg is supported by USPHS Grants MH-13688 and MH-06489. C. M. Kuhn is supported by USPHS Grant DA-02739.

133

Marked suppression of growth and behavioral development in humans, or "psychosocial dwarfism," results in children who are deprived of the normal nurturing care provided by the mother (or father). These children fail to grow normally, are often mentally retarded, and demonstrate a number of abnormal behaviors, even if they receive adequate nutrition and appropriate medical care (Barbero & Shaheen, 1967; Casler, 1961; Glaser, Heagarty, Bullard, & Pivchik, 1968; Patton & Gardner, 1963; Powell, Brasel, & Hansen, 1967a; Silver & Finkelstein, 1967). The suppression of growth associated with human psychosocial dwarfism is reversed rapidly when adequate maternal care is provided, but persistent behavioral abnormalities and permanent decreases in body size and even death are observed in humans subjected to repeated or chronic maternal deprivation (Patton & Gardner, 1963; Thoman & Arnold, 1968).

The overall suppression of growth and behavioral development that characterizes psychosocial dwarfism is suggestive of a disturbance of endocrine regulation because only such a general process could affect development of all tissues. In fact, it has been demonstrated that maternal deprivation dwarfism in humans is associated with a specific endocrine abnormality that might mediate the suppression of growth. Powell *et al.* (1967a, 1967b) have reported that maternally deprived children do not secrete growth hormone following administration of insulin or arginine, stimuli that usually elicit brisk secretion in normal children. Furthermore, serum levels of somatomedin, the peptide that mediates the stimulation of skeletal growth caused by growth hormone, also appear to be depressed in maternally deprived children (D'Ercole, Underwood, & Van Wyk, 1977). This effect on growth hormone secretion seems to be fairly specific, as other endocrine parameters like thyroid function and glucose tolerance appear to be normal in maternally deprived children.

In this laboratory, we have developed an animal model of psychosocial dwarfism that appears to be useful for investigating the biochemical and physiological responses of developing animals to maternal deprivation. We have shown that a biochemical index of tissue maturation appears to be decreased during maternal deprivation and that changes in serum hormone levels correlate with this response. Maternal deprivation of preweanling rat pups decreases the activity of brain, heart, and liver ornithine decarboxylase (ODC), as well as tissue levels of its product, putrescine (Butler & Schanberg 1977). Both ODC activity and tissue putrescine content decline rapidly when pups are removed from the mother and remain low for as long as pups are kept away from the mother (Figures 7.1 and 7.2). ODC activity returns as soon as pups are returned to the mother (Figure 7.3).

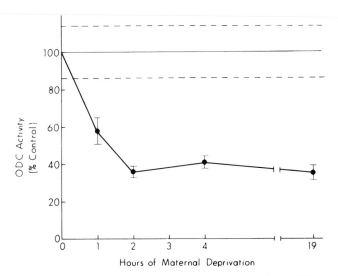

FIGURE 7.1   Effect of maternal deprivation on 10-day-old rat brain ODC activity. All values are expressed as percentage control ± *SEM*, *n* = 5 in each group. All differences are significant, *p* < .05. Control ODC activity = 1.3 nCi/mg protein/30 min.

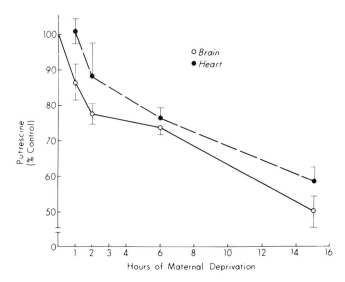

FIGURE 7.2   Comparison of the effect of maternal deprivation on 10-day-old rat cerebellum and heart putrescine levels. All values are expressed as percentage control ± *SEM*. *n* = 10 in each group. Values at 6 and 15 hours are significantly different from control, *p* < .05. Control values = 30 nmol/cerebellum, 15 nmol/heart.

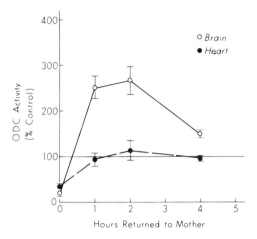

FIGURE 7.3   Comparison in 10-day-old rat brain and heart of the recovery of ODC activity after a 2-hour deprivation and return to the mother. All values are expressed as percentage control ± *SEM*. *n* = 5 in each group. Brain and heart values are significantly below control (*p* < .001) after 2 hours of deprivation and no return. Brain and heart values are significantly above control at each point after return (*p* < .05). Control brain ODC activity = 1.3 nCi/mg protein/30 min, heart = 5.2 nCi/mg protein/30 min.

ODC is the first and probably the rate-limiting enzyme in the synthesis of the polyamines putrescine, spermine, and spermidine, compounds that are intimately involved in regulation of nucleic acid and protein synthesis (Bachrach, 1973; Raina & Janne, 1970). Its activity and the concentration of its product are high in tissues with a high rate of growth and protein synthesis (Russell & Durie, 1978). The half-life of ODC is so short (10–30 min) that its activity can serve as an earlier and more sensitive index of tissue development than more conventional indices like protein synthesis (Janne & Raina, 1969; Russell & Snyder, 1969). ODC activity has proven to be such an accurate and sensitive index of cell growth and development that its decline during maternal deprivation in rats suggests that this environmental manipulation might have significant effects on tissue development, as it does in humans. During the past 2 years, we have used this model to help elucidate the physiological and biochemical mechanisms involved in the responses of neonatal mammals to maternal deprivation.

The first aim of these studies was to determine which aspect of the mother–pup interaction regulated the fall in ODC activity after separation. Some behavioral responses of neonatal rats to separation from the mother are caused by alterations in nutrition and temperature (Hofer, 1973, 1975; Stone, Bonnet, & Hofer, 1976). However, we found that pup

TABLE 7.1
Effect of 2-Hour Suckling with an Anesthetized Mother on Pup Brain ODC Activity[a]

| Experimental conditions | n | ODC activity (% control) | |
		Brain	Heart
Pups with non-anesthetized mother	18	100 ± 13	100 ± 12
Pups with anesthetized mother	19	44 ± 4*	20 ± 3*
Pups injected with urethane	10	118 ± 15	81 ± 15

[a]Brain ODC activity is expressed as a percentage of littermate controls. *Indicates statistically significant difference from controls.

body temperature was not altered during experimental maternal deprivation, nor was the decline in ODC activity related to food deprivation (Butler, Suskind, & Schanberg, 1978).

Maternal deprivation also interrupts several other interactions between the mother and pups, including some initiated by the mother, such as licking and retrieving. To determine the role of active maternal behavior in maintaining ODC activity, pups were placed with lactating female rats that had been anesthetized with urethane. This treatment does not interfere with milk production or ejection, or with suckling by the pups (Lincoln, Hill, & Wakerly, 1973). However, it obviously eliminates active maternal behavior. We found that ODC activity declines in pups placed with an anesthetized mother (Table 7.1). The only change in the pups' environment in this experiment is the absence of active stimulation by the mother; this fall in activity occurs in the presence of all other sensory cues provided by the mother (olfactory, gustatory, and the like). The results of this experiment suggest that active tactile stimulation by the mother is required to maintain ODC activity. Neither the sensory stimuli provided by littermates nor those received by the pups when they initiate contact with the anesthetized mother restore ODC activity to normal.

To further investigate the hypothesis that active tactile stimulation of the pups is involved in the maintenance of ODC activity, we tested the ability of tactile stimulation alone to prevent the decrease in ODC activity associated with maternal deprivation. Pups were removed from the mother and either left undisturbed or stroked vigorously on the back and head for 2 hours with a moist brush. The results of this study are shown in Table 7.2. ODC activity in brain, heart, and liver decreased significantly in maternally deprived pups. However, none of these parameters decreased in pups that were separated from the mother but stroked. In additional studies, we have shown that only a specific type

TABLE 7.2
Effect of Stroking on Maternally Deprived Rat Pups[a]

	ODC activity (% control)			Serum GH (% control)
	Brain	Heart	Liver	
Control	100 ± 13	100 ± 6	100 ± 13	100 ± 20
Deprived	$68 \pm 8^*$	$36 \pm 7^*$	$32 \pm 6^*$	$25 \pm 7^*$
Deprived + Stroked	134 ± 15	93 ± 15	199 ± 41	82 ± 17

[a]8-day-old rat pups were maternally deprived for 2 hours and either left untouched or stroked 10–20 times every 5 min with a small moistened brush. Control pups were left with mother for 2 hours. Results are expressed as percentage control $\pm$ SEM. Control ODC activity was 0.147, 0.188, and 0.048 nmol ornithine/g tissue/hour respectively for brain, heart, and liver. *Indicates $p < .05$ or better compared to controls. Number of animals in each group was 12–15.

of stimulation will prevent the effects of maternal deprivation. Fairly heavy stroking that is roughly similar to that used by the mother in grooming the pups prevents the effects of maternal deprivation on tissue ODC activity, while light stroking and tail pinching are ineffective (Figure 7.4). These results further support our hypothesis that the removal of active tactile stimulation triggers the fall in ODC activity that is associated with maternal deprivation. This finding is of particular interest because tactile stimulation is thought to be one aspect of the mother–neonate interaction that is vital for normal somatic growth and general development in many mammalian species, including rats, cats, dogs, monkeys, and humans. For example, there is a report that tactile manipulation of premature babies increased their weight significantly over controls (White & Labarba, 1976).

Another goal of our studies is identification of physiological changes in the pups which could mediate the fall in ODC activity. Data from our early studies suggested that the fall in ODC activity probably was triggered by a hormonal or metabolic stimulus. The strongest evidence supporting this hypothesis is the finding that neither the decline in ODC activity in the heart nor the return is affected even when neural activity to the heart is blocked pharmacologically (Table 7.3). Furthermore, a deprivation-induced decline in ODC activity occurs on the second day of life before functional innervation is established in most peripheral tissues. Finally, the decrease in ODC activity induced by maternal deprivation occurs in all tissues studied, including heart, liver, brain, and kidney; such a general effect is probably mediated by some metabolic or hormonal signal.

Elevation of serum glucocorticoids is one of the most common hor-

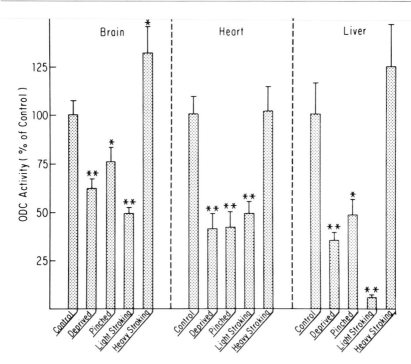

FIGURE 7.4 Effect of stimulation on ODC activity in maternally deprived pups. Pups were maternally deprived for 2 hours and either left untouched or stroked heavily, stroked lightly, or pinched on the tail every 5 min, and then killed. Controls were left undisturbed with the mother for 2 hours. Results are expressed as percentage control ± SEM. Control ODC activity = 0.147, 0.188, and 0.048 nmol ornithine/g tissue/hour respectively for brain, heart, and liver. *$p < .05$ or better compared to controls. **$p < .001$ or better compared to controls. $N > 15$ except pinched and light stroking $N > 8$.

monal responses to stress, and these hormones have been reported to cause numerous effects on tissue growth and maturation, including stimulation and inhibition of ODC activity in various tissues (Anderson & Schanberg, 1975, Friedman, Ader, Grota, & Larson, 1967; Zarrow, Haltmeyer, & Denenberg, 1966). However, when 4-day-old pups were adrenalectomized before deprivation, neither basal ODC activity in brain nor the deprivation-induced decline was affected (Butler *et al.*, 1978). Furthermore, serum levels of corticosterone were not changed after 2 hours of maternal deprivation (Kuhn *et al.*, 1978). These results indicate that stress-induced secretion of adrenal glucocorticoids is not involved in the deprivation response.

Previous studies from this laboratory and elsewhere have shown that growth hormone is involved in regulation of ODC activity in many

TABLE 7.3
Effect of Blocking Agents on Heart ODC Activity Following Return to
Mother[a]

Experimental conditions	n	ODC activity (% control)
Non-deprived		
no injection	10	100 ± 10
Deprived		
no injection		
not returned to mother	10	$33 \pm 2^*$
Deprived		
chlorisondamine injection		
returned to mother	11	106 ± 12
Deprived		
saline injection		
returned to mother	12	100 ± 10
Deprived		
propranolol injection		
returned to mother	12	$139 \pm 16^*$

[a]Heart ODC activity of 10-day-old pups maternally deprived for 2 hours, deprived for 2 hours and returned for 2 hours, and deprived for 2 hours, injected with saline, propranolol or chlorisondamine and returned for 2 hours. ODC activity is expressed as percentage of control $\pm$ SEM. *Indicates statistically different from control, $p < .05$ or better. Neither drug had any effect on heart ODC activity when injected into deprived and non-deprived control pups.

tissues, including brain and liver (Roger, Schanberg, & Fellows, 1974). Furthermore, growth hormone secretion is altered by various stresses (Martin, 1976). Therefore, we next investigated the possibility that altered secretion of growth hormone contributes to the fall in ODC activity associated with maternal deprivation. We found that serum growth hormone concentration declines rapidly when pups are removed from the mother and increases rapidly when pups are returned. This decrease is not accompanied by changes in serum content of other stress-responsive hormones such as thyroid-stimulating hormone, prolactin, or corticosterone (Table 7.4). These studies suggest that maternal deprivation elicits a specific neuroendocrine response that is distinct from the "nonspecific" stress response typically characterized by a decrease in serum growth hormone and an increase in prolactin and corticosterone (Brown & Martin, 1974; Krulich, Hefco, Illner, & Read, 1974; Pecile, Ferrario, Falconi, & Muller, 1967; Zarrow et al., 1966).

The endocrine response of rats to maternal deprivation is similar to that observed in humans, a surprising finding since serum growth hormone typically increases in response to stress in human adults but decreases in rats. Since neural regulation of anterior pituitary hormone

TABLE 7.4
Effect of Maternal Deprivation and Return to the Mother on 10-Day-Old Pup Serum Growth Hormone[a]

	n	GH	PRL	TSH	CS
		% control			
Non-deprived	28	98 ± 3	100 ± 7	100 ± 13	100 ± 10
Deprived					
1 hour	10	53 ± 8*			
2 hours	16	60 ± 6*	129 ± 14	92 ± 4	86 ± 10
6 hours	5	59 ± 12*			
Deprived and returned					
15 min	5	155 ± 32			
1 hour	8	99 ± 7			
2 hours	13	94 ± 7			
4 hours	5	100 ± 4			

[a]Pups were maternally deprived for various times in the water bath incubator, killed and trunk blood collected for hormone determinations. Pups returned to the mother were deprived in the incubator for 2 hours. Equally handled littermates served as controls for all experiments. Results are expressed as percentage control ± *SEM*. Control serum GH (growth hormone) = 80 ng/ml, PRL (prolactin) = 1.4 ng/ml, TSH (thyroid-stimulating hormone) = 237 ng/ml, CS (corticosterone) = 2 ug%. *Indicates significantly different from control ($p < .05$).

secretion in neonatal mammals is considerably different from that observed in adults (Cocchi *et al.*, 1977; Dohler & Wuttke, 1974; Kaplan & Grumbach, 1976; Ojeda & McCann, 1974), it is possible that this response represents a universal neuroendocrine response of immature animals to stress. This hypothesis is supported by the report that serum growth hormone in human neonates decreases rather than increases in response to stress (Stubbe & Wolf, 1971).

Studies from this laboratory suggest that the altered secretion of growth hormone which occurs during maternal deprivation contributes to the decline in ODC activity. Both the decline in ODC activity and the decrease in serum growth hormone which occur are initiated by removal of active tactile stimulation by the mother. Placing the pups with an anesthetized mother causes a decrease in both parameters, while stroking of pups increases both (Table 7.2, Figure 7.5). In addition, we have shown that pharmacological suppression of growth hormone secretion with cyproheptadine (a serotonin antagonist) causes a decrease in brain and liver ODC activity, while stimulation of growth hormone release by injection of 5-HTP (the precursor of serotonin) results in an increase of ODC activity in these organs (Stuart, Lazarus, Smythe, Moore, & Sara, 1977; Table 7.5).

We have recently identified another marked disruption of growth

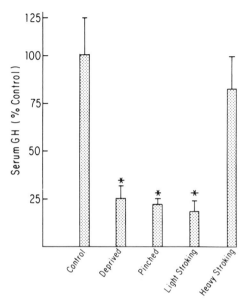

FIGURE 7.5   Effect of stimulation on serum growth hormone (GH) in maternally deprived pups. Pups were maternally deprived and stimulated as described in Figure 7.4. Results are expressed as percentage control ± *SEM*. Control serum GH = 54 ng/ml. *$p < .002$ or better compared to controls. $N > 15$ except pinched and light stroking $N > 10$.

hormone mechanisms in maternally deprived rat pups. To test our hypothesis that inhibition of growth hormone secretion during maternal deprivation contributes to the fall in ODC activity, we tried to restore ODC activity in maternally deprived rat pups by administration of

TABLE 7.5
Effect of Cyproheptadine and 5-HTP on Serum Growth Hormone and Tissue ODC Activity[a]

			ODC activity (% control)	
	n	Serum GH (% control)	Brain	Liver
Control	6	100 ± 20	100 ± 4	100 ± 10
Cyproheptadine	6	34 ± 13*	60 ± 7*	37 ± 9*
5-HTP	10	240 ± 75*	—	377 ± 83*

[a]10-day-old pups were injected intraperitoneally with cyproheptadine (10 mg/kg), or 5-HTP (15 mg/kg), or saline, killed 2 hours later and serum GH (growth hormone) and tissue ODC activity determined. Results are expressed as percentage control ± *SEM*. *Indicates significant difference from saline injected control, $p < .05$ or better.

TABLE 7.6
Effect of Growth Hormone on Brain and Liver ODC Activity in
Maternally Deprived Rat Pups[a]

	ODC activity (% control)	
Treatment	Brain	Liver
Control	100 ± 6	100 ± 22
Deprived	59 ± 6*	11 ± 3*
Control-growth hormone	166 ± 7*	437 ± 36*
Deprived-growth hormone	67 ± 9* +	10 ± 1* +

[a]8-day-old rat pups were maternally deprived for 2 hours, injected intra-peritoneally (for liver) or intracisternally (for brain) with growth hormone (100 μg), returned to the deprivation cages and killed 4 hours later. Control pups were left with the mother and injected with saline or hormone at the same time as experimental animals. Results are expressed as percentage control ± SEM. Control ODC activity was 40 nCi/30 min/g tissue for brain and 13 nCi/30 min/g tissue for liver. *Indicates statistically different from controls, $p < .05$. +Indicates statistically different from growth hormone-injected control, $p < .001$. $n = 10$ for all groups.

growth hormone. We found that when pups are deprived for 2 hours and then injected with growth hormone, neither brain nor liver ODC activity increases, although growth hormone injected into normal litter-mates induces a marked rise in ODC activity in both tissues (Table 7.6). The tissue response to growth hormone returns when pups are returned to the mother. The loss of tissue sensitivity to growth hormone, like the decline in tissue ODC activity and serum growth hormone, appears to be triggered by the removal of active tactile stimulation by the mother. Placing the pups with an anesthetized mother causes a similar loss of tissue responsivity to growth hormone, while starving the pups by transfer to a nipple-ligated mother does not interfere with responsivity (Table 7.7).

The biochemical mechanism that is responsible for the observed loss of growth hormone sensitivity in tissue remains unknown. However, ODC activity can be stimulated by other agents (Table 7.8). Therefore, it does not appear to result from a general impairment of protein synthesis or a similarly general metabolic phenomenon. In addition, these data indicate that the loss of tissue responsivity to growth hormone does not result from the presence of a previously described inhibitor of ODC, as this inhibitor also inhibits dexamethasone-stimulated activity.

The loss of tissue responsivity to growth hormone during maternal deprivation is particularly interesting in light of a report that maternally deprived children are resistant to the actions of growth hormone. While

TABLE 7.7
Response of Liver ODC to Growth Hormone in Pups with an Anesthetized or Nipple-Ligated Mother[a]

Treatment	ODC activity (% control)
Experiment 1	
control	100 ± 11
control + growth hormone	1097 ± 144*
pups with anesthetized mother + vehicle	38 ± 4*
pups with anesthetized mother + growth hormone	41 ± 6*+
Experiment 2	
pups with nipple-ligated mother	100 ± 16
pups with nipple-ligated mother + growth hormone	1029 ± 17*

[a]8-day-old pups were placed with urethane anesthetized or nipple-ligated mother for 2 hours, injected subcutaneously with vehicle or growth hormone (100 μg), returned to the mother and killed 4 hours later. Control pups were left with a normal mother and injected with saline or hormone at the same time. Control activity in Experiment 1 = 10 nCi/30 min/g tissue, in Experiment 2 = 30 nCi/30 min/g tissue. *Indicates statistically different from control, $p < .05$. +Indicates statistically different from growth hormone-injected control, $p < .05$. $n = 10$ or more for each group.

growth of hypopituitary dwarfs is stimulated by administration of growth hormone, treatment of maternally deprived children with growth hormone seems to be less effective than treatment of normal children (Rayner & Rudd, 1973).

TABLE 7.8
Effect of Hormones on Liver ODC Activity in Maternally Deprived Rat Pups[a]

		ODC activity (% control)			
Treatment	Dose	Control	n	Deprived	n
Vehicle		100 ± 22	60	11 ± 3+	60
oGrowth hormone	100 μg	437 ± 136*	20	11 ± 2*+	20
oPlacental lactogen	100 μg	315 ± 54*	10	10 ± 1*+	10
Dexamethasone	200 μg	366 ± 62*	10	532 ± 51*	10
Dibutyryl cAMP	800 μg	518 ± 172*	10	539 ± 183*	10
PGE-1	50 μg	510 ± 66*	10	620 ± 213*	10
Insulin	10 μg	1306 ± 422*	10	2040 ± 594*	15

[a]8-day-old pups were maternally deprived for 2 hours, injected subcutaneously with vehicle or hormone, returned to the deprivation cages and killed 4 hours later. Control pups were left with the mother and injected with vehicle or hormone at the same time. Results are expressed as percentage control ± *SEM*. Control ODC activity was 37 nCi/30 min/g tissue. *Indicates statistically different from control, $p < .05$. +Indicates statistically different from paired, hormone-injected control, $p < .05$. n = number of animals in each group.

The finding of decreased growth hormone responsivity in maternally deprived rat pups also raises a significant question about the role of growth hormone in the loss of ODC activity during deprivation. If a decline in serum growth hormone triggers the decline in ODC associated with maternal deprivation, then one should expect that an increase in serum growth hormone should mediate the return. However, pharmacological elevation of serum gorwth hormone in deprived pups failed to raise ODC activity. Furthermore, return of sensitivity was not complete until 1.5–2 hours after return to the mother. These findings cast doubt on the hypothesis that the surge of growth hormone that occurs within 15 min of return mediates the subsequent increase in ODC activity. Although altered growth hormone secretion might contribute to the observed change in ODC activity, apparently other factors also are involved.

In summary, we have shown that maternal deprivation of neonatal rat pups is associated with a marked decrease in both serum growth hormone as well as a loss of sensitivity in various tissues to growth hormone. These studies indicate that this animal model is similar in many ways to human psychosocial dwarfism. The latter condition also is characterized by a suppression of growth and inhibition of growth hormone secretion in response to physiological stimuli. Furthermore, the finding that ODC activity in both brain and peripheral tissue declines in parallel during maternal deprivation of rats suggests that the retardation of behavioral development observed in maternally deprived humans might be mediated by the same hormonal mechanism that triggers the suppression of somatic growth.

Many questions about the sequelae of maternal deprivation in rats remain. The most important of these for evaluating the relevance of this animal model to human psychosocial dwarfism is whether the decrease in growth hormone secretion results from a suppression of hypothalamo–hypophyseal responsivity as observed in humans. The loss of tissue sensitivity to growth hormone observed in rats raises questions about the primary role of decreased growth hormone secretion in mediation of the alterations in polyamine metabolism observed in rats and, therefore, the role of growth hormone in mediating the retardation of growth observed in human psychosocial dwarfism. Perhaps alterations in the secretion of other substances contribute to the retardation of growth via the suppression of tissue reactivity to various physiological stimuli. It is apparent that this animal model offers a unique opportunity for the investigation of biochemical and physiological mechanisms which mediate the developmental effect of maternal–infant interactions.

References

Anderson, T. R., & Schanberg, S. M. (1972). Ornithine decarboxylase activity in developing rat brain. *Journal of Neurochemistry, 19*, 1471–1481.

Bachrach, U. (1973). *Function of naturally occurring polyamines.* New York: Academic Press.

Barbero, G. J., & Shaheen, E. (1967). Environmental failure to thrive: A clinical view. *Journal of Pediatrics, 71*, 639–644.

Brown, G. M., & Martin, J. H. (1974). Corticosterone, prolactin and growth hormone responses to handling and new environment in the rat. *Psychosomatic Medicine, 36*, 241–247.

Butler, S. R., & Schanberg, S. M. (1977). Effect of maternal deprivation on polyamine metabolism in preweanling rat brain and heart. *Life Sciences, 21*, 877–884.

Butler, S. R., Suskind, M. R., & Schanberg, S. M. (1978). Maternal behavior as a regulator of polyamine biosynthesis in brain and heart of the developing rat pup. *Science, 199*, 445–447.

Casler, L. (1961). Maternal deprivation: A critical review of the literature. *Monographs for research in child development, 26*(2).

Cocchi, D., Gil-Ad, I., Panerai, A. E., Locatelli, V., & Muller, E. E. (1977). Effect of 5-hydroxytryptophan on prolactin and growth hormone release in the infant rat: evidence for different neurotransmitter mediation. *Neuroendocrinology, 24*, 1–13.

D'Ercole, A. J., Underwood, L. E., & Van Wyk, J. J. (1977). Serum somatomedin-C in hypopituitarism and in other disorders of growth. *Journal of Pediatrics, 90*, 375–381.

Dohler, K. D., & Wuttke, W. (1974). Serum LH, FSH, prolactin and progesterone from birth to puberty in female and male rats. *Endocrinology, 94*, 1003–1008.

Friedman, S. B., Ader, R., Grota, L. J., & Larson, T. (1967). Plasma corticosterone response to parameters of electric shock stimulation in the rat. *Psychosomatic Medicine, 29*, 323–328.

Glaser, H. H., Heagarty, M. C., Bullard, D. M., & Pivchik, B. A. (1968). Physical and psychological development of children with early failure to thrive. *Journal of Pediatrics, 73*, 690–698.

Harlow, H. F., & Harlow, M. K. (1965). Effects of various mother–infant relationships on rhesus monkey behaviors. In B. Foss (Ed.), *Determinants of infant behavior* (pp. 15–30). London: Methuen.

Harlow, H. F., & Zimmerman, R. R. (1959). Affectional responses in the infant monkey. *Science, 130*, 421–432.

Hinde, R. A., & Spencer-Booth, Y. (1971). Effects of brief separation from mother on rhesus monkeys. *Science, 173*, 111–118.

Hofer, M. A. (1970). Physiological responses of infant rats to separation from their mothers. *Science, 168*, 871–873.

Hofer, M. A. (1973). The role of nutrition in the physiological and behavioral effects of early maternal separation in infant rats. *Psychosomatic Medicine, 35*, 350–364.

Hofer, M. A. (1975). Studies on how early maternal separation produces behavioral change in young rats. *Psychosomatic Medicine, 37*, 245–264.

Janne, J., & Raina, A. (1969). On the stimulation of ornithine decarboxylase and RNA polymerase activity in rat liver after treatment with growth hormone. *Biochemica et Biophysica Acta, 174*, 769–772.

Kaplan, S. L., & Grumbach, M. M. (1976). Development of hormonal secretion by the human fetal pituitary gland. In L. Martini & W. F. Ganong (Eds.), *Frontiers in neuroendocrinology* (Vol. 4, pp. 255–276). New York: Raven Press.

Krulich, L., Hefco, E., Illner, P., & Read, C. B. (1974). The effects of acute stress on the secretion of LH, FSH, prolactin and GH in the normal male rat with comments on their statistical evaluation. *Neuroendocrinology, 16*, 293–311.

Kuhn, C. M., Butler, S. R., & Schanberg, S. M. (1978). Selective depression of serum growth hormone during maternal deprivation in rat pups. *Science, 201*, 1034–1036.

Lincoln, L. W., Hill, A., & Wakerly, J. B. (1973). The milk ejection reflex of the rat: Intermittent function not abolished by surgical levels of anesthesia. *Journal of Endocrinology, 57*, 459–476.

Martin, J. B. (1976). Brain regulation of growth hormone secretion. In L. Martini & W. F. Ganong (Eds.), *Frontiers in neuroendocrinology* (Vol. 4, pp. 129–168). New York: Raven Press.

Ojeda, S. R., & McCann, S. M. (1974). Development of dopaminergic and estrogenic control of prolactin release in the female rat. *Endocrinology, 95*, 1499–1505.

Patton, R. G., & Gardner, L. I. (1963). *Growth failure in maternal deprivation.* Springfield, IL: Charles Thomas.

Pecile, A., Ferrario, G., Falconi, G., & Muller, E. E. (1967). Pituitary growth hormone content and hypothalamic growth hormone releasing activity in neonatal rats after stress. *Proceedings of the Society for Experimental Biology and Medicine, 130*, 425–427.

Plaut, S. M., & Davis, J. M. (1972). Effects of mother–litter separation on survival, growth and brain amino acid levels. *Physiology and Behavior, 8*, 43–51.

Plaut, S. M., Thal, A., Haynes, E. E., & Wagner, J. E. (1974). Maternal deprivation in the rat: Prevention of mortality by nonlactating adults. *Psychosomatic Medicine, 36*, 311–320.

Powell, G. F., Brasel, J. A., & Hansen, J. D. (1967a). Emotional deprivation and growth retardation simulating idiopathic hypopituitarism. Clinical evaluation of the syndrome. *New England Journal of Medicine, 276*, 1271–1278.

Powell, G. F., Brasel, J. A., & Hansen, J. D. (1967b). Emotional deprivation and growth retardation simulating idiopathic hypopituitarism. II. Endocrinologic evaluation of the syndrome. *New England Journal of Medicine, 276*, 1279–1283.

Raina, A., & Janne, J. (1970). Polyamines and the accumulation of RNA in mammalian systems. *Federation Proceedings, 29*, 1563–1574.

Rayner, P. H. W., & Rudd, B. T. (1973). Emotional deprivation in three siblings associated with functional pituitary growth hormone deficiency. *Australian Paediatric Journal, 9*, 79–84.

Roger, L. J., Schanberg, S. M., & Fellows, R. E. (1974). Growth and lactogenic hormone stimulation of ornithine decarboxylase in neonatal rat brain. *Endocrinology, 95*, 904–911.

Russell, D. H., & Durie, B. G. M. (1978). *Polyamines as biochemical markers of normal and malignant growth.* New York: Raven Press.

Russell, D. H., & Snyder, S. H. (1969). Amine synthesis in regenerating rat liver: Extremely rapid turnover of ornithine decarboxylase. *Molecular Pharmacology, 5*, 253–262.

Silver, H. K., & Finkelstein, M. (1967). Deprivation dwarfism. *Journal of Pediatrics, 70*, 317–324.

Stone, E. A., Bonnet, K. S. A., & Hofer, M. A. (1976). Survival and development of maternally deprived rats: Role of body temperature. *Psychosomatic Medicine, 38*, 242–249.

Stuart, M., Lazarus, I., Smythe, G. A., Moore, S., & Sara, V. (1977). Biogenic amine control of growth hormone secretion in the fetal and neonatal rat. *Neuroendocrinology, 22*, 337–342.

Stubbe, P., & Wolf, H. (1971). The effect of stress on growth hormone, glucose and glycerol levels in newborn infants. *Hormone and Metabolic Research, 3,* 175–179.

Thoman, E. B., & Arnold, W. J. (1968). Maternal behavior in rats. *Journal of Comparative Physiology and Psychology, 65,* 441–446.

White, J. L., & Labarba, R. C. (1976). The effects of tactile and kinesthetic stimulation on neonatal development in the premature infant. *Developmental Psychobiology, 9,* 569–577.

Zarrow, M. X., Haltmeyer, G. C., Denenberg, V. H., & Thatcher, J. (1966). Response of the infantile rat to stress. *Endocrinology, 79,* 631–634.

8

Biochemical Simulation of Anxiety Stress Employing Natural and Synthetic Corticoids: Influences on Neoplastic Processes

DARREL H. SPACKMAN,
M. A. FITZMAURICE, AND VERNON RILEY

Introduction

Although anxiety stress is undoubtedly a complex phenomenon in its overall manifestations, one basic physiological aspect is a rapid increase in circulating adrenal corticoids following exposure to a perturbing or disquieting stimulus (Friedman & Ader, 1965; Riley, 1981; Riley, Fitzmaurice, & Spackman, 1981a, 1981b, 1982; Santisteban, 1959; Spackman & Riley, 1976, 1978a, 1978b; Spackman, Riley, & Bloom, 1978). The resulting anxiety is transmitted through the CNS, and the corticoid elevation is effected via the thalamus, the cerebral cortex, the hypothalamus, the pituitary, ACTH, and the adrenal cortex (Stein, Schiavi, & Camerino, 1976; Turner & Hagnara, 1971). In the case of the mouse and other rodents, the adrenal glucocorticoid produced is corticosterone (CSR), while in the human and other primates it is mainly cortisol (Claman, 1972, 1975).

In the mouse, CSR elevation in the plasma occurs rapidly following natural or experimentally induced anxiety, and its time-course can be measured with precision. Tangible stress-induced physiological effects can be induced by remarkably mild procedures such as the simple capturing and handling of quiescent experimental animals. This results in a

PERSPECTIVES ON BEHAVIORAL MEDICINE, Vol. 2
Neuroendocrine Control and Behavior

natural increase in plasma CSR from the quiescent range of 0–40 ng/ml to over 200 ng/ml. These CSR concentrations can be measured accurately by appropriate microassay techniques (Riley & Spackman, 1977b; Spackman, Riley, & Bloom, 1978).

Such stress-induced increases of CSR in the plasma, which are physiologically derived, induce a conspicuous thymus involution, a T-cell lymphocytopenia (Blomgren & Anderson, 1971; Dougherty, 1952; Riley, 1981; Riley, Fitzmaurice, & Spackman, 1981a, 1981b, 1982; Santisteban, 1958, 1959; Wira & Munck, 1974), various inhibitory effects upon the functions of T-cell and natural killer cell subsets involved in cell-mediated immunity (Balow, Hurley, & Fauci, 1975; Berenbaum, Cope, & Bundick, 1976; Fauci & Dale, 1975; Fauci, Pratt, & Whalen, 1977; Feldman, 1975; Gillis, Crabtree, & Smith, 1979; Haynes & Fauci, 1978; Hochman, & Cudcowicz, 1979; Lotzova & Savary, 1981; Mendelsohn, Multer, & Bernheim, 1977; Monjan, 1981; Monjan & Collector, 1977; Parillo & Fauci, 1978; Rousseau & Schmit, 1977; Santoni, Herberman, & Holden, 1979), as well as a loss of tissue mass of the spleen and peripheral lymph nodes (Dougherty, 1952; Santisteban, 1958, 1959; Santisteban & Dougherty, 1954). These alterations of lymphoid cell populations and critical organs, whether induced by elevations of endogenous adrenal cortical hormones following stress, or by the administration of natural or synthetic exogenous corticoids, have been shown to have adverse effects upon the ability of the animal to cope with incipient or latent pathological processes (Riley, 1975, 1978, 1979a, 1979b, 1981a, 1981b, 1982; Riley & Fitzmaurice, 1982a, 1982b; Riley et al., 1981a, 1981b, 1982; Riley & Spackman, 1976, 1977a, 1977b; Riley, Spackman, Hellstrom, & Hellstrom, 1978). Both the incidence and the growth behavior of various stress-sensitive latent and transplantable malignancies have been experimentally altered by intentionally increasing the concentration of natural (CSR, cortisol) or synthetic (dexamethasone, fluocinolone acetonide, and the like) glucocorticoids in the blood. This is consistent with the known adverse influences that these hormones have upon various aspects of cell-mediated immunological competence.

Materials, Methods, and Assay Procedures

Animals

Housing and Environment. The mice employed in these experiments were protected by a special barrier system consisting of ventilated enclosed shelves with a filtered, laminar airflow that is vented outside of the building following contact with the animals and their released odors and aerosols (Riley, 1972, 1981a; Riley *et al.*, 1981a, 1981b, 1982; Riley & Spackman, 1976, 1977a, 1977b). When the Plexiglas doors of these facilities are closed, each shelf becomes a separate, independent, and isolated unit within a larger protected facility. Standard 12-hour intervals of light and dark were controlled by automatic light switches, and the temperature was maintained at 24°C (±2). Standard plastic cages, 28 × 18 × 13 cm (11 × 7 × 5 in.), containing about 2 cm of San-I-Cel ground corncob bedding were employed. The food consisted of Wayne Lab Blox pellets, which were supplied *ad libitum* through the cage-top food hopper. Clean water was constantly available through the use of pint glass bottles and stainless steel drinking tubes. High standards of sanitation were employed in the routine changing and sterilization of drinking bottles, tubes, and cages. Cages and bedding were changed once a week with a minimum of disturbance of the animals.

Experimental Mice.   Mice used in any given experiment consisted of uniform groups in terms of age, sex, strain, and origin. Mice were either bred in our laboratories or were obtained from reliable commercial breeders in batches of 50 or 100. In either case their age range was limited to about 5 days. Any abnormal-appearing mice were discarded. At the time of weaning, or upon receipt, the animals were randomly segregated into groups of 10 in standard plastic cages. If received from other breeders, the new mice were held in low-stress protective facilities to recover from the stressful effects of shipping (Riley *et al.*, 1981b; Riley & Spackman, 1977a). They were thus equilibrated for a minimum of 2 weeks prior to use. At the time of experimentation, the mice were usually young adults, 8–12 weeks of age, weighing 20–25 grams. Blood samples were drawn using the rapid and nondestructive retro-orbital technique (Riley, 1960). All mice, as well as the tumors and Moloney sarcoma virus employed in these experiments, were free from contamination with the LDH-elevating virus. When present, this virus is capable of inducing a wide variety of physiological alterations which include changes in immunological competence and tumor behavior (Riley, 1973, 1981a; Riley *et al.*, 1981a, 1981b; Riley & Spackman, 1976, 1977b; Riley, Spackman, Hellstrom, *et al.*, 1978; Riley, Spackman, Santisteban, *et al.*, 1978).

Organ Weights and Blood Counts.   Where organs were to be examined, mice were euthanized in a jar containing carbon dioxide, and the organs of interest were carefully removed and placed in covered petri dishes equipped with filter paper disks. The disks were moistened with saline to provide a high humidity and to prevent the drying of the tissues during the removal of fat and connective tissue, so that the weights could be determined accurately. The time between removal of the organs and their weight determination was kept to a minimum. Each organ was weighed individually to at least 0.1 mg accuracy. Leukocyte counts were determined with a Research Model B Coulter Counter.

Assay Procedures for Plasma Corticosterone in Mice

In any study of the biochemical simulation of anxiety stress by the administration of exogenous corticoids, it is essential that normal, quiescent, nonstressed animals be employed, and that their plasma levels of endogenous corticoids (CSR, in the mouse) be known. The micro-fluorometric assay procedure currently employed in our laboratories for the assay of CSR was developed specifically for use with the small samples of plasma or serum available from mice or rats (Spackman & Riley, 1976, 1978a, 1978b; Spackman *et al.*, 1978). Blood samples were drawn using the retro-orbital technique (Riley, 1960); plasma aliquots of 50 μl were assayed, and duplicate determinations were made for each unknown sample.

Assay Modifications.   Since the initial description of our assay method, several modifications have been incorporated to improve the assay procedure. Liquinox cleaning solution is used for all glassware cleaning (the use of chromic acid has been discontinued); fluorescence is developed in an incubator at 27°C; a Turner Model 430 spectrofluorometer, fitted with an adaptor to accept the 6 × 50-mm round cuvettes, is now used to determine fluorescence, and the wavelengths used are 470 and 525 nm for excitation and emission, respectively. Also, procedures have been developed for the recognition and determination of unidentified fluorogens (UF) in plasma and serum samples, the routine use of which allows corrected, "true" CSR values to be reported.

Determination of Unidentified Fluorogens in Plasma.   Almost all plasma CSR values for rats and mice reported in the literature have been determined by fluorescence methodology, and, other than in publications from our laboratory, are uncorrected for UF. UF compounds, also referred to as residual fluorescence, nonspecific fluorogens, and the like, have been recognized by several authors as being present in plasma. To our knowledge, our laboratory has been the only one to have chromatographically separated these UF compounds from CSR or cortisol and to have established the extent and reproducibility of their contribution to uncorrected CSR assay results (Spackman & Riley, 1978b). Uncorrected CSR values are, thus, higher than corrected, true CSR values, and true CSR values can only be established if the UF correction value has been determined under the conditions of assay used in the laboratory. Results from our laboratory, published after late 1978, contain corrected CSR values.

Our studies have shown that the total of UF compounds in plasma is stable and reproducible under our conditions of assay and does not vary measurably in samples containing a wide range of CSR values. In pooled plasmas from 21 groups of normal female mice maintained under low-stress conditions, and in plasma pools from 20 groups, bearing various tumors, that were housed similarly (range of CSR = 4–148 ng/ml), the average UF correction values were 23 ± 2 SD and 23 ± 3 SD, respectively. The average UF value for male mice was 19. In collaborative studies with members of the Bioelectromagnetic Research Laboratory at the University of Washington, several groups of samples, each consisting of 200 serum samples from Sprague-Dawley male rats, were analyzed for CSR. From each large group of 200 samples, 20–30 samples with apparent low to moderate CSR values were further analyzed for UF compounds. The average of the UF compounds, determined from the small sampling, was then subtracted from each of the samples in the large group of 200 to yield corrected, true CSR assay values for each of those samples. The average UF correction values from several such large groups of 200 samples were highly consistent, the values being from 18 to 20 ng/ml. It further appears that under the conditions of our assay, fluorescence contributions from the UF compounds in rats and mice are very similar, and the UF correction value for males is slightly less than for females.

The significance of correcting for the UF compounds seems apparent. In samples from animals kept in low-stress housing and handling conditions, the UF correction value frequently is greater than half the uncorrected CSR value. In such samples, if the UF correction could not be made accurately, the uncorrected, apparent CSR value might be 100% or more too high.

Environmental Factors Affecting Corticosterone Levels

Protective Housing.   Low-stress, protective housing units consisting of individually ventilated, enclosed shelves, as described previously, have been proven to be essential, in our experience, if one is to maintain mice or rats under conditions in which the physiological effects of stress are to be determined (Riley, 1972, 1975, 1978, 1979a, 1979b, 1981a, 1981b, 1982;

Riley & Fitzmaurice, 1982a, 1982b; Riley *et al.*, 1981a, 1981b, 1982; Riley & Spackman, 1976, 1977a, 1977b; Riley, Spackman, Hellstrom, *et al.*, 1978; Riley, Spackman, McClanahan, & Santisteban, 1979; Santisteban, Riley, & Fitzmaurice, 1972; Spackman & Riley, 1976, 1978a, 1978b; Spackman *et al.*, 1978). In conventional facilities, animals are usually exposed to routine daily noises, rack motion, the disturbance of cleaning operations, thermal fluctuations, pheromones, and other stressful disturbances. Rodents raised in most conventional facilities are stressed, as evidenced by their chronically elevated daytime plasma CSR levels, when compared to the low CSR values observed in animals in low-stress, protective housing facilities.

Handling Procedures. Even mild handling is capable of producing profound CSR elevations in normal, previously quiescent mice and rats. To obtain plasma samples in which CSR levels are in the nonstressed, quiescent range, a maximum "safe" time of 4 min is available, starting with the first disturbance of the animals such as the technician entering the animal room or lifting the cage from the shelf, until the blood sample is obtained. After 4 min from the initial disturbance, plasma CSR concentrations increase markedly and may be 10–15 times normal as a result of 30 min of mild disturbance associated with handling, weighing, cage changing, or the like (Riley, 1979b; Riley *et al.*, 1981b, 1982; Riley & Spackman, 1977a).

Stress Communication. Even with the use of low-stress protective housing, mice should not be bled in the same room where other mice are housed. Mice being bled are able to communicate their distress to other mice in the immediate vicinity through sounds both audible and inaudible to the human ear. Even mice behind ventilated barrier shelves awaiting their turn to be bled will exhibit stress-induced elevations of plasma CSR if other mice are bled near them in the same room (Riley *et al.*, 1981b).

Other Factors. Other conditions have also been found to contribute to elevated levels of CSR and should be evaluated if a minimum-stress environment is to be maintained. These include proximity to the opposite sex in separate cages on the same shelf; the type of cage used (i.e., wire-bottom versus all-plastic); the length of equilibration time since the animals were received in shipment; uncontrolled noises, such as heavy construction noise and vibration outside the building; and disturbance from radios or shouting in or near the animal rooms (Kelley, 1980; Riley, 1975, 1978, 1979a, 1979b, 1981a, 1981b, 1982; Riley & Fitzmaurice, 1982a, 1982b; Riley *et al.*, 1981a, 1981b, 1982; Riley & Spackman, 1976, 1977a). In addition, we are acquiring evidence which shows that sex, strain, and age all have an effect on the extent of plasma CSR elevation induced in mice following a given stressor (Riley et al., 1981b).

Corticosterone Levels in Low-Stress versus Stressful Housing Conditions

Low-Stress Ranges. Under optimal conditions of animal housing, care, and treatment, and of sample analysis, as discussed in the foregoing sections, we have found that 0–40 ng/ml of plasma CSR (corrected for UF) is the low-stress, normal resting range for mice and rats when plasma samples are obtained in the morning and early afternoon. We have also observed that the CSR levels in male rats and mice are somewhat lower than in females when both are maintained in low-stress protective housing and completely isolated from the opposite sex. These values agree well with the results of Barrett and Stockham (1963), who studied the effects of housing conditions, handling, and noise on the plasma CSR levels in rats. They reported an average value of 58 ± 0.5 ng/ml of CSR for 78 male Wistar rats housed individually, undisturbed for 18 hours prior to the determination, and bled within 2 min. They also reported that the handling (kept to a minimum) associated with weighing a different group of animals resulted in an average plasma CSR value of 219 ± 26 ng/ml, 15 min after the procedure (Barrett & Stockham, 1963).

Our studies have shown that daytime plasma CSR values for mice housed in conventional facilities ranged from 150 to 500 ng/ml (Riley, 1981a; Riley et al., 1981b). A study employing CBA female mice gave average plasma CSR values of 37 ng/ml for mice housed in protective animal facilities, as compared to 197 ng/ml for analogous mice maintained in a conventional animal room (Riley et al., 1979).

Determination of Chronic Stress. Various forms and durations of handling and treatment of mice and rats performed prior to the procurement of the blood sample, and that exceed the 4-min time limit, will almost certainly result in elevated plasma CSR values. An exception may be in rats that have been gentled by regular and repeated handling from an early age. Stressful events or disturbances (e.g., weighing an animal or giving an intraperitoneal injection) that occur in mice housed in protective facilities, and that are of short duration, cause only temporary elevations of plasma CSR. In such mice, plasma CSR levels are usually back to normal after 1.5 to 2 hours. Whether animals exhibiting elevated plasma CSR levels are chronically stressed, however, can only be determined by obtaining blood samples for the plasma CSR assay within 4 min of first entering the vicinity of the cage in which the animal is housed, following overnight, or longer, undisturbed equilibration. Also, the animal should have been maintained in its housing under normal or typical conditions for 10–14 days following a highly stressful event, such as shipment from a breeder (Riley *et al.*, 1981b; Riley & Spackman, 1977a).

For the morning and early afternoon hours, we consider the range of 50 to 100 ng/ml for plasma CSR in rats and mice to result from mild stress, and from 100 to 200 ng/ml to represent moderately stressed animals. Mice that have continuously elevated daytime plasma CSR values as a result of stressful housing conditions are chronically stressed. They will have smaller than normal thymus weights and may have other measurable changes in lymphatic tissue elements as well.

Circadian Patterns of Corticosterone and Stress. Mice and rats exhibit a circadian pattern of plasma CSR fluctuation, with the highest levels occurring between 9 and 11 P.M. for mice in protective housing (Riley & Spackman, 1977b). After 1 A.M., the CSR levels decrease to low levels that are maintained until about 3 P.M., when they start to rise again. We have no comparable nocturnal data for mice in conventional, stressful housing in which the mice exhibit elevated daytime CSR levels. However, since CSR values are elevated during the early part of the night in all rodents, protective housing, which is conducive to low daytime plasma CSR levels, is apparently highly important in producing animals which exhibit low-stress physiological characteristics. Whether the maximum nighttime CSR values differ appreciably between animals in protective housing as compared to those in conventional housing is not known. One would assume, however, that mice in conventional housing would have relatively low plasma CSR levels during the 1 A.M. to 8 A.M. waning part of the circadian CSR cycle, in the absence of disturbances caused by technicians or other personnel. This might explain why mice in conventional housing could continue to exhibit chronically elevated daytime CSR levels without suffering adrenal exhaustion.

Results

Some Physiological Effects of Stress from Construction Noise and Vibration

It is relevant to report data resulting from an unanticipated environmental stressor which influenced all mice in our colony and, therefore, our experimental plans. During 1981 and 1982, new-building construc-

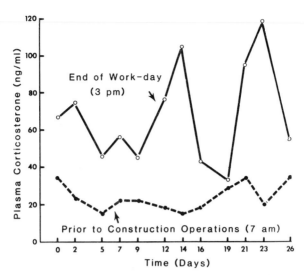

FIGURE 8.1   Effect of construction noise and vibration on plasma CSR levels during a 4-week period. The CSR levels of the plasma samples obtained at 7 A.M. were all within the nonstressed quiescent range of 0–40 nm/ml. In contrast, at 3 P.M., after the mice had been exposed to a day of construction-related noise and vibration, their CSR levels indicated that the mice had been stressed. The differences between the 7 A.M. and 3 P.M. CSR levels were statistically significant ($p < .005$). Each point represents the mean level of a separate group of five mice. Mice were C3H/He females, 8–12 weeks old.

tion was carried on just outside of our (minimal-stress) animal facilities. As a consequence, our mice were subjected to noises and vibrations associated with bulldozers, jackhammers, diesel trucks, drilling machines, and various other disturbances. Figure 8.1 illustrates the effect of this construction-associated stress upon the plasma CSR levels of animals within our facilities during a representative 4-week period. This figure shows the low CSR levels from mice bled at 7 A.M., prior to the start of the daily construction operations, in comparison with the elevated levels seen in analogous animals bled at 3 P.M., the end of the construction workday. Diurnal effects are not responsible for the observed differences, since murine plasma CSR concentrations have been determined in our laboratory to be essentially the same between 7 A.M. and 3 P.M. under quiescent conditions.

During the same construction period, uncontrolled thymus involutions occurred in otherwise untreated mice, as shown in Figure 8.2. The upper curve in Figure 8.2 shows the systematic decrease in thymus weight usually observed in nonstressed mice housed in low-stress facilities, as a function of mouse age. In contrast, the lower curve indicates that the mice undergoing uncontrolled environmental stress in the form

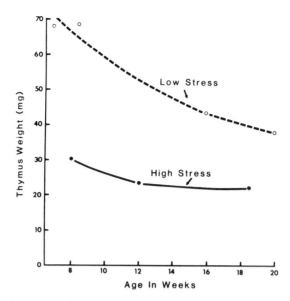

FIGURE 8.2 Thymus weight data observed under conditions of low stress and high stress. The lower thymus weights resulted from endogenous CSR elevation present during this high stress period as indicated by the elevated CSR data shown in Figure 8.1. Each point represents the mean of a minimum of 10, C3H/He, male mice. Similar data were obtained from BALB/c female mice.

of construction noise underwent a much more rapid thymus involution, and they prematurely reached the degree of thymus involution that is usually observed in old mice, when they were only 12 weeks of age. This accelerated thymus involution resulting from uncontrolled environmental stress rendered such animals useless in experiments in which a relatively intact thymus in the control mice was essential; it also demonstrates the deleterious accumulative effects of uncontrolled background noises upon the immune system.

Simulation of Stress Effects on the Thymus by Exogenous
Corticosterone

Figure 8.3 illustrates the simulation of environmental stress by the direct administration of exogenous CSR to mice of various ages, resulting in thymus involution which is apparently similar to that seen in the chronically stressed mice as shown in Figure 8.2.

Figure 8.4 illustrates the observed relationship between CSR dose and the resulting thymus involution. As indicated by the semilog graph plot,

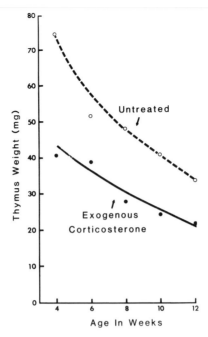

FIGURE 8.3   Thymus involution following administration of 1 mg of exogenous CSR to mice of various ages. This chart also demonstrates the natural thymus involution which occurs as a function of the animals' age (untreated mice). Each point represents the mean thymus weight of a separate group of five, male, BALB/c mice. The thymus weights of the mice which had received exogenous CSR (1 mg/mouse) were determined 48 hours following CSR administration.

the degree of thymus involution relative to the CSR dose, plotted logarithimcally, approaches a linear relationship.

Effects of a Synthetic Corticoid on Peripheral Leukocytes

Figure 8.5 illustrates the typical lymphocytopenic response of circulating mouse leukocytes to a single injection of a suspension of the synthetic corticoid dexamethasone (DMS). Although the data of Figure 8.5 represent the entire peripheral leukocyte population, a substantial portion of this leukocytopenia is due to a depletion of T-lymphocytes, since the majority of murine leukocytes are T cells (J. Clagett, personal communication, 1975; Gillius, Crabtree, & Smith, 1979; Santisteban, Guslander, & Willhight, 1969). In the mouse, both emotional stress-evoked elevations of plasma CSR and elevations from exogenously administered glucocorticoids cause a decrease of lymphocytes in the peripheral

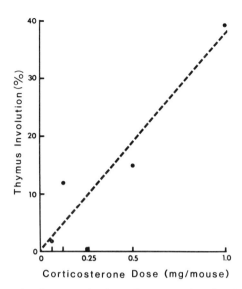

FIGURE 8.4   Relationship between the dose of exogenously administered CSR and the resultant percentage thymus involution (correlation coefficient = .92). Thymuses were weighed 48 hours after the various doses of CSR were administered. Each point represents the mean of a separate group of five 11-week-old BALB/c mice.

blood, due to cell lysis and also through sequestration in bone marrow and other organs (Claman, 1972, 1975; Dougherty, 1952; Fauci & Dale, 1975; Haynes & Fauci, 1978; Santisteban, 1958, 1959; Santisteban & Dougherty, 1954; Santisteban et al., 1969, 1972). This response is more rapid than the involution of the thymus as shown in Figures 8.2, 8.3, and 8.6. However, the leukocyte count returns to normal levels more rapidly than do the weights of the involuted organs once the stressor is removed or returns to normal. Thus, the lowest leukocyte counts following injection of a saline suspension of DMS equal to 1 mg per 20 gm mouse (50 mg/kg) were usually observed between 2 and 8 hours following the corticoid administration, with an average reduction in peripheral leukocyte counts of approximately 60% being maintained during the first 24 hours following treatment.

Lymphoid Organ Involution Following Administration of Synthetic Corticoids

Figure 8.6 illustrates the weight losses occurring in the thymus, spleen, and lymph nodes of mice injected with a single 50 mg/kg (1 mg per 20 gm mouse) dose of DMS as a saline suspension. The rapid thy-

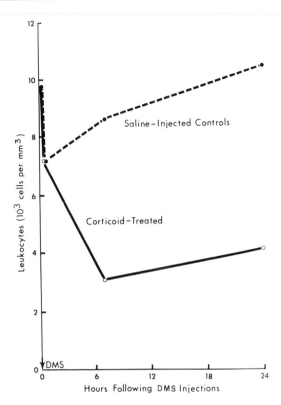

FIGURE 8.5 Influence of a single dose of dexamethasone (DMS) administered intra-peritoneally upon circulating peripheral leukocytes. C3H/He female mice, 9–10 weeks of age, were employed, with each point representing the average of 5 mice. The differences between the saline-injected controls and the DMS-treated mice were statistically signifi-cant at both 7 and 24 hours following injection ($p < .0005$).

mus involutions were followed by a similar weight loss in the spleens and peripheral lymph nodes. Two weeks following the corticoid admin-istration, the thymus weights were still about 70% below normal, al-though the spleens and nodes exhibited partial recovery.

Similar results were obtained with another synthetic corticoid, fluocinolone acetonide (FCA). Figure 8.7 shows that the extent of the involution of thymus, spleen, and lymph nodes 48 hours after intra-peritoneal corticoid administration was dependent upon the initial con-centration of the injected corticoid. In this experiment a corn oil suspen-sion of FCA was injected into mice to give a dose of 100 μg per 20 gm mouse (5 mg/kg). Four, tenfold dilutions of the initial preparation in corn oil were also injected into other groups of mice to give injected

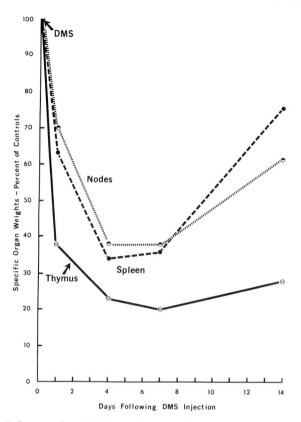

FIGURE 8.6   Influence of a single dose of dexamethasone (DMS) upon elements of the immunological apparatus and the reticuloendothelial system. The DMS was administered (50 mg/kg) as an insoluble suspension either subcutaneously or intraperitoneally. Since no statistically significant difference in response was noted between the two routes, the data were combined. Each point of the combined data represents the average of the organ weights obtained from 10 mice. C3H/He females, 9–10 weeks of age, were employed.

doses of 10, 1, 0.1 and 0.01 μg per 20 gm mouse, respectively. While significant organ involution was observed at the highest concentration of the corticoid, subsequent dilutions resulted in diminishing effects, until at the lowest FCA concentration of 0.01 μg per mouse (10^{-4} dilution), no significant organ weight loss occurred.

Enhancement of the Growth of Transplantable Tumors by Biochemically Simulated Stress

Selection of the proper tumor–host model is critical for studies that are designed to utilize the growth rates or regressions of transplantable

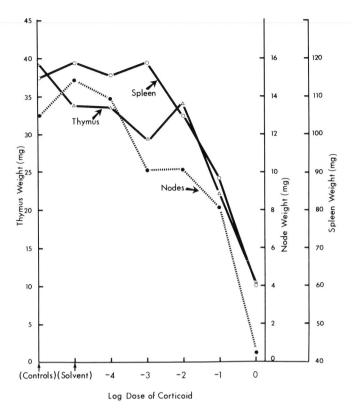

FIGURE 8.7   Effect of a synthetic adrenocorticoid, fluocinolone acetonide (FCA), upon various organs associated with the reticuloendothelial and immunological systems. Eight-week-old C3H/He female mice were employed. The highest dose of FCA employed was 100 μg per 20 gm mouse (5 mg/kg). In order to examine the influence of lower doses, four tenfold dilutions of this FCA concentration were prepared in corn oil and injected intraperitoneally. During a 60-day observation period, no deaths were observed.

tumors as indicators of the subtle impairment of host immunocompetence. For example, the primary growth of rapidly growing tumors such as the B-16 pigmented melanoma are largely unaffected by impairment of the immune system induced by stress or by injections of exogenous corticoids. However, in contrast, the primary growth of the more slowly growing nonpigmented variant of the B-16 melanoma is partially under host immunological control, and thus may be employed as a sensitive indicator of either impaired or enhanced immunocompetence (Riley, 1981a; Riley *et al.*, 1981b, 1982; Riley & Spackman, 1976). Preliminary work in our laboratories has also shown that the rate and number of lung metastases of the pigmented B-16 melanoma are also stress sensitive (Riley, 1982; Riley & Fitzmaurice, 1982a, 1982b).

As indicated by Figure 8.8, the 6C3HED lymphosarcoma growing in C3H/He mice responds to an implant of the synthetic corticoid DMS by an enhanced tumor growth. This tumor–host model is also responsive to rotation-caused, mild anxiety stress, which induces a natural elevation of endogenous CSR in the plasma. Figure 8.9 shows the increased tumor growth response to exogenously administered CSR at plasma levels which we believe simulated those resulting from anxiety stress. However, when the same lymphosarcoma was implanted into C3H/Bi mice, a more histocompatible substrain, the tumor grew rapidly even in the absence of elevated CSR levels, and its behavior in this substrain was not significantly altered by either endogenously induced or exogenously administered CSR, or by related synthetic corticoids (Riley, 1981a; Riley *et al.*, 1981a, 1981b, 1982). Thus, rapidly growing tumors which are not responsive to immunological control, such as the primary pigmented B-16 melanoma or the 6C3HED lymphosarcoma, when implanted into C3H/Bi mice represent examples of tumor–host models that may be

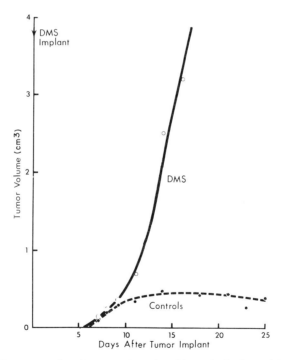

FIGURE 8.8   Tumor growth enhancement produced by a single dose of dexamethasone (DMS) administered on the day of tumor implantation. An aqueous suspension of 50 mg/kg of DMS (1 mg per mouse) was administered intraperitoneally into 10-week-old, C3H/He, female mice implanted with the 6C3HED lymphosarcoma. Each point represents the average tumor volume of 10 mice.

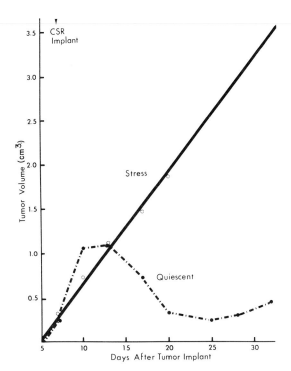

FIGURE 8.9 Biochemical simulation of the effects of stress upon the growth of the 6C3HED lymphosarcoma in C3H/He mice. Each mouse in the stress group was implanted subcutaneously with a slow-release pellet originally containing 6.7 mg of CSR, 7 days following tumor implantation. Each point represents the average tumor volume of 10 mice. Female mice, 10 weeks of age, were employed. In a similar quiescent control group, the mice received only the tumor implantation.

unsuitable for studies on the effects of stress or of administered corticoids upon immunocompetence (Riley, 1981a; Riley et al., 1981b, 1982).

Effects of Administered Corticoids on the Behavior of Moloney Sarcoma Virus-Induced Tumors

The Moloney sarcoma virus (MSV) tumor system is a useful model for studying the unusual phenomenon of the spontaneous regression of autochthonous tumors (Amkraut & Solomon, 1972; Fefer, McCoy, Perk, & Glynn, 1968; Riley, 1981a; Riley et al., 1982; Riley, Spackman, Hellstrom, et al., 1978). Figure 8.10 compares the tumor growth-enhancing effects of slow-release pellet implants of CSR (10 mg per 20 gm mouse) or DMS (1 mg per 20 gm mouse) with the minimal tumor growth observed in untreated controls following inoculation with the MSV. Tumor

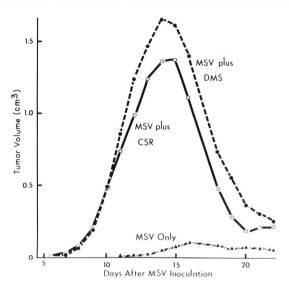

FIGURE 8.10   Enhanced growth of autochthonous tumors induced by the Moloney sarcoma virus (MSV) following implantation of single slow-release pellets of either CSR (10 mg/20 gm mouse) or dexamethasone (DMS).

The recipient, 9-week-old BALB/c female mice were inoculated intramuscularly in the right hip with 0.05 ml of a Moloney sarcoma virus preparation.

The slow-release corticoid pellets were implanted subcutaneously in the left hip on the day of MSV inoculation. Each mouse received a total of either 10 mg of CSR or 1 mg of DMS. All mice were housed 10 per cage in plastic cages with bedding, within low-stress facilities.

growth enhancement in the corticoid-treated groups was expressed by (1) significantly larger maximum tumor volumes, (2) a shortening of the tumor latent periods, (3) higher tumor incidence, and (4) a significant lengthening of the time required for the tumors to regress. These data may be interpreted as further evidence that these various tumor enhancements were a result of the partial impairment of host immunocompetence following administration of corticoids. These findings are consistent with other related data demonstrating the adverse effects of corticoids upon lymphocytes and upon the thymus and other organs involved in immunological competence.

Effects of the Timing of Biochemically Simulated Stress on Tumor Growth

The data of Figure 8.11 illustrate an example of the importance of the timing of biochemically simulated stress upon immunological competence. In this experiment, both enhancement and suppression of the normal growth behavior of the 6C3HED lymphosarcoma in C3H/He mice were observed. The growth of the 6C3HED lymphosarcoma in this

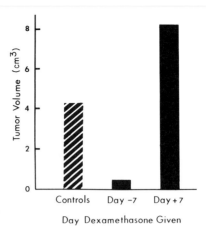

FIGURE 8.11   The influence of the synthetic corticoid, dexamethasone (DMS), upon tumor growth following administration at different times in respect to the implantation of the 6C3HED lymphosarcoma in C3H/He mice.

DMS was injected intraperitoneally as a saline suspension of low solubility at a dose of 1 mg per 20 gm mouse (50 mg/kg) either 7 days prior to, or 7 days after tumor implantation. The tumors were implanted subcutaneously as cell suspensions in the hips of female mice, 10 weeks of age, 10 mice per group. The tumor volumes shown were measured on day 21 following tumor implantation.

C3H substrain is usually limited under low-stress conditions, with a high percentage of tumor regressions occurring. When DMS was administered 7 days after tumor implantation, an apparent immunological impairment occurred, permitting the lymphosarcomas to escape the usual host control and grow rapidly, with lethal consequences for the hosts. However, when an identical dose of the corticoid was administered 7 days prior to tumor implantation, enough time elapsed between the DMS administration and the growth of the tumors to allow the immune competence to recover from the corticoid-induced impairment and be followed by an apparent overshoot of immune functions, as indicated by the observed suppression of tumor growth. In another experiment (data not shown) employing rotation-induced anxiety stress as a means for elevating endogenous plasma CSR levels, similar effects were observed on the growth of tumors induced by the MSV. Rotation on days 4 through 6 after virus inoculation resulted in a significant enhancement of tumor growth, in contrast to tumor inhibition observed when the mice were rotated for 3 days prior to MSV inoculation.

Another facet of the effects of timing upon the results of biochemically simulated stress is illustrated by Figure 8.12. This figure demonstrates the differences in tumor growth resulting from single injections of the synthetic corticoid fluocinolone acetonide (FCA) at various times following implantation of the 6C3HED lymphosarcoma into C3H/He mice, in

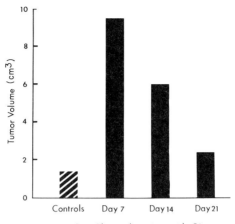

FIGURE 8.12 The influence of the time of administration of a synthetic corticoid, fluocinolone acetonide (FCA), on the growth of the transplantable 6C3HED lymphosarcoma in C3H/He mice. A slow-release suspension of FCA was implanted intraperitoneally at the various times indicated following tumor implantation. The tumor volumes shown were those observed on day 22 after tumor implantation. Ten female mice 9 weeks of age were employed in each group.

which a high percentage of tumor regressions are usually observed under low-stress conditions. The maximum tumor growth enhancement observed in this experiment occurred following a single FCA dose administered 7 days after tumor implantation. Similar but lesser tumor growth enhancement was observed when the compound was injected 14 or 21 days after tumor implantation. Thus, in this experiment, the FCA-induced, tumor-enhancing effects were systematically diminished when the corticoid was administered at longer intervals after tumor implantation, when the average tumor volume of the hosts was changing slowly. A tentative interpretation of this phenomenon is that, in the slowly growing or regressing tumors present at this stage, a smaller number of viable tumor cells remained to respond to the corticoid-induced immunosuppression (Riley, 1981a; Riley *et al.*, 1981b).

Effects of Elevated Corticoid Concentrations on
Mortality Apparently Associated with Spontaneous
Tumors in Aging Mice

Aging has been widely reported to be accompanied by a decrease in immunocompetence in both experimental animals and humans. Of possible relevance, we have observed a significant difference in the survival of old (20-month-old), C3H/He, female mice as compared with analogous young adult (2-month-old) mice, following injection of both groups with identical doses of DMS, as shown in Figure 8.13. Single injections of this hormone at 50 mg/kg (1 mg per 20 gm mouse) are usually well tolerated by normal weanling and young adult mice with essentially no deaths. A second injection of DMS administered to the young adult mice in this experiment at 14 days, however, may have contributed to the few deaths in this group, as shown in Figure 8.13. This low mortality is in contrast to the 47% mortality observed in the DMS-treated, 20-month-old mice during the same 24-day experimental period. Untreated 20-

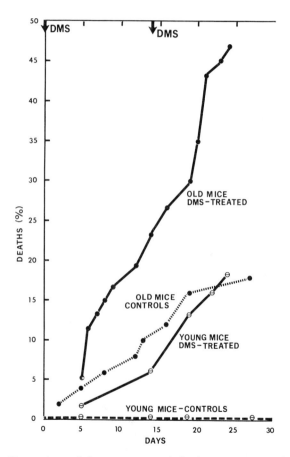

FIGURE 8.13 Comparison of the percentage of deaths occurring in old and young C3H/He female mice following identical administrations of the synthetic corticoid dexamethasone (DMS). The initial injection of a suspension of the hormone (50 mg/kg, or 1 mg per mouse) was given at experimental time zero, at which time the old mice were 20 months of age, and the young mice were 2 months old. A second injection of DMS was given to both groups 14 days later.

month-old mice that were employed as controls exhibited less than a 20% mortality during this period. It is of interest that the old, C3H/He mice apparently had an overall spontaneous tumor incidence also of 47%, as indicated when representative groups of the untreated old mice were autopsied at the termination of the experiment. An interpretation that is consistent with the other data of this report is that the DMS injections administered to the old mice may have permitted latent tumors that were already present to escape the immunological control of their hosts (Riley, 1981a; Riley et al., 1981b).

Discussion

By utilizing appropriate murine tumor–host models permitting the detection of modest changes in immunocompetence, the tangible increased risk of stressed animals with respect to either incipient or selected overt malignancies has been demonstrated (Amkraut & Solomon, 1972; Kelley, 1980; Nieburgs et al., 1979; Riley, 1975, 1978, 1979a, 1979b, 1981a, 1981b, 1982; Riley & Fitzmaurice, 1982a, 1982b; Riley et al., 1981a, 1981b; Riley, Spackman, Hellstrom, et al., 1978; Riley & Spackman, 1976, 1977a, 1977b; Spackman & Riley, 1976, 1978a; Spackman et al., 1978). Certain neoplastic processes respond to increased plasma concentrations of glucocorticoid hormones, whether derived endogenously from stress-induced psychoneural activation of the adrenal cortex, or through the direct administration of exogenous natural or synthetic corticoids, as indicated by Figures 8.8 through 8.12. The primary effects of elevated plasma corticoid levels upon these stress-sensitive neoplasms are associated with corticoid-induced alterations of thymus integrity, as indicated by Figures 8.2, 8.3, 8.4, 8.6, and 8.7, and various other host-cell mediated, immunological processes (Balow, Hurley, & Fauci, 1975; Barrett & Stockham, 1963; Berenbaum, Cope, & Bundick, 1976; Berenbaum, Fluch, & Hurst, 1973; Blomgren & Andersson, 1971; Borysenko, 1982; Burnet, 1969; Claman, 1972, 1975; Djeu, Heinbaugh, Viera, Holden, & Herberman, 1979; Fauci & Dale, 1975; Fauci et al., 1977; Feldman, 1975; Gillis, Crabtree, & Smith, 1979; Gisler, 1974; Haynes & Fauci, 1978; Herberman, 1982; Herberman & Holden, 1978; Hochman & Cudcowicz, 1979; Kelley, 1980; Kiessling & Wigzell, 1979; Klein, 1975; Lippman, 1982; Lotzova & Savary, 1981; Mendelsohn et al., 1977; Monjan, 1981; Monjan & Collector, 1977; Nicol & Bilbey, 1958; Oehler & Herberman, 1978; Parrillo & Fauci, 1978; Reichard, Edelman, & Gordon, 1956; Santoni, Herberman, & Holden, 1979).

Although there is continuing controversy over the role of immunological surveillance in controlling cancer, the accumulated data, from our laboratory and others, strongly suggest that such protective monitoring is a reality. For immunosurveillance to function effectively, at least two conditions must be met: (1) appropriate elements of the immunological system must be capable of recognizing foreign or neoplastic entities, and (2) the immunological system must be sufficiently competent to effectively negate or destroy transformed malignant cells or other invaders. A reasonable function of a low-stress environment in assisting immunosurveillance is through a continuing maintenance of the integrity of the organs and cellular constituents that permit cell-mediated immunity to function effectively (Riley, 1975, 1978, 1979a, 1979b, 1981a, 1981b, 1982; Riley & Fitzmaurice, 1982a, 1982b; Riley *et al.*, 1979, 1981a, 1981b, 1982; Riley & Spackman, 1976, 1977a, 1977b; Riley, Spackman, Hellstrom, *et al.*, 1978; Santisteban *et al.*, 1972; Spackman & Riley, 1976, 1978a).

The advantages of utilizing mouse models for studies embracing stress influences and the effects of aging relative to neoplasms and immune responses are that the various processes are greatly magnified and accelerated. It is probably permissible to assume that this intentional experimental magnification will yield useful clues concerning stress-induced enhancements of pathological processes that occur in humans at subliminal rates (Fox, 1978).

Stress-Induced Hormones

Stress elicits a cascade of changes in hormonal secretions (Mason, 1974; Pierpaoli, Baroni, Fabris, & Sorkin, 1969; Tache, Ruisseau, Ducharme, & Collu, 1978). In the rat, the profile of the modifications induced by acute stress includes increased secretions of ACTH, CSR, prolactin, luteinizing hormone, and, to a lesser degree, of follicle-stimulating hormone (Tache *et al.*, 1978). Sustained chair restraint of monkeys resulted in elevations in corticosteroids, epinephrine, norepinephrine, and thyroxins, with concomitant decreases in insulin and gonadal hormones; on the other hand, exposure to gradually decreasing temperatures over a one-week period induced elevations in corticosteroids, epinephrine, norepinephrine, and thyroid and growth hormones (Mason, 1974). The single consistent response involving a variety of species and stressors was the elevation of ACTH and plasma corticosteroids. Second were elevations in plasma epinephrine and growth hormone; the rest of the responses varied considerably depending upon the stressor. It is due to this observed consistency in the increased levels of plasma corticosteroids following stress that natural or synthetic corticosteroids have been employed to simulate stress-induced responses. However, it should also be borne in mind that, due to the complex interrelationships between various hormonal secretions, the administration of exogenous corticosteroids in amounts sufficient to attain the levels observed in the plasma of stressed animals might radically alter the concentration levels of others of the various hormones mentioned above. This is especially true of the catecholamines and growth hormone (Glick, 1975).

The Importance of the Thymus

There is an impressive body of literature on the importance of the thymus to the proper development and continuing functioning of the immune system. It is widely recognized that neonatal thymectomy results in severe immunological deficiencies which frequently result in death (Luckey, 1973; Metcalf, 1966). The thymectomy of adult animals, while not having immediate consequences under ideal environmental and nutritional circumstances, can have lethal consequences in malnourished or stressed animals, and eventually may lead to immune deficiencies similar to those following neonatal thymectomy, even under ideal conditions (Luckey, 1973; Metcalf, 1966; Pierpaoli, 1981). The age-related involution of the thymus, as depicted by Figures 8.2 and 8.3, commences at puberty in response to the changing hormonal secretions at this time and to the sensitivity of thymocytes to the increased output of glucocorticoids and sex hormones (Luckey, 1973; Metcalf, 1966). This normal process has no immediate consequences upon the immune defences of the young adult animal, but it eventually is correlated with, and may be responsible for, the immune deficiencies found in old age, as indicated by the data of Figure 8.13 and in animals housed under conditions of severe environmental stress (Kelley, 1980; Riley, 1975, 1978, 1979a, 1979b, 1981a, 1981b, 1982; Riley & Fitzmaurice, 1982a, 1982b; Riley et al., 1978, 1979, 1981a, 1981b, 1982; Riley & Spackman, 1976, 1977a, 1977b; Riley, Spackman, Hellstrom, et al., 1978; Santisteban, 1958, 1959; Santisteban & Dougherty, 1954). As indicated in Figure 8.2, the rate at which this natural process takes place can be increased in the presence of stressful environmental conditions which produce elevations in plasma glucocorticoid levels, shown in Figure 8.1. Of interest in this regard is the presence in the mouse thymus of corticoid-sensitive and corticoid-resistant cells (Blomgren & Andersson, 1971; Claman, 1972, 1975; Rousseau, 1977; Trainin, Levo, & Rotter, 1974; Wira & Munck, 1974). Corticoid-resistant thymocytes have been indicated to be immunologically more competent than corticoid-sensitive cells (Wira & Munck, 1974), and it is possible to hypothesize that the destruction of corticoid-sensitive cells, which occurs preferentially following endogenous corticoid elevation induced by an acute stress, might serve some long-range, useful purpose (Monjan, 1981; Monjan & Collector, 1977). However, our data indicate that the cell-mediated immune responses to tumor growth are indeed rapidly suppressed by both endogenous and exogenous corticoids, as expressed in various tumor–host models. This is true of mammary tumor incidence in susceptible C3H mice subjected to long-term environmental stress (Riley, 1975, 1981a; Riley et al., 1982); in incidence and numbers of B-16 melanoma metastases following subjection of the tumor-bearing mice to rotation-induced stress (Riley, 1982; Riley & Fitzmaurice, 1982b); in the survival time of B-16 melanoma-bearing mice recovering from shipping stress (Riley et al., 1982); in the growth rate and regressions of 6C3HED lymphosarcomas in mice under various stressful conditions (Riley, 1981a, 1981b; Riley et al., 1981a, 1981b, 1982); and in the enhanced growth of autochthonous tumors induced by the MSV (Amkraut & Solomon, 1972; Riley, 1981a; Riley et al., 1982; Riley, Spackman, Hellstrom, et al., 1978). As indicated by Figures 8.8 through 8.12, several of these stress-induced, tumor-enhancing effects can be simulated by the administration of exogenous glucocorticoids. Because of experimental design, thymus weights in the stressed, tumor-bearing mice in many of the above experiments were not determined. However, the thymus involution seen in Figures 8.2, 8.3, 8.4, 8.6, and 8.7 as a result of elevated levels of glucocorticoids, as well as the thymus involution previously observed in stressed, nontumor-bearing mice (Blomgren & Andersson, 1971; Riley, 1981a; Riley et al., 1981b, 1982; Santisteban, 1958, 1959), makes it difficult to dismiss the assumption that thymus involution brought about by stress-induced elevations of glucocorticoids was a key factor in the tumor-enhancing effects of stress.

Of relevance to the connection between the integrity of the thymus and various tumor-related parameters are the functions of the thymus as a programmer in the maturation of various cytotoxic lymphoid cells (Haynes & Fauci, 1978; Metcalf, 1966; Pierpaoli, 1981; Trainin et al., 1973, 1974), and as a source of endocrine secretions (Bach, Dardenne, Pleau, & Bach, 1975; Goldstein, Slater, & White, 1966; Luckey, 1973; Metcalf, 1966; Pierpaoli, 1981; Potop & Mileu, 1973; Robey, 1973; Trainin et al., 1973, 1974). Of further relevance to this relationship between thymus integrity and tumor-related immunocompetence may be the effect of thymic hormones on the development and maintenance of other endocrine functions, notably those of the pineal gland and, hence, the hypothalamic–pituitary axis (Pierpaoli, 1981). Some thymus-produced hormones have also been reported to have antitumor activities. For example, the thymic factor(s) described by Bach *et al.* (1975) and Trainin *et al.* (1973, 1974) are active in the promotion of cell-mediated, antitumor immunity. On the other hand, thymosterin, which has a steroid config-uration, demonstrates antitumor activity both *in vitro* and *in vivo* (Potop & Milcu, 1973). It is also of relevance that at least some of these impor-tant thymic hormones exhibit a decrease in concentration in thymus weight ordinarily seen as a concomitant of age and precede the dimunu-tion of cell-mediated immunity usually associated with aging (Bach *et al.*, 1975). The intrinsic hormonal activity of the thymus may explain the older observation that thymus grafts involute according to the age of the donor animal, and not the recipient host (Metcalf, 1966).

The Effects of Glucocorticoids on Lymphocytes and Other Cells Involved in Cell-Mediated Immunity

The primary cellular defenses of the host against neoplastic processes are mediated by mature T-lymphocytes, which have been processed by the thymus; by natural cytotoxic cells comprising killer (K) and natural killer (NK) cells; and by macrophages (Herberman & Holden, 1978; Par-rillo & Fauci, 1978; Santoni *et al.*, 1979). B cells derived directly from the bone marrow apparently play a lesser part. Helper T cells and mac-rophages play accessory roles by releasing interleukins, which stimulate the proliferation of mature cytolytic T cells (Monjan, 1981).

A rapid leukocytopenia in the peripheral blood of mice is seen imme-diately following the injection of glucocorticoid hormones, as shown in Figure 8.5 and elsewhere; similar results are also seen if intermittent rotation is used to induce an endogenous elevation of plasma CSR (Riley, 1981a; Riley *et al.*, 1981a, 1981b, 1982). It is relevant to note that the majority of the circulating leukocytes in the mouse are thymus-processed lymphocytes, or T cells, subsets of which are involved in cell-mediated defenses against neoplasia (J. Clagett, personal communica-tion, 1975; Djeu *et al.*, 1979; Gillis *et al.*, 1979; Santoni *et al.*, 1979; Trainin *et al.*, 1973, 1974). The rapid glucocorticoid-induced lymphocytopenia assumes even greater significance in view of the concomitant corticoid-induced damage to the integrity of the thymus, as shown in Figures 8.2, 8.3, 8.4, 8.6, and 8.7. This loss of thymus integrity delays the processing of replacement immunocompetent T cells (Gillis *et al.*, 1979; Trainin *et al.*, 1973, 1974).

In the mouse, the observed glucocorticoid-induced suppression in cell-mediated immunity against various neoplastic processes, as indi-cated by Figures 8.8 through 8.12, may result largely from changes in the numbers and functional capabilities of subsets of immune cells. Several subsets of murine T cells have been shown to be sensitive to acute doses of corticoids (Blomgren & Andersson, 1971; Monjan, 1981; Nieburgs *et al.*, 1979). Other murine lymphocyte subsets respond to chronic, but not to the acute administration of, glucocorticoids. The rosette-forming T cells in the spleen and lymph nodes, which may be functionally mature cells, decrease significantly following chronic glucocorticoid administration (Balow *et al.*, 1975). Murine NK cells have also been shown to be detrimentally affected by glucocorticoids. A rapid decrease in NK-cell activity has been observed within 3 hours after cortisone acetate administration (Lotzova & Savary, 1981). These results suggested that two populations of murine NK cells exist, a great majority of which are corticoid sensitive; the corticoid-resistant minority appear to be pre-NK cells, which can later be activated (Herberman, 1982). The inhibition of NK cells by glucocorticoids may be mediated by suppressor cells in the spleen that are probably of T-cell origin (Hochman & Cudcowicz, 1979). Kiessling and Wigzell (1979) reported that NK-cell activity was suppressed in mice following the stress of shipping. We have shown that shipping stress both induced high plasma CSR levels and predisposed such stressed mice, when implanted with the 6C3HED lymphosarcoma, to higher mortality rates (Riley & Spackman, 1977a). A decreased NK-cell activity may well be involved in such stress-induced decreases of immunocompetence.

Since histamine has been shown to modulate lymphocyte functions (Roszkowski, Plaut, & Lichenstein, 1977), the inhibitory effects of glucocorticoids on histamine decarboxlase activity (Parrot & Laborde, 1955), the tissue binding of newly formed histamine (Schayer, Davis, & Smiley, 1955), and the amount of histamine released by the tissues (Schmutzler & Freundt, 1975; Yamasaki & Yamamoto, 1963) may play a role in the various effects of glucocorticoids on lymphocyte subsets.

In addition to their accessory role in T cytolytic proliferation, macrophages can directly lyse tumor cells via antibody arming and phagocytosis (Monjan, 1981). It is thus of importance to note that glucocorticoids affect macrophage functions adversely, inhibiting phagocytic efficiency (Nicol & Bilbey, 1958; Reichard *et al.*, 1956) and the induction of armed macrophages, by interference with macrophage-arming factor (Monjan, 1981).

Immunological Impairment or Enhancement as a Function of Timing

The experiments shown in Figures 8.11 and 8.12 illustrate that in producing biochemically simulated stress with glucocorticoid injections, timing may be a critical factor in influencing host immunocompetence, as judged by tumor behavior. For this to be true, however, the tumor growth must be partially under the control of the immune system of the host (Riley & Fitzmaurice, 1982b; Riley & Spackman, 1977b; Riley, Spackman, Hellstrom, *et al.*, 1978). Rotation-evoked anxiety stress, accompanied by plasma CSR elevations, has also been shown to enhance or inhibit the growth of the MSV-induced tumors, depending upon the timing of the intermittent rotation relative to tumor cell inoculation (Riley & Fitzmaurice, 1982b; Riley & Spackman, 1977b).

An immunosuppression followed by a subsequent immunoenhancement was observed by Monjan and Collector (1977) in mice exposed to nocturnal auditory stress. The initial suppression of the responsiveness of T and B cells to mitogens *in vitro* was undoubtedly a consequence of the observed, elevated plasma CSR levels during the early phase of the experiment. The mechanisms responsible for the subsequent immunoenhancement are less clear.

Corticosteroids and Lymphoid Tissues in Man and Mouse

The effects of adrenal corticosteroids on the lymphoid tissues of laboratory animals and man have been reviewed in detail (Claman, 1972, 1975). In corticosteroid-sensitive species such as the mouse, rat, rabbit, and hamster, acute stress causes an involution of the thymus (Doughterty, 1952; Riley, 1981a, 1981b; Riley *et al.*, 1981a, 1981b, 1982; Santisteban, 1958, 1959; Santisteban & Dougherty, 1954; Santisteban *et al.*, 1969, 1972). In these species, corticoids have been shown to act directly on small lymphoid cells in the thymus, spleen, and peripheral blood (Claman, 1972, 1975), and they actually lyse lymphocytes (Borysenko, 1982). On the other hand, the lymphoid cells of steroid-resistant species such as man, the monkey, ferret, and guinea pig are not easily lysed by steroids.

While the experimental data reported here have been derived from rodent models, which are more corticoid-sensitive than the human, many inhibitory actions of corticosteroids on human immunological responses have been reported (Balow *et al.*, 1975; Fauci & Dale, 1975; Fauci *et al.*, 1977; Haynes & Fauci, 1978; Mendelsohn *et al.*, 1977; Parrillo & Fauci, 1978). Treatment of mice, rats, or humans with corticosteroids *in vivo* caused substantial transient reductions in both NK and antibody-dependent cytotoxic activities measured *in vitro* (Djeu *et al.*, 1979; Hochman & Cudcowicz, 1979; Lotzova & Savary, 1981; Oehler & Herberman, 1978; Parillo & Fauci, 1978; Santoni *et al.*, 1979). However, normal levels of lymphocyte-mediated cytotoxic activity could be restored by the discontinuation of corticosteroid administration (Santoni *et al.*, 1979) or by stimulation with interferon inducers (Djeu *et al.*, 1979; Oehler *et al.*, 1978).

It should be noted that many of the inhibitory effects of corticosteroids upon lymphocyte functions have been reported (Balow, 1975; Lippman, 1982) to occur at very low plasma corticosteroid concentrations, which is consistent with our observations that stress-induced physiological elevations of endogenous corticosteroids are capable of modifying immune responses and tumor growth. It should also be borne in mind that even in corticoid-resistant species such as the guinea pig and primates, corticoid administration has been reported to suppress the normal antigenic proliferation response of cytolytic T cells (Balow, 1975), inhibit mitogen-stimulated lymphocyte proliferation and metabolism *in vitro* (Berenbaum *et al.*, 1976; Fauci & Dale, 1975; Mendelsohn *et al.*, 1977), as well as to drastically decrease NK-cell activity (Parrillo & Fauci, 1978). Thus, even in these relatively resistant species, chronic stress with concomitant elevation of endogenous corticoids can result in progressive atrophy of the lymphoid organs (Borysenko, 1982).

Summary

The earliest and most conspicuous biochemical event following the onset of anxiety stress in the mouse and other mammals is a rapid elevation of plasma levels of adrenal glucocorticoids such as corticosterone or cortisol. In mammals undergoing anxiety stress, the elevation of endogenous corticoids is accomplished through well-known neurohormonal pathways involving the CNS, the hypothalamus, the pituitary, and the adrenal cortex. It is useful, from the experimental standpoint, to bypass these endogenous hormonal pathways in order to directly determine the effects of administered glucocorticoids on specific lymphatic tissues and on overall immunocompetence. In this way greater insight may be obtained as to the effects of stress-induced endogenous corticoid elevations on neoplastic processes.

Inhibitory effects of elevated levels of adrenocorticoids on virtually every aspect of the immune apparatus have been described; a special emphasis on those involving cell-mediated immunity is appropriate for studies involving neoplastic processes. Exogenously administered natural or synthetic corticoids, at levels simulating those occurring in the early stages of controlled anxiety stress, induce adverse effects on lymphocytes, the thymus, and other lymphoid tissues. Enhancement of various neoplastic processes, due to this impairment of host defense mechanisms, thus can result from either the induction of elevated endogenous corticoids by anxiety stress, or by the injection of exogenous corticoids at levels simulating those exhibited by stressed subjects.

Acknowledgments

The authors are appreciative of the contributions of H. Brent Solvason in discussions, and the correlation of the work of other investigators.

These studies were partially supported by the National Cancer Institute Grants: CA 12188 and CA 16308; the American Cancer Society, Grant No. PDT-73; the Alexander Medical Foundation; the Eagles Cancer Fund; the National Science Foundation; the Council for Tobacco Research, Special Project No. 111; and the M.J. Murdock Charitable Trust.

References

Amkraut, A., & Solomon, G. F. (1972). Stress and murine sarcoma virus (Moloney)—induced tumors. *Cancer Research, 32,* 142B.

Bach, J. F., Dardenne, M., Pleau, J. M., & Bach, M. A. (1975). Isolation, biochemical characteristics and biological activity of a circulating thymic hormone in the mouse and in the human. *Annals of the New York Academy of Science, 249,* 186–210.

Balow, J., Hurley, D., & Fauci, A. (1975). Immunosuppressive effects of glucocorticosteroids: Differential effects of acute vs. chronic administration on cell-mediated immunity. *Journal of Immunology, 114,* 1072–1076.

Barrett, A. M., & Stockham, M. A. (1963). The effect of housing conditions and simple experimental procedures upon the corticosterone level in the plasma of rats. *Journal of Endocrinology, 26,* 97–105.

Berenbaum, M. C., Cope, W. A., and Bundick, R. A. (1976). Synergistic effect of cortisol and prostaglandin E on the PHA response. *Clinical and Experimental Immunology, 26,* 534–541.

Berenbaum, M. D., Fluch, P. A., & Hurst, N. P. (1973). Depression of lymphocyte responses after surgical trauma. *British Journal of Experimental Pathology, 54,* 597–607.

Blomgren, H., & Andersson, B. (1971). Characteristics of the immunocompetent cell in the mouse thymus: Cell population changes during cortisone-induced atrophy and subsequent regeneration. *Cellular Immunology, 1,* 545–560.

Borysenko, J. A. (1982). Higher cortical function and neoplasia: Psychoneuroimmunology. In S. Levy (Ed.), *Biological mediators of behavior and disease: Neoplasia* (pp. 27–53). New York: Elsevier Biomedical.

Burnet, M. (1969). *Cellular immunology.* Carlton: Melbourne University Press, and London: Cambridge University Press.

Claman, H. N. (1972). Corticosteroids and lymphoid cells. *New England Journal of Medicine, 287,* 388–397.

Claman, H. N. (1975). How corticosteroids work. *Journal of Allergy and Clinical Immunology, 5,* 145–151.

Djeu, J. Y., Heinbaugh, J., Viera, W. D., Holden, H. T., & Herberman, R. B. (1979). The effect of immunopharmacological agents on mouse natural cell-mediated cytotoxicity and on its augmentation by poly I:C. *Immunopharmacology, 1,* 231–244.

Dougherty, T. F. (1952). Effects of hormones on lymphatic tissue. *Physiological Reviews, 32,* 379–401.

Fauci, A. S., & Dale, D. C. (1975). The effect of hydrocortisone on the kinetics of normal human lymphocytes. *Blood, 46,* 235–243.

Fauci, A. S., Pratt, K. R., & Whalen, G. (1977). Activation of human B lymphocytes IV. Regulatory effects of corticosteroids on the triggering signal in the plaque-forming cell response of human peripheral blood B lymphocytes to polyclonal activation. *Journal of Immunology, 119,* 598–603.

Fefer, A., McCoy, J. L., Perk, K., & Glynn, J. P. (1968). Immunologic, virologic, and pathologic studies of regression of autochtonous Moloney sarcoma virus-induced tumors in mice. *Cancer Research, 28,* 1157.

Feldman, D. (1975). The role of hormone receptors in the action of adrenal steroids. In W. P. Creger, C. H. Coggins, & E. W. Hancock (Eds.), *Annual review of medicine* (pp. 83–90). *26,* 83–90.

Fox, B. M. (1978). Premorbid psychological factors as related to cancer incidence. *Journal of Behavioral Medicine, 1*(1), 45–133.

Friedman, S. B., & Ader, R. (1965). Parameters relevant to the experimental production of "stress" in the mouse. *Psychosomatic Medicine, 27,* 361.

Gillis, S., Crabtree, G. R., & Smith, K. A. (1979). Glucocorticoid-induced inhibition of T cell growth factor production. *Journal of Immunology, 123,* 1624–1638.

Gisler, R. H. (1974). Stress and the hormonal regulation of the immune response in mice. *Psychotherapy and Psychosomatics, 23,* 197–208.

Glick, S. M. (1975). Normal and abnormal secretion of growth hormone. *Annals of the New York Academy of Science, 148,* 471–485.

Goldstein, A. L., Slater, F. D., & White, A. (1966). Preparation, assay and partial purification of a thymus lymphocytopoietic factor. *Proceedings of the National Academy of Sciences, U.S.A., 56,* 1010–1017.

Haynes, B. F., & Fauci, A. S. (1978). The differential effect of in vivo hydrocortisone on the kinetics of subpopulations of human peripheral blood thymus-derived lymphocytes. *Journal of Clinical Investigation, 61,* 703–707.

Herberman, R. B. (1982). Possible effects of central nervous system on natural killer (NK) cell activity. In S. Levy (Ed.), *Biological mediators of behavior and disease: Neoplasia* (pp. 235–249). New York: Elsevier Biomedical.

Herberman, R. B., & Holden, H. T. (1978). Natural cell-mediated immunity. *Advances in Cancer Research, 27,* 305–377.

Hochman, P. S., & Cudcowicz, G. (1979). Suppression of natural cytotoxicity by spleen cells of hydrocortisone-treated mice. *Journal of Immunology, 123,* 968–976.

Kelley, K. W. (1980). Stress and immune function: A bibliographic review. *Annales de Recherches Veterinaires, 11*(4), 445–478.

Kiessling, R., & Wigzell, H. (1979). An analysis of the murine NK cell as T1 structure, function and biological significance. *Immunological Reviews, 44,* 165–208.

Klein, G. (1975). Immunological surveillance against neoplasia. *Harvey Lectures, 69,* 71–102.

Lippman, M. (1982). Interactions of psychic and endocrine factors with progression of neoplastic diseases. In S. Levy (Ed.), *Biological mediators of behavior and disease: Neoplasia* (pp. 55–82). New York: Elsevier Biomedical.

Lotzova, E., & Savary, C. (1981). Parallelism between the effect of cortisone acetate on hybrid resistance and natural killing. *Experimental Hematology, 9,* 766–774.

Luckey, T. D. (1973). Perspective of thymic hormones. In T. D. Luckey (Ed.), *Thymic hormones* (pp. 275–314). Baltimore: University Park Press.

Mason, J. W. (1974). Specificity in the organization of neuroendocrine response profiles. In P. Seeman & G. M. Brown (Eds.), *Frontiers in neurology and neuroscience research* (pp. 68–80). Toronto: Neuroscience Institute, Univ. of Toronto.

Mendelsohn, J., Multer, M. M., & Bernheim, J. L. (1977). Inhibition of human lymphocyte stimulation by steroid hormones: Cytokinetic mechanisms. *Clinical and Experimental Immunology, 27,* 127–134.

Metcalf, D. (1966). *Recent results in cancer research: The thymus* (Vol. 5, pp. 1–144). New York: Springer-Verlag.

Monjan, A. A. (1981). Stress and immunologic competence: Studies in animals. In R. Ader (Ed.), *Psychoneuroimmunology* (pp. 185–217). New York: Academic Press.

Monjan, A. A., & Collector, M. I. (1977). Stress-induced modulation of the immune response. *Science, 196,* 307–308.

Nicol, T., & Bilbey, D. L. (1958). Substances depressing the phagocytic activity of the reticuloendothelial system. *Nature, 182,* 606.

Nieburgs, H. E., Weiss, J., Navarrete, M., Strax, P., Tierstein, A., Grillione, G., & Siedlecke, B. (1979). The role of stress in human and experimental oncogenesis. *Cancer Detection and Prevention, 2,* 307–336.

Oehler, J. R., & Herberman, R. B. (1978). Natural cell-mediated immunity in rats. III. Effects of immunopharmacologic treatments on natural reactivity and on reactivity augmented by polyinosinic-polycytidylic acid. *International Journal of Cancer, 21,* 221–229.

Parrillo, J. E., & Fauci, A. S. (1978). Comparison of the effector cells in human spontaneous cellular cytotoxicity and antibody-dependent cellular cytotoxicity: Differential sensitivity of effect of cells to in vivo and in vitro corticosteroids. *Scandinavian Journal of Immunology, 8,* 99–107.

Parrot, J. L., & Laborde, C. (1955). Inhibition d'histidine-decarboxylase par la cortisone et par le salicylate de sodium. *Journal of Physiology, 53,* 441–442.

Pierpaoli, W. (1981). Integrated phylogenetic and ontogenetic evolution of neuroendocrine and identity-defense, immune functions. In R. Ader (Ed.), *Psychoneuroimmunology* (pp. 575–606). New York: Academic Press.

Pierpaoli, W., Baroni, C., Fabris, N., & Sorkin, E. (1969). Hormone and immunologic capacity. II. Reconstitution of antibody production in hormonally deficient mice by somatotrophic hormone, thyrotropic hormone, and thyroxin. *Immunology, 16,* 217–230.

Potop, I., & Milcu, S. M. (1973). Isolation, biologic activity, and structure of thymic lipids and thymosterin. In T. D. Luckey (Ed.), *Thymic hormones* (pp. 205–273). Baltimore: University Park Press.

Reichard, S. M., Edelmann, A., & Gordon, A. S. (1956). Adrenal and hypophyseal influences upon the uptake of radioactive gold (Au^{198}) by the reticuloendothelial system. *Endocrinology, 59,* 55–68.

Riley, V. (1960). Adaptation of orbital bleeding technique to rapid serial blood studies. *Proceedings of the Society for Experimental Biology and Medicine, 104,* 751–754.

Riley, V. (1972). Protective ventilated shelves for experimental animal storage. *Proceedings of the 23rd Annual Session of the American Association of Laboratory Animal Science,* No. 22A.

Riley, V. (1973). Persistence and other characteristics of the lactate-dehydrogenase-elevating virus (LDH-virus). *Progress in Medical Virology, 18,* 198–213.

Riley, V. (1975). Mouse mammary tumors: Alteration of incidence as an apparent function of stress. *Science, 189,* 465–467.

Riley, V. (1978). Stress and cancer: Fresh perspectives. In H. E. Nieburgs (Ed.), *Detection and prevention of cancer* (Part 1, Vol. 2, pp. 1769–1775). New York: Marcel Dekker.

Riley, V. (1979a). Introduction: Stress-cancer contradictions: A continuing puzzlement. *Cancer Detection and Prevention, 2*(2), 159–162.

Riley, V. (1979b). Cancer and stress: Overview and critique. *Cancer Detection and Prevention, 2*(2), 163–195.

Riley, V. (1981a). Psychoneuroendocrine influences on immunocompetence and neoplasia. *Science, 212,* 1100–1109.

Riley, V. (1981b). Biobehavioral factors in animal work on tumorigenesis. In S. Weiss, J. Herd, & B. Fox (Eds.), *Perspectives on behavioral medicine* (pp. 183–214). New York: Academic Press.

Riley, V. (1982). Psychoneuroendocrine modulation of tumor metastases associated with anxiety stress. *Proceedings of the 13th International Cancer Congress, 466.*

Riley, V., & Fitzmaurice, M. A. (1982a). Influence of anxiety stress and adrenal corticoids upon the incidence of melanoma metastases. *Proceeding of the American Association for Cancer Research, 23,* 235.

Riley, V., & Fitzmaurice, M. A. (1982b). Thymus involution during melanoma growth: Possible relationship to metastatic spread. *Proceedings of the 13th International Cancer Congress, 466.*

Riley, V., Fitzmaurice, M. A., & Spackman, D. H. (1981a). Animal models in biobehavioral research: Effects of anxiety stress on immunocompetence and neoplasia. In S. Weiss, J. Herd, & B. Fox (Eds.), *Perspectives on behavioral medicine* (pp. 371–400). New York: Academic Press.

Riley, V., Fitzmaurice, M. A., & Spackman, D. H. (1981b). Psychoneuroimmunological factors in neoplasia: Studies in animals. In R. Ader (Ed.), *Psychoneuroimmunology* (pp. 31–102). New York: Academic Press.

Riley, V., Fitzmaurice, M. A., & Spackman, D. H. (1982). Immunocompetence and neoplasia: Role of anxiety stress. In S. Levy (Ed.), *Biological mediators of behaviors and disease: Neoplasia* (pp. 175–218). New York: Elsevier Press.

Riley, V., & Spackman, D. H. (1976). Melanoma enhancement by viral-induced stress. In V. Riley (Ed.), *The pigment cell; Melanomas: Basic properties and clinical behavior* (Vol. 2 pp. 163–173) Basel: Karger.

Riley, V., & Spackman, D. H. (1977a). Housing stress. *Laboratory Animals, 6,* 16–21.

Riley, V., & Spackman, D. H. (1977b). Modifying effects of a benign virus on the malignant process and the role of physiological stress on tumor incidence. In M. A. Chirigos (Ed.), *Modulation of host immune resistance in the prevention or treatment of induced neoplasias* (DHEW Publication No. (NIH) 77-894, pp. 319–336). Washington, DC: U.S. Government Printing Office.

Riley, V., Spackman, D. H., Hellstrom, K. E., & Hellstrom, I. (1978). Growth enhancement of murine sarcoma by LDH-virus, adrenocorticoids, and anxiety stress. *Proceedings of the American Association for Cancer Research, 19,* 57.

Riley, V., Spackman, D. H., McClanahan, H., & Santisteban, G. A. (1979). The role of stress in malignancy. *Cancer Detection and Prevention, 2(2),* 235–255.

Riley, V., Spackman, D. H., Santisteban, G. A., Dalldorf, G., Hellstrom, I., Hellstrom, K. E., Lance, E. M., Rowson, K. E. K., Mahy, B. W. J., Alexander, P., Stock, C. C., Sjogren, H. O., Hollander, V. P., & Horzinck, M. C. (1978). The LDH-virus: An interfering biological contaminant. *Science, 200,* 124–125.

Robey, W. G. Thymosin reviewed. In T. D. Luckey (Ed.), *Thymic hormones* (pp. 159–166). Baltimore: University Park Press.

Rousseau, G. G., & Schmit, J. P. (1977). Structure-activity relationships for glucocorticoids. I. Determination of receptor binding and biological activity. *Journal of Steroid Biochemistry, 8,* 911–919.

Roszkowski, W., Plaut, M., & Lichenstein, L. M. (1977). Selective display of histamine receptors on lymphocytes. *Science, 195,* 683–685.

Santisteban, G. A. (1958). Studies on the relationships of the acute involution of lymphatic organs to the severity of stress stimuli. *Anatomical Record, 130,* 2.

Santisteban, G. A. (1959). Comparison of the influences of various forms of stress stimuli upon the adrenocortico–thymico–lymphatic system in CBA mice. *Anatomical Record, 133,* 331.

Santisteban, G. A., & Dougherty, T. F. (1954). Comparison of the influences of adrenocortical hormones on the growth and involution of lymphatic organs. *Endocrinology, 54,* 130–146.

Santisteban, G. A., Guslander, C., & Willhight, K. (1969). Studies on the maturation of the adrenal cortical–lymphatic tissue interrelationships. *Anatomical Record, 163,* 2.

Santisteban, G. A., Riley, V., & Fitzmaurice, M. A. (1972). Thymolytic and adrenal cortical responses to the LDH-elevating virus. *Proceedings of the Society for Experimental Biology and Medicine, 139,* 202–206.

Santoni, A., Herberman, R. B., & Holden, H. T. (1979). Correlation between natural and antibody-dependent cell-mediated cytotoxicity against tumor targets in the mouse. II. Characterization of the effector cells. *Journal of the National Cancer Institute, 63,* 995–1003.

Schayer, R. W., Davis, J. K., & Smiley, R. L. (1955). Binding of histamine in vitro and its inhibition by cortisone. *American Journal of Physiology, 182,* 54–56.

Schmutzler, W., & Freundt, G. P. (1975). The effect of glucocorticoids and catecholamines on cyclic AMP and allergic histamine release in guinea pig lung. *International Archives of Allergy and Applied Immunology, 49,* 209–212.

Spackman, D. H., & Riley, V. (1976). The modification of cancer by stress: Effects of plasma corticosterone elevations on immunological system components in mice. *Federation Proceedings, 35,* 1693.

Spackman, D. H., & Riley, V. (1978a). True adrenal glucocorticoid values in experimental animals: Implications for cancer research. *Proceedings of the 12th International Cancer Congress, Abstracts,* Vol. 2, p. 26.

Spackman, D. H., & Riley, V. (1978b). Corticosterone concentrations in the mouse. *Science, 200,* 87.

Spackman, D. H., Riley, V., & Bloom, J. (1978). True plasma corticosterone levels of mice in cancer/stress studies. *Proceedings of the American Association for Cancer Research, 19,* 57.

Stein, M., Schiavi, R. C., & Camerino, M. (1976). Influence of brain and behavior on the immune system. *Science, 191,* 435–440.

Tache, Y., Ruisseau, P. D., Ducharme, J. R., & Collu, R. (1978). Pattern of adenohypophyseal hormone changes in male rats following chronic stress. *Neuroendocrinology, 26,* 208–219.

Trainin, N., Levo, Y., & Rotter, V. (1974). Resistance to hydrocortisone conferred upon thymocytes by a thymic humoral factor. *European Journal of Immunology, 4,* 634–637.

Trainin, N., Small, M., & Kimhi, Y. (1973). Characteristics of a thymic factor involved in the development of cell-mediated immune competence. In T. D. Luckey (Ed.), *Thymic hormones* (pp. 135–158). Baltimore: University Park Press.

Turner, C. D., & Hagnara, J. T. (1971). *General endocrinology.* (5th ed.). Philadelphia: Sanders.

Wira, C. R., & Munck, A. (1974). Glucocorticoid-receptor complexes in rat thymus cells. *Journal of Biological Chemistry, 249,* 5328–5336.

Yamasaki, H., & Yamamoto, T. (1963). Inhibitory effect of adrenal glucocorticoids on histamine release. *Japanese Journal of Pharmacology, 19,* 223–224.

9

Behavioral Influences and Beta-Adrenergic Mechanisms: The Kidney and Sodium Retention*

PAUL A. OBRIST,
ALBERTO GRIGNOLO, JOHN P. KOEPKE,
ALAN W. LANGER, AND KATHLEEN C. LIGHT

Introduction

This report describes our first efforts in evaluating beta-adrenergic influences on renal handling of sodium and water during a behavioral task. An overview of two experiments is presented. In the first (Grignolo, 1980; Grignolo, Koepke, & Obrist, 1981), we were able to demonstrate that a shock avoidance task facilitated sodium retention, while the second (Koepke, Grignolo, & Obrist, 1981) demonstrated that a beta-adrenergic mechanism was involved in this effect. Before describing these experiments, we would like to outline the rationale for these efforts.

This research stems from our interest in the delineation of beta-adrenergic influences on the myocardium and vasculature in behavioral paradigms. One basis for this has been the possibility that myocardial beta-adrenergic mechanisms are of significance in the etiology of hypertension (Buhler *et al.*, 1980; Julius & Esler, 1975). Relevant to this have been

---

*This research was supported by research grants HL 18976, HL 23718, and HL 24643 from the National Heart, Lung and Blood Institute, National Institute of Health.

PERSPECTIVES ON BEHAVIORAL MEDICINE, Vol. 2
Neuroendocrine Control and Behavior

our observations that certain behavioral challenges, that is, laboratory tasks, evoke beta-adrenergic influences on the myocardium in both young adult, normotensive humans as well as dogs, as indexed by heart rate and several indirect measures of cardiac contractility (Grignolo, Light, & Obrist, 1981; Light, 1981; Light & Obrist, 1980a; Obrist *et al.*, 1978; Obrist, Light, McCubbin, Hutcheson, & Hoffer, 1979). As important are the observations of appreciable individual differences in beta-adrenergic reactivity in our human subjects that are directly related to the incidence of hypertension in their parents (Hastrup, Light, & Obrist, 1981; Light, 1981; Light & Obrist, 1980b; Obrist, 1981; Obrist, Light, Langer, & Koepke, 1981).

We initiated this study because renal processes, particularly those involved in the maintenance of sodium balance, have also been hypothesized to be involved in the hypertensive process (Brown *et al.*, 1977; Guyton, 1980); thus, renal processes may also involve beta-adrenergic mechanisms (Zanchetti & Bartorelli, 1977). The intent is to evaluate behavioral influences on the renal handling of sodium, and whether such renal effects might act in conjunction with myocardial activity, because of common neurogenic mechanisms, to influence the control of the blood pressure.

While there has been sporadic interest over the years in behavioral influences on renal processes such as renal blood flow and plasma renin activity (see Grignolo, 1980, for a review), there has been no systematic efforts focusing directly upon sodium and water handling and the mechanisms involved. Thus, the present work directly concerns the influence of behavioral challenges on sodium and water excretion and an evaluation of neurogenic influences.

Survey of Experiments

Two experiments are discussed here. Both used a dog preparation since control of sodium intake and excretion would be easier to achieve, and thus, any effect of our experimental procedures would be more readily observable. The experimental procedures of the two studies are similar with certain exceptions. In any given experimental session, the dogs were volume loaded with saline so as to amplify excretion rates. Once these rates had stabilized, the dogs were either allowed to continue resting (baseline conditions) or exposed to a shock avoidance task. In the first study but not the second, treadmill exercise was also used so as to determine the effects of a more metabolically demanding task (Grignolo, Koepke, & Obrist, 1982).

Shock avoidance was observed in Experiment 1 to result in a reduction of both water and sodium excretion relative to the baseline, or control, condition. This effect was most pronounced in those sessions where the largest heart rate and systolic blood pressure changes were evidenced. Exercise, typically, resulted in an increase of excretion rates. Since GFR (Glomular filtration rate) (inulin clearance) and free water clearance did not change, but the fractional excretion rates of sodium and water decreased, the retention effects appeared to be mediated via increased tubular reabsorption.

In the second experiment (Koepke, Light, & Obrist, 1983), we were able to replicate the effects of shock avoidance on sodium and water retention if the innervations were intact. However, no retention of sodium or water was found during avoidance after systemic pharmacological blockade of beta-receptors (propranolol). For example, during the 20-min avoidance session, sodium excretion in the five dogs evaluated decreased on the average by 37% with intact innervation, but no change was evidenced with blocked innervation (also see Koepke, Light, Obrist, & Morris, 1984; Koepke & Obrist, 1983).

Sodium retention under these circumstances can be a pronounced effect, approaching a 50% reduction in excretion rates on some occasions. This we find a little sobering in the light of the already increased excretion rates initiated by volume loading. Considering the critical role the kidney plays in maintaining balance between sodium ingestion and excretion, these effects seem to reflect an appreciable disruption in this fundamental metabolic process. They are consistent with Weiner's (1977) view of hypertension as a "disease of regulation" (p. 608) and Mason's (1975) comment as to the "concept of disease as resulting from intergrative disorders" (p. 177). We have one other line of evidence illustrating a disruption of metabolic processes, but this time concerning the myocardium. There is the observation, also during shock avoidance in dogs, of an inappropriately elevated cardiac output (Langer, 1978; Langer, Obrist, & McCubbin, 1979; see also Sherwood *et al.*, 1985). In this instance, the appropriateness of the cardiovascular response is evaluated with respect to oxygen consumption, where it is found that, as compared to exercise, similar levels of cardiac output are associated with lesser arteriovenous blood oxygen content difference. While we have not as yet evaluated beta-adrenergic mechanisms when measuring cardiac output and O_2 consumption, their influence appears likely, since we have been able to demonstrate an appreciable beta-adrenergic influence on heart rate and intraventricular dP/dt in dogs under similar conditions (Grignolo, Light, & Obrist, 1981).

It is observations of this nature which we believe begin to point to ways behavioral factors can be implicated in the etiology of hypertension. With both the kidney and myocardium, we are dealing with events intimately associated with blood pressure control mechanisms either directly (e.g., cardiac output) or indirectly (e.g., changes in vascular resistance due to sodium retention or autoregulation). The possibility that both the myocardial and renal effects involve a common neurogenic (beta-adrenergic) influence indicates that the disruption of metabolic processes is pervasive. While we have not as yet evaluated renal events or cardiac output in humans, our evidence is reasonably definitive with respect to behaviorally evoked, beta-adrenergic influences on other aspects of myocardial performance. The methodology required to obtain a more complete picture of myocardial events in humans, as well as to evaluate renal functioning, is difficult but not insurmountable. For example, we developed a sensitive system for the measurement of oxygen consumption on a breath-by-breath basis (Langer, Hutcheson, Charlton, McCubbin, & Obrist, 1981), and we are working on a methodology to obtain stabile, baseline sodium excretion rates. In any case, we believe our mechanistic strategy gives us a better handle on the etiological process than working with blood pressure as an index and in isolation of control mechanisms.

References

Brown, J. J., Fraser, R., Lever, A. F., Morton, J. J., Robertson, J. I. S., & Schalekamp, M. A. D. (1977). Mechanisms in hypertension: A personal view. In J. Genest, E. Koiw, & O. Kuchel (Eds.), *Hypertension: Physiopathology and treatment* (pp. 529–548). New York: McGraw-Hill.

Buhler, F. R., Kiowski, W., van Brummelen, P., Amann, F. W., Bertel, O., & Landman, R. (1980). Plasma catecholamines and cardiac, renal and peripheral vascular adrenoceptor-mediated responses in different age groups of normal and hypertensive subjects. *Clinical and Experimental Hypertension, 2*, 409–426.

Grignolo, A. (1980). *Renal function and cardiovascular dynamics during treadmill exercise and shock-avoidance in dogs.* Unpublished doctoral dissertation, University of North Carolina, Chapel Hill.

Grignolo, A., Koepke, J. P., & Obrist, P. A. (1982). *Renal function and cardiovascular dynamics during treadmill exercise and shock avoidance in dogs. American Journal of Physiology, 242,* R482–R490.

Grignolo, A., Light, K. C., & Obrist, P. A. (1981). Beta adrenergic influences on the canine myocardium: A behavioral and pharmacological study. *Pharmacology, Biochemistry, and Behavior, 14*, 313–319.

Guyton, A. C. (1980). *Arterial pressure and hypertension.* Philadelphia: Saunders.

Hastrup, J. L., Light, K. C., & Obrist, P. A. (1982). *Parental history of hypertension in relationship to sympathetic response to stress. Psychophysiology, 19,* 615–622.

Julius, S., & Esler, M. D. Autonomic nervous cardiovascular regulation in borderline hypertension. *American Journal of Cardiology, 36*, 685–696.

Koepke, J. P., Grignolo, A., Light, K. C., & Obrist, P. A. (1983). Central beta-adrenoceptor mediation of the antinatriuretic response to behavioral stress in conscious dogs. *Journal of Pharmacology and Experimental Therapeutics, 227,* 73–77.

Koepke, J. P., Grignolo, A., & Obrist, P. A. (1983). Decreased urine and sodium excretion rates during signaled shock avoidance in dogs: Role of beta-adrenergic receptors. *Journal of Pharmacology and Experimental Therapeutics, 227,* 73–77.

Koepke, J. P., Light, K. C., & Obrist, P. A. (1983). Neural control of renal excretory function during behavioral stress in conscious dogs. *American Journal of Physiology, 245,* R251–R258.

Koepke, J. P., Light, K. C., Obrist, P. A., & Morris, M. (1984). Vasopressin and urine flow rate responses to stress in conscious dogs. *American Journal of Physiology,* in press.

Langer, A. W. (1978). *A comparison of the effects of the treadmill exercise and signaled shock avoidance training on hemodynamic processes and the arterial-mixed venous oxygen content difference in conscious dogs.* Unpublished doctoral dissertation, University of North Carolina, Chapel Hill.

Langer, A. W., Hutcheson, J. S., Charlton, J. D., McCubbin, J. A., & Obrist, P. A. (1985). On-line minicomputerized measurement of respiratory gas exchange during exercise. *Psychophysiology, 22,* 50–58.

Langer, A. W., Obrist, P. A., & McCubbin, J. A. (1979). Hemodynamic and metabolic adjustments during exercise and shock avoidance in dogs. *American Journal of Physiology: Heart and Circulatory Physiology, 5,* H225–H230.

Light, K. C. (1981). Cardiovascular responses to effortful active coping: Implications for role of stress in hypertension development. *Psychophysiology, 18,* 216–225.

Light, K. C., & Obrist, P. A. (1980a). Cardiovascular response to stress: Effects of opportunity to avoid shock, experience and performance feedback. *Psychophysiology, 17,* 243–252.

Light, K. C., & Obrist, P. A. (1980b). Cardiovascular reactivity to behavioral stress in young males with and without marginally elevated systolic pressure: A comparison of clinic, home and laboratory measures. *Hypertension, 2,* 802–808.

Mason, J. W. (1975). Emotion as reflected in patterns of endrocrine integration. In L. Levi (Ed.), *Emotions—Their parameters and measurement* (pp. 143–181). New York: Raven.

Obrist, P. A. (1981). *Cardiovascular psychophysiology: A perspective.* New York: Plenum.

Obrist, P. A., Gaebelein, C. J., Teller, E. S., Langer, A. W., Grignolo, A., Light, K. C., & McCubbin, J. A. (1978). The relationship among heart rate, carotid dp/dt and blood pressure in humans as a function of the type of stress. *Psychophysiology, 15,* 102–115.

Obrist, P. A., Light, K. C., Langer, A. W., & Koepke, J. P. (1981). Psychosomatics. In M. Coles, E. Donchin, & S. Porges (Eds.), *Psychophysiology: Systems processes and applications.* New York: Guilford, in press.

Obrist, P. A., Light, K. C., McCubbin, J. A., Hutcheson, J. S., & Hoffer, J. L. (1979). Pulse transit time: Relationship to blood pressure and myocardial performance. *Psychophysiology, 16,* 292–301.

Sherwood, A., Allen, M. T., Obrist, P. A., & Langer, A. W. (1985). Evaluation of beta-adrenergic influences on cardiovascular and metabolic adjustments to physical and psychological stress. *Psychophysiology,* in press.

Weiner, H. (1977). *Psychobiology and human disease.* New York: Elsevier.

Zanchetti, A., & Bartorelli, C. (1977). Central nervous mechanisms in arterial hypertension: Experimental and clinical evidence. In J. Genest, E. Koiw, & O. Kuchel (Eds.), *Hypertension: Pathophysiology and treatment* (pp. 59–75). New York: McGraw-Hill.

10

Type A Behavior: Mechanisms Linking Behavioral and Pathophysiological Processes

DAVID C. GLASS

A large body of data on the role of psychosocial factors in the etiology and pathogenesis of coronary heart disease (CHD) has accumulated over the past few decades (e.g., Jenkins, 1976). Two promising variables have been identified, namely psychological stress and what has been called the Type A, coronary-prone behavior pattern (e.g., Rosenman & Friedman, 1974). *Stress* may be defined as an internal state of the individual when he is faced with threats to his physical or psychic well-being. An individual who shows Pattern A behavior is competitive and hard driving, time urgent and impatient, hostile and aggressive. By contrast, Pattern B individuals display these characteristics to a much lesser degree. Type A behavior is the outcome of a person–situation interaction. It is elicited only in the presence of appropriate environmental circumstances, including the challenge of doing well at a difficult task, or the stress of uncontrollable aversive stimulation (Glass, 1977).

Psychological Stress and Coronary Heart Disease

Several classes of psychological stressors have been linked to the major cardiovascular disorders, including dissatisfaction with marital rela-

---

*The preparation of this paper was supported, in part, by funds from NIH Research Grant HL 22514. A slightly modified version of this paper appeared in J. Siegrist and M. J. Halhuber (Eds.), *Myocardial infarction and psychosocial risk.* Berlin: Springer-Verlag, 1981. Reproduced by permission of Springer-Verlag.

PERSPECTIVES ON BEHAVIORAL MEDICINE, Vol. 2
Neuroendocrine Control and Behavior

tionships and other interpersonal relations. Excessive work and responsibility, which lead to feelings that job demands are beyond the person's control, have also been implicated in the development of coronary disease. There is, in addition, some data to suggest that acutely stressful events, such as the death of a close relative or a sudden loss of self-esteem, increases the likelihood of a coronary event. More detailed discussion of these matters can be found in a number of review papers and books (e.g., Glass, 1977; Jenkins, 1976).

The physiological mechanisms whereby psychological stress may enhance the development of cardiac disorders include: repeated increases in serum lipids (e.g., cholesterol) and blood pressure, acceleration of the rate of damage to the coronary arteries over time, facilitation of platelet aggregation, induction of myocardial lesions, and precipitation of cardiac arrhythmias. It is believed, in some quarters, that these effects are mediated by enhanced activity of the sympathetic nervous system and consequent discharge of cathecholamines such as epinephrine and norepinephrine (e.g., Eliot, 1979; Haft, 1974).

Type A Behavior and Coronary Heart Disease

Perhaps the most thoroughly studied behavioral factor contributing to coronary disease is the Type A behavior pattern. Issues of Type A measurement and classification cannot be discussed within the confines of this paper. Suffice it to note here that the major diagnostic tools are a structured interview developed by Friedman and Rosenman and a self-administered questionnaire called the Jenkins Activity Survey for Health Prediction. More detailed considerations of measurement can be found in Dembroski *et al.* (1978a).

The strongest available evidence on the association between Type A behavior and CHD comes from the Western Collaborative Group Study (WCGS). The results indicate that Type A men experienced about twice the incidence of acute clinical events over an $8\frac{1}{2}$-year follow-up period compared to Type B men (Rosenman *et al.*, 1975). This difference occurred independently of other risk factors, including total serum cholesterol, systolic blood pressure, and daily cigarette smoking. Still other research, using coronary arteriography, has documented more severe occlusion of the coronary arteries in Pattern A compared to Pattern B patients (e.g., Blumenthal, Williams, Kong, Schanberg, & Thompson, 1978).

If we accept the results showing a linkage between behavior pattern A and coronary disease, the next question to be posed concerns the physiological mechanisms underlying the association. Clinical studies indicate that lipid and related hormonal differences exist between Type A and Type B individuals (Rosenman and Friedman, 1974). Other research shows increased urinary norepinephrine (NE) excretion in Type A's during an active working day compared to more sedentary evening activities (Byers, Friedman, Rosenman, & Freed, 1962). Also relevant here is a study indicating elevated plasma NE responses to competition and stress among Type A compared to Type B men (Friedman, Byers, Diamant, & Rosenman, 1975).

Elevated catecholamine responses are likely to be associated with changes in cardiovascular function which could be crucial in the potentiation of CHD and sudden death. A number of studies have, in fact, shown that Type A's display greater episodic increases in systolic blood pressure and heart rate than do Type B's in stressful and challenging situations (e.g., Dembroski *et al.*, 1977; Manuck *et al.*, 1978; Pittner, & Houston, 1980). There is typically little difference between the two types of individuals in basal levels of these cardiovascular variables.

Consider, by way of illustration, an experiment from my own laboratory which studied Type A and B men from the work force of the New York City Transit Authority (Glass *et al.*, 1980a). All subjects were free of the major risk factors for CHD, including hypertension, diabetes mellitus, excessive cigarette smoking, and elevated levels of serum cholesterol. The purpose of the study, conducted in collaboration with Lawrence R. Karkoff of the Mount Sinai Medical School in New York, was to assess the effects upon arterial pressure, heart rate, and plasma catecholamines of simple competition in a game versus competition with a hostile and harassing opponent. The 22 Type A and 22 Type B subjects were assigned randomly to either Harass or No-Harass experimental conditions.

The protocol for the study can be summarized as follows. After a 25-min baseline period, subjects played a series of 9 games of Pong, a computerized television game similar to tennis, against an opponent who pretended to be another subject. He was actually a member of the research staff who had been trained at the game so that he was virtually unbeatable. Throughout the "tournament," this opponent was either nonharassing, or he exhibited hostility by delivering a series of pre-programmed comments such as: "Come on, can't you keep your eye on the ball"; "Damn, you're not even trying"; "I don't understand why you're having so much trouble hitting the ball." The 9-game competition was played for a prize, the winner receiving a $25 gift certificate to a major department store in New York. The certificate was prominently displayed atop the TV set throughout the contest.

Systolic and diastolic blood pressure (SBP and DBP) and heart rate (HR) were monitored every 2 min over the course of the session. Blood pressure determinations were made using a Roche Arteriosonde, which ultrasonically detects arterial wall motion. Heart rate was measured with a photocell plethysmograph, which allowed the recording of digital pulsation. Blood for plasma epinephrine (E) and norepinephrine was obtained by means of an indwelling venous catheter. Samples were taken at the end of the baseline period, and again after the third and sixth games. A final sample was drawn after the ninth, and final, game, when the subject had lost to the opponent, who received the gift certificate.

Plasma E and NE were measured by radioassay, using catechol O-methyl transferase in the presence of $3H$-methyl S-adenosyl-methonine. A thin layer chromatography was employed for separation of the reaction products, which were then converted to vanillin for counting by liquid scintillation spectrometry (Vlachakis, Ribeiro, & Krakoff, 1978). The interassay coefficients of variation were 31% and 24% for E and NE, respectively. Intra-assay variation of duplicates was 10% for E and 9% for NE.

The results for each dependent measure were averaged for each of the three experimental periods (i.e., blocks of 3-game segments) and compared to their respective baseline values. Statistical analyses of these data revealed the following effects:

1. There were no differences between Type A's and B's, or between the two experimental conditions, in mean baseline values for SBP, DBP, HR, plasma E, and plasma NE ($p > .20$).
2. All increases in the five dependent measures relative to baseline values were statistically significant ($p < .05$).
3. The increase in SBP for Harassed Type A's was significantly greater than for No-Harassed Type A's and for each of the two Type B groups ($p < .05$). The relevant data can be seen in Table 10.1.

TABLE 10.1
Systolic Blood Pressure: Mean Changes for Each Third of the Contest (in mm Hg)

Condition	1st third	2nd third	Last third
Type A, Harass	+37.5	+41.9	+38.5
Type A, No Harass	+24.5	+27.9	+27.4
Type B, Harass	+24.2	+26.5	+26.4
Type B, No Harass	+24.1	+25.8	+25.3

TABLE 10.2
Heart Rate: Mean Changes for Each Third of the Contest (in bpm)

Condition	1st third	2nd third	Last third
Type A, Harass	+26.1[a]	+24.6	+21.4
Type A, No Harass	+15.6[a]	+17.8	+14.9
Type B, Harass	+12.4	+13.4	+12.8
Type B, No Harass	+14.0	+12.1	+10.9

[a]Apparatus failure interfered with the recording of heart rate from one case in this group.

4. The effect of harassment on DBP was near-significant at the .06 level, but there was no difference between Type A's and B's ($p > .20$).

5. The increase in HR for the Type A's was significantly greater than for the Type B's ($p < .05$), and the source of this difference was attributable to the elevations of the Harassed Type A's. Table 10.2 presents these results.

6. The increase in plasma E for the Harassed Type A's was also significantly greater than for any other experimental group, as can be seen in Table 10.3.

7. Although the mean change scores for the plasma NE were in the same direction as those for plasma E, they did not attain acceptable levels of statistical significance. There was simply too much within-groups variability.

TABLE 10.3
Plasma Epinephrine: Mean Changes during and after the Contest
(in pg/ml)

Condition	During the contest	After the contest
Type A, Harass	+100.2[a]	+120.5[b]
Type A, No Harass	+3.7	+19.8
Type B, Harass	+16.9[a]	+2.0[b]
Type B, No Harass	+16.1	+20.0[b]

[a]Two cases each were lost from the Harass A and Harass B groups because of technical difficulties connected with assay and blood sampling procedures.

[b]Four cases (one Harass A, one Harass B, and two No-Harass B's) were eliminated from analysis of E levels in the third (i.e., "after-contest") blood sample. Hemolyzed samples made it virtually impossible to calculate accurate values for these subjects.

The conclusions of this experiment can be summarized as follows:

1. Competition elicits significant and similar increases in BP, HR, and plasma catecholamines in Type A and B men.
2. The effect of a hostile opponent causes no reliable differences in cardiovascular and plasma catecholamine responses of Type B's.
3. In Type A's, however, the harassing opponent elicits greater increases in SBP, HR, and plasma E during competition.
4. It would appear, then, that behavior pattern A is predisposed selectively to enhanced reaction to hostile interactions, but competition alone does not distinguish between Type A's and B's.

This experiment, as well as others conducted in my laboratory over the past few years (e.g., Glass & Contrada, 1984; Glass *et al.*, 1980b), suggests some of the cardiovascular and hormonal variables that might account for the greater tendency of Type A individuals to develop coronary disease. It is, of course, speculative to argue that excess production of epinephrine and heightened systolic pressor responses serve as the intermediary process by which Type A behavior enhances the risk of cardiovascular disease. However, it is probably reasonable to assume that the observed physiological responses of Type A's to environmental stress are mediated via the sympathetic nervous system.

Pattern A as a Psychological Construct

My remarks have thus far emphasized physiological mechanisms underlying the Type A–coronary disease relationship. There is, however, a more basic issue, namely, whether behavior pattern A is a valid psychological construct.

A large proportion of the population is typically classified as Type A, estimates having ranged from 45% to as high as 65% in some populations (e.g., Howard, Cunningham, Rechnitzer, 1976; Rosenman *et al.*, 1964). Nevertheless, there is a relatively low incidence of CHD among Type A's, albeit significantly greater than in Type B's (e.g., Rosenman *et al.*, 1975). Therefore, the causal mechanisms underlying cardiovascular disease may not be distributed evenly throughout the Type A group. It is possible that some facets of behavior pattern A have little or no relationship to the disease, since they appear in all Type A's rather than in only those who show increased risk. On the other hand, it may be that Type A behaviors of any kind always lead to physiological changes culminating in illness, but CHD occurs only in some Type A's because they lack psychological or physiological protective mechanisms. In either case, these considerations underscore the importance of understanding the psychological mechanisms giving rise to and sustaining Type A behavior.

There are at least three approaches to identifying such mechanisms. The first derives from a factor analysis of the structured interview responses of 186 men from the WCGS (Matthews, Glass, Rosenman, & Bortner, 1977). Although five primary factors were revealed, only two— competitive drive and impatience—were associated with the later onset of clinical CHD. Subsequent analyses indicated that of the more than 40 interview ratings, only seven items discriminated CHD cases from age-matched healthy controls. Of the seven, four items were directly related to hostility, one was concerned with competitiveness, and the remaining two dealt with vigorousness of voice stylistics. Dembroski (e.g., Dembroski, MacDougall, Shields, Petitto, & Lushene, 1978b) has developed a component scoring system for the structured interview based on the Matthews *et al.* (1977) findings. The same dimensions that predicted CHD were found to predict experimentally induced elevations in systolic blood pressure and heart rate.

A somewhat different approach to the association between Type A behavior and CHD comes from the work of Scherwitz, Berton, & Levanthal, (1978a). They identified and measured certain speech characteristics that occurred continuously in the structured interview. These characteristics were correlated with simultaneously occurring changes in heart rate, finger pulse amplitude, and blood pressure. Type A individuals who used many self-references (I, me, my, mine) in answering the interview questions showed the highest levels of systolic blood pressure. By contrast, the Type B group had very few significant correlates of self-references. These results have led to the suggestion that self-involvement might account for both the speech characteristics and autonomic reactions of Type A subjects. Indeed, there is evidence that individuals with acute awareness of themselves behave like Type A's. For example, individuals whose attention is focused on themselves are likely to be aggressive when provoked (Scheier, 1976). While performing a task, self-aware individuals are more likely to compare their performance to their internal standards of excellence (e.g., Carver, Blaney, & Scheier, 1979). To the extent that these standards are high, salient discrepancies between performance and goals may lead to excessive striving, frustration, and helplessness. Thus, Scherwitz *et al* (1978a) suggest that the construct of self-involvement is useful not only because it may explain why Type A behaviors arise, but also because its correlation with cardiovascular and behavioral variables underscore its potential importance as a key construct in explaining the linkage between Type A behavior and CHD.

A third approach to the issue of mechanism comes from my own past work on Type A behavior (e.g., Glass, 1977). In several studies, my students and I have found that Type A's work hard to succeed, suppress subjective states (such as fatigue) that might interfere with task performance, conduct their activities at a rapid pace, and express hostility after being frustrated or harassed in their efforts at task completion. It might be argued that these behaviors reflect an attempt by the Type A individual to assert and maintain control over stressful aspects of his environment. Type A's engage in a continual struggle for control and, in consequence, appear hard driving and aggressive, easily annoyed, and competitive. Furthermore, this struggle by A's may lead them, when confronted by clear threats to that control, to increase their efforts to assert mastery. On the other hand, if these efforts meet with repeated failure, Type A's might be expected to give up responding and act helpless. Stated somewhat differently, initial exposure to threatened loss of control accelerates control efforts, whereas prolonged exposure leads to a decrement in these behaviors. This pattern of responding has been described elsewhere as *hyper-responsiveness* followed by *hypo-responsiveness* (Glass, 1977).

Experimental results with healthy human subjects reported elsewhere have tended to support the foregoing hypothesis (e.g., Glass, 1977). However, it should be emphasized that there is no evidence to date which bears on the interactive effects of depression and Type A on clinical CHD. Such an association would, of course, be consistent with the hypo-responsiveness part of our hypothesis. While it has been suggested that depression is a risk factor for a variety of illnesses and for delayed recovery from such illnesses (e.g., Engel, 1970; Greene, Goldstein, & Moss, 1972), nevertheless there are no data showing that Type A's, when depressed, are at a greater risk of CHD than their Type B counterparts. A test of this notion must await future research.

Central to our view of Type A behavior is the idea that active efforts by Type A's to control their environment are accompanied by sympathetic activation and elevated levels of circulating catecholamines. When efforts at control fail—as they inevitably will with an uncontrollable stressor—the theory predicts a shift from sympathetic to parasympathetic dominance. Such abrupt shifts have been implicated in sudden cardiac death (e.g., Engel, 1970). Still other research, some of which was cited earlier in this paper, indicates that elevated catecholamines are important factors in the pathogenesis of cardiovascular disease and acute clinical events.

The foregoing paradigms are but three of many possible avenues for further differentation of the psychological processes underlying Type A behavior and the connection of these processes to physiological changes that may enhance cardiovascular risk. As these and other models are more fully developed and tested, we may expect the Type A concept to be superseded by more differentiated factors that are closely linked to pathophysiological mechanisms (cf. Scherwitz *et al.*, 1978b).

Conclusions

I conclude this paper with some remarks about directions for future research—at least as I see these directions. As I have suggested already, attention should be given to conceptualizing Type A behavior and identifying the psychological processes that produce and sustain it. Most of the existing literature simply describes a behavior pattern and its behavioral and physiological correlates. We must define more precisely those behaviors in Pattern A that are risk inducing. In this connection, serious consideration should be given to the notion that Type A behavior is an outgrowth of a person–situation interaction. It follows from this view that efforts need to be directed toward a delineation of the classes of environmental stimuli that elicit the primary facets of the behavior pattern. It is not enough to speak loosely about appropriately challenging or stressful events. We need to define these terms with precision. We need to specify the relevant parameters, such that we will be able to determine, *a priori*, which types and levels of stress or challenge are sufficient to produce Type A behaviors and concomitant physiological responses in both laboratory and field settings.

Another direction for future research should concentrate on linking the behavior pattern or, more appropriately, the underlying dimensions of the pattern, to physiological processes believed to be routes to atherosclerosis and clinical CHD. Once such correlations are established, subsequent studies (probably with animal models) might be undertaken to elucidate cause-and-effect; that is, are the physiological changes observed in Type A's under stress the result of behavioral responses, or vice-versa? Indeed, both behavioral and physiological reactions may be consequences of a third, higher-order variable located in the brain. When such causal research is well underway, it would be time for moderate-sized field studies aimed at evaluating whether the principles derived from psychophysiological experimentation can predict disease end points. At that time, too, it might be appropriate to consider the advisability and feasibility of altering Type A behavior, or at least those facets of the behavior pattern that have been established as enhancing the risk of cardiovascular disease.

References

Blumenthal, J. A., Williams, R., Kong, Y., Schanberg, S. M., & Thompson, L. W. (1978). Type A behavior and angiographically documented coronary disease. *Circulation, 58,* 634–639.

Byers, S. O., Friedman, M., Rosenman, R. H., and Freed, S. C. (1962). Excretion of VMA in men exhibiting behavior pattern (A) associated with high incidence of clinical coronary artery disease. *Federation Proceedings, 21,* 99–101.

Carver, C. S., Blaney, P. H., & Scheier, M. F. (1979). Focus of attention, chronic expectancy, and responses to a feared stimulus. *Journal of Personality and Social Psychology, 37,* 1186–1195.

Dembroski, T. M., MacDougall, J. M., and Shields, J. L. (1977). Physiologic reactions to social challenge in persons evidencing the Type A coronary-prone behavior pattern. *Journal of Human Stress, 3,* 2–10.

Dembroski, T. M., Weiss, S. M., Shields, J. L., Haynes, S. G., & Feinleib, M. (1978). *Coronary-prone behavior.* New York: Springer-Verlag.

Dembroski, T. M., MacDougall, J. M., Shields, J. L., Petitto, J., & Lushene, R. (1978). Components of the Type A coronary-prone behavior pattern and cardiovascular responses to psychomotor performance challenge. *Journal of Behavioral Medicine, 1,* 159–176.

Eliot, R. S. (1979). *Stress and the major cardiovascular disorders.* Mount Kisco, NY: Futura.

Engel, G. L. (1970). Sudden death and the 'medical model' in psychiatry. *Canadian Psychiatric Association Journal, 15,* 527–538.

Friedman, M., Byers, S. O., Diamant, J., & Rosenman, R. H. (1975). Plasma catecholamine response of coronary-prone subjects (Type A) to a specific challenge. *Metabolism, 24,* 205–210.

Glass, D. C. (1977). *Behavior patterns, stress and coronary disease.* Hillsdale, NJ: Erlbaum Associates.

Glass, D. C., & Contrada, R. J. (1984). Type A behavior and catecholamines: A critical review. In M. G. Ziegler & C. R. Lake (Eds.), *Frontiers of clinical neuroscience: norepinephrine, Vol. 2.* Baltimore, MD: Williams and Wilkins.

Glass, D. C., Krakoff, L. R., Contrada, R., Hilton, W. F., Kehoe, K., Mannucci, E. G., Collins, C., Snow, B., and Elting, E. (1980a). Effect of harassment and competition upon cardiovascular and plasma catecholamine responses in Type A and Type B individuals. *Psychophysiology, 17,* 453–463.

Glass, D. C., Krakoff, L. R., Finkelman, J., Snow, B., Contrada, R., Kehoe, K., Mannucci, E. G., Isecke, W., Collins, C., Hilton, W. F., & Elting, E. (1980b). Effect of task overload upon cardiovascular and plasma catecholamine responses in Type A and B individuals. *Basic and Applied Social Psychology, 1,* 199–218.

Greene, W. A., Goldstein, S., & Moss, A. J. (1972). Psychosocial aspects of sudden death: A preliminary report. *Archives of Internal Medicine, 129,* 725–731.

Haft, J. I. (1974). Cardiovascular injury induced by sympathetic catecholamines. *Progress in Cardiovascular Diseases, 17,* 73–86.

Howard, J. H., Cunningham, D. A., & Rechnitzer, P. A. (1976). Health patterns associated with Type A behavior: A managerial population. *Journal of Human Stress, 2,* 24–31.

Jenkins, C. D. (1976). Recent evidence supporting psychologic and social risk factors for coronary disease. *New England Journal of Medicine, 294,* 987–994.

Manuck, S. B., Craft, S. A., & Gold, K. J. (1978). Coronary-prone behavior pattern and cardiovascular response. *Psychophysiology, 15,* 403–411.

Matthews, K. A., Glass, D. C., Rosenman, R. H., & Bortner, R. W. (1977). Competitive drive, pattern A, and coronary heart disease: A further analysis of some data from the Western Collaborative Group Study. *Journal of Chronic Diseases, 30,* 489–498.

Pittner, M. S., & Houston, B. K. (1980). Response to stress, cognitive coping strategies, and the Type A behavior pattern. *Journal of Personality and Social Psychology, 39,* 147–157.

Rosenman, R. H., Friedman, M., Straus, R., Wurm, M., Kositchek, R., Hahn, W., & Werthessen, N. T. (1964). A predictive study of coronary heart disease: The Western Collaborative Group Study. *Journal of the American Medical Association, 189,* 15–22.

Rosenman, R. H., and Friedman, M. (1974). Neurogenic factors in pathogenesis of coronary heart disease. *Medical Clinics of North America, 58,* 269–279.

Rosenman, R. H., Brand, R. J., Jenkins, C. D., Friedman, M., Straus, R., & Wurm, M. (1975). Coronary heart disease in the Western Collaborative Group Study: Final follow-up experience of $8\frac{1}{2}$ years. *Journal of the American Medical Association, 223,* 872–877.

Scheier, M. F. (1976). Self-awareness, self-consciousness, and angry aggression. *Journal of Personality, 44,* 627–644.

Scherwitz, L., Berton, K., & Leventhal, H. (1978a). Type A behavior, self-involvement, and cardiovascular response. *Psychosomatic Medicine, 40,* 593–609.

Scherwitz, L., Leventhal, H., Cleary, P., & Laman, C. (1978b). Type A behavior: Consideration for risk modification. *Health Values: Achieving High Level Wellness, 2,* 291–296.

Vlachakis, N. D., Ribeiro, A. B., & Krakoff, L. R. (1978). Effect of saralasin upon plasma catecholamines in hypertensive patients. *American Heart Journal, 95,* 78–80.

11
Psychological and Endocrinological Correlates of Chronic Stress at Three Mile Island

ANDREW BAUM,
MARC A. SCHAEFFER, C. RAYMOND LAKE,
RAYMOND FLEMING, AND DANIEL L. COLLINS

Psychoendocrine involvement in stress is well documented. Research reported in this volume as well as elsewhere suggests that a wide variety of threatening or stressful conditions gives rise to a complex of psychological, behavioral, physiological, and biochemical changes such as emotional disturbance, task performance decrements, heightened cardiovascular response, and increased systemic concentrations of catecholamines and corticosteroids (e.g., Baum, Grunberg, & Singer, 1982; Frankenhaeuser, 1975; Mason, 1975; Rose, Jenkins, & Hurst, 1978; Selye, 1976). Some have argued that these responses to threatening environmental events are integrated aspects of the same response and that they are partially interdependent (Lang, Rice, & Sternbach, 1974; Mason, 1975). Recent research has suggested that there is a modest degree of overlap among different aspects of stress response and that the use of psychoendocrine measures of stress can provide a useful adjunct to assessments of affective changes and behavioral difficulties (Baum, Gatchel, & Schaeffer, 1983; Frankenhaeuser, 1978). In this chapter, we discuss research that has considered endocrinological responses to chronic stress experienced by people living near the damaged Three Mile Island Nuclear Station (TMI) near Middletown, Pennsylvania. Specifically, adrenal activity was considered in the context of psychological,

PERSPECTIVES ON BEHAVIORAL MEDICINE, Vol. 2
Neuroendocrine Control and Behavior

behavioral, and physiological markers of stress, all of which were used to measure responses to the threats associated with living near TMI.

Stress

As a number of researchers have noted, stress is best viewed as a process that links environmental events with psychological analysis and interpretation of them, and a "whole-body" response to those events interpreted as threatening, challenging, or harmful (Baum, Singer, & Baum, 1981; Jenkins, 1979; Lazarus, 1966; Lazarus & Launier, 1978). It may involve a single powerful event, such as a change of jobs or a natural disaster that is encountered against an otherwise benign background. Or, stress may involve a summation of several sources of threat or harm experienced on a more day-to-day basis. The duration of the event, its power, suddenness, and predictability, and the number of people affected by it may all influence interpretation of, and response to, these events.

The notion of a whole-body response is the antithesis of dualism, suggesting integration of central and peripheral systems. It includes both preparatory physiological responses and coping. Thus, any stimulus that is appraised as stressful can be manifested in both psychological and biological responses. For example, an individual confronted with job stress may exhibit bouts of depression, which would be labeled as a mental health symptom. A second worker experiencing the same occupational stress may experience lower back pain, typically considered a psychosomatic disorder. And both of the workers probably would be prone to a decrement in performance or reduced efficiency on the job. Therefore, it is moot whether depression, pain, or decrements in performance is the key to the stress response. The most salient symptoms often mask secondary manifestations that more fully depict the whole-body nature of the stress response. Secondary manifestations can be as meaningful an index of stress as the more overt primary ones.

A number of studies have been reported that underscore the importance of appraisal of events at some level. Some show that stress-related psychiatric or organic pathologies appear only when subjects are conscious or aware of threat or danger (Adler, 1943; Mason, 1975; Symington, Currie, Curran, & Davidson, 1955). Other studies demonstrate that changing people's appraisal of events alters their response and the degree to which stress is experienced (Johnson, 1973; Johnson & Leventhal, 1974; Lazarus & Alfert, 1964; Nomikos, Opton, Averill, & Lazarus, 1968). The interpretation of events appears to influence subsequent responses, including coping.

Bodily response during stress appears to be governed principally by the sympathetic nervous system and the pituitary–adrenocortical system. Both are ultimately controlled by the hypothalamus, which, during stress, stimulates both sympathetic and pituitary activity. Adrenal medullary activity, including the release of epinephrine and, to a lesser extent, norepinephrine, is triggered by sympathetic arousal. Once in the circulation, these catecholamines heighten and extend the effects of sympathetic arousal, including increased cardiovascular and respiratory activity, decreased blood flow to the skin and viscera, and so on. These mechanisms of arousal are similar to Cannon's (1914, 1929) description of the emergency "fight or flight" response. Cannon's *centralist* view on emotion and arousal was developed to counter the *peripheralist* view of James (1890). While James argued that autonomic responses precede appraisal, Cannon cited empirical results to the contrary. Separation of the viscera from the CNS in animals did not appear to alter their emotional responding; drug-induced physiological changes did not seem to produce emotional states; and autonomic responses appeared to be similar across emotional states. Today, although centralist and peripheralist factions still exist, the two biases have been largely hybridized by 50 years of thought and research. Research addressing the central–peripheral issue has demonstrated that with differing circumstances, either central or peripheral elements provides the first measurable responses (Duffy, 1962; Lindsley, 1956; Schachter & Singer, 1962).

Adrenocortical activity during stress appears to require some central appraisal of stimuli. Higher brain centers transmit signals to the hypothalamus, which secretes corticotropin-releasing factor (CRF). This, in turn, stimulates pituitary activity and secretion of adrenocorticotropic hormone (ACTH), which results in releases of corticosteroids, including cortisol, increasing the availability of energy in cells and heightening overall metabolism. In addition to describing this sequence, Selye (1976) pioneered research on the importance of the pituitary–adrenocortical axis with his description of the "general adaptation syndrome." Working with laboratory rats, Selye reported findings that indicated that a host of different specific stressors produced the same nonspecific response pattern. This pattern included secretion of adrenocorticoids, involution of the thymus, and ulceration of the stomach. Adrenocortical activity and increases in circulating corticosteroids were viewed as being responsible for these changes.

A wide variety of psychological and physical stressors can evoke these responses, and they are clearly directed at mobilization to overcome threat. However, these aspects of the stress response also have a number of negative effects, including suppression of the immune system, damage to the cardiovascular system, and general wear and tear on various organs (Riley, 1981; Riley, Fitzmaurice, & Spackman, 1981; Schneiderman, 1983; Selye, 1976; Stein, 1983).

Psychological and behavioral responses during stress take several forms. On one level, stress appears to be associated with increases in symptom reporting and negative affective tone. Emotional disturbances, such as anxiety or depression, may become troublesome, and somatic distress (e.g., headaches, back pain, digestive discomfort) may also be experienced. Problem solving and task performance also appear to suffer during or after experiencing stress, due to some combination of motivational, skill, and cognitive changes (Glass & Singer, 1972). Finally, overt and intrapsychic coping responses are directed at reduction or management of stress. These may include attempts to leave the situation or to modify it directly; to gain information about the situation; or to regulate emotional response (e.g., reduce fear or anxiety) by reinterpreting the situation or by managing the response (Lazarus & Launier, 1978).

Our studies of stress have examined all of these levels of response, allowing evaluation of the degree of interdependence among them. Fifteen-hour urine samples were collected and subsequently assayed for levels of cortisol and free epinephrine and norepinephrine. Symptom reporting, depression, and perceived threat were also measured, and performance on tasks requiring concentration and motivation was observed.

Our interest in chronic stress brought us to the attention of the Nuclear Regulatory Commission (NRC), the federal agency responsible for preparing impact statements on the decontamination of TMI. The NRC was interested in assessing levels of stress experienced by residents of the TMI area, and we saw this as a unique opportunity for application of research technologies to the real-world assessment of stress. It also provided the opportunity to investigate adrenal activity in the context of an ongoing and persistently stressful situation. Of course, before proceeding, we had to consider whether there were adequate reasons to expect TMI-area residents to exhibit symptoms of stress long after the accident.

Sources of Stress at Three Mile Island

The situation at TMI remains confused even now, more than 6 years after the accident there. The accident began during the early hours of 28 March 1979. Through a series of human errors, confusing and contradictory reports from responsible officials, and a general information crisis, what was a mechanical malfunction escalated into an emergency, with a major evacuation of people living near the plant. The actual dangers presented by this incident were unclear; estimates of how much radiation was released vary, and the imminence of explosion during the accident has been questioned. It was, however, a disruptive and frightening experience, particularly for people living near the plant.

Few disagree that the accident caused acute problems for local residents. Several studies have reported evidence of emotional distress among residents of the TMI area shortly after the accident (Bromet, 1980; Dohrenwend *et al.*, 1979; Flynn, 1979; Flynn & Chalmers, 1980; Houts, Miller, Tokuhata, & Ham, 1980). The threats posed by the accident, the evacuation, and the uncertainty generated by contradictory assurances and alarms appear to have engendered acute stress among area residents.

Whether stress has persisted beyond the emergency and become chronic is less certain. Some research has found continuing effects of stress 9 months after the accident (Bromet, 1980; Houts *et al.*, 1980), but another study found that demoralization among TMI-area residents was short lived (Dohrenwend *et al.*, 1979). There are a number of reasons, however, to believe that TMI-area residents may be experiencing chronic stress.

First, sources of threat in the TMI area have not disappeared. The accident left radioactive gas trapped in the concrete containment building and more than 400,000 gallons of radioactive water in the reactor building. The gas leaked into the atmosphere several times during the year following the accident, and it was finally released to the atmosphere during July 1980. The radioactive accident water remained on the reactor building floor for several years. Thus, the possibility of exposure to radiation did not end with the accident.

The probability that residents will ever be exposed to this continuing source of radiation is not likely to be high, but some area residents are not convinced of their safety. Likewise, though most officials agree that there were no dangerous radiation releases during and after the accident, some residents believe that there were. Also, one should not expect that concerns about past exposure to radiation should disappear quickly. Many of the effects of radiation take years or generations to be manifested. Neoplastic diseases typically have long periods of development and possible genetic damage may take even longer to become apparent. Some TMI-area residents fear these effects of radiation, and their vigilance about these effects can lead to interpretation of one's symptoms or other people's illnesses as being related to radiation. This, of course, can fuel already existing concerns.

We feel that these sources of stress are experienced as chronic uncertainty or ambiguity. Residents perceive the possibilities of new exposure to radiation, are uncertain of whether they have already been exposed, and are uncertain about possible effects if they have been exposed. Added to this are uncertainties about whether the undamaged reactor at TMI will be reopened, when (or if) decontamination of the crippled reactor will be accomplished, whether the damaged reactor will be repaired and recommissioned, and the economic implications of all of these events. Finally, the information crisis during and after the accident has reduced the credibility of the utility operating TMI as well as a number of agencies, and many area residents do not know who or what to believe. This kind of continued uncertainty may well be associated with chronic stress and may evoke hormonal responses similar to those described by Mason (1975) as Pattern II responses. The Pattern II response was derived from a series of studies with monkeys which involved a high degree of unpredictability, uncertainty, or ambiguity (Mason, Mangan, Brady, Conrad, & Rioch, 1961; Mason, Brady, & Tolson, 1966). In these situations the animals were alerted to possible unpleasant events but were not made aware of the nature of the events or when to expect them. Under these conditions, norepinephrine, epinephrine, and cortisol levels increased. Mason contrasted this with a Pattern I response to challenges or threats that are known and expected. In situations involving low levels of ambiguity and uncertainty (such as exercise), no dramatic increase in epinephrine was observed. The Pattern I response involved increases in norepinephrine and cortisol only. Although unpleasant elements are found in Pattern I and Pattern II responses, the most characteristic distinction between the two patterns appears to be the presence of a high degree of unpredictability, uncertainty, or ambiguity.

Field Study of Chronic Stress at Three Mile Island

Our research at TMI began 15 months after the accident at TMI, in June 1980. Since then, we have continued to collect data from a number of groups. We confine ourselves in this chapter, however, to the first phase of the continuing study.

The initial study compared the responses of 44 people living within 5 miles of TMI with those of 31 residents living in a control site approximately 80 miles away. The control area was selected because of its demographic comparability to the area surrounding TMI. Residents of the TMI and control sites were sampled in quasi-random fashion, and response rates averaged 70%. The two samples were comparable on all demographic variables considered (e.g., education, age, income), and these variables were not related to our findings in any systematic way.

Subjects were tested in their homes. They were asked to complete the SCL-90 (Derogatis, Rickels, & Rock, 1976), a symptom checklist assessing frequency of bothersome somatic and psychological problems (e.g., headache, nausea, depression, anxiety) over a 2-week period. Participants also performed a timed proofreading task that has provided a reliable behavioral index of stress in previous research (Glass & Singer, 1972), and were tested for persistence on a series of complex embedded figures. During proofreading, subjects had to detect as many misspelling, typographical, and similar types of errors as they could within the time limit. The embedded figures task involved finding and tracing a simple target figure hidden in a more geometrically complex one. Subjects were given as much time as they wanted to complete the embedded figures task. Finally, subjects provided 15-hour urine samples. These samples were frozen and subsequently assayed using radioenzymatic COMT assay procedures for estimates of free epinephrine and norepinephrine in the urine (Durrett & Ziegler, 1980). A competitive binding site assay was performed to obtain estimates of cortisol in the urine (Yalow & Berson, 1971). All measures were collected during four consecutive weekdays in June 1980. Foods and beverages consumed during the collection period were also recorded. Subsequent reanalyses suggested that these variables did not contribute to differences between groups in levels of hormones.

Evidence of Chronic Stress at Three Mile Island

Assays of subjects' urine samples indicated that, overall, TMI-area residents exhibited higher levels of epinephrine, norepinephrine, and cortisol than did control subjects. These findings are summarized in Table 11.1. Differences in epinephrine approached significance, and norepinephrine and cortisol differences were statistically significant. The averaging nature of long-term urine samples makes precise interpretation of these findings more difficult, but they do suggest that TMI-area residents exhibited chronically elevated levels of adrenal activity and sympathetic arousal. However, a number of questions about these findings have to be considered, and we discuss them in the next section.

Symptom reporting and other self-report measures of emotional dis-

TABLE 11.1
Mean Levels of Urinary Epinephrine, Norepinephrine, and Cortisol
Exhibited by TMI and Control Subjects

	Epinephrine (ng/ml)	Norepinephrine (ng/ml)	Cortisol (μg/24 hr)
TMI	15.0	38.9	54.9
Control	10.6	20.9	10.9

tress and perceived threat showed the same pattern. Residents of the
TMI area reported experiencing more bothersome symptoms than did
subjects living far from the damaged plant (see Table 11.2), and they
reported significantly more somatic distress, anxiety, depression, aliena-
tion, difficulty in concentrating, and fear. The differences in symptom
reporting between the TMI and control samples were substantial and
highly significant, further suggesting that TMI-area residents experienced chronic stress.

Answers to questions about threats peculiar to living near TMI also
suggested that TMI-area residents were experiencing chronic difficulties. They were more likely to regard TMI as a threat to their health and
their family's health; they reported greater concern about the effects of
emissions from TMI during and after the accident; and they were more
negative about future operations at TMI than were control subjects. This
partially confirms our notion that the damaged plant continued to be
perceived as threatening by area residents long after the accident.

Performance on the proofreading measure also suggested that chronic
stress continued to be a problem for TMI-area residents. Stress is manifested on this task by poorer performance, and TMI-area residents
found fewer of the errors contained in the passage that they read than
did control subjects (see Table 11.2). Similarly, decrements in performance were found on the embedded figures task with TMI-area resi-

TABLE 11.2
Mean Number of Bothersome Symptoms Reported and Mean
Performance on Proofreading Task

	Symptoms reported	Proofreading errors (%)
TMI	36	44
Control	18	74

TABLE 11.3
Correlations among Measures of Stress

Measure	r
Epinephrine	
× Norepinephrine	.41
× Cortisol	.24
× Proofreading performance	−.29
Cortisol	
× Norepinephrine	.67
× Proofreading performance	−.38
× Prescriptions written	.26
Norepinephrine	
× Proofreading performance	−.39
× Symptoms reported	.38
× Somatic distress	.32
× Anxiety	.27
× Depression	.31
× Prescriptions written	.26
× Complaints noted by physician	.37
× Change in SBP	.37
× Change in DBP	.32
Proofreading performance	
× Symptoms reported	−.25
× Somatic distress	−.31
× Anxiety	−.23
× Depression	−.30
Complaints noted by physician	
× SBP	.45
× DBP	.29

dents solving fewer of the puzzles and exhibiting less persistence than did controls.

The correlations among most of these measures suggested a modest degree of overlap or interdependence. As can be seen in Table 11.3, epinephrine levels were significantly correlated with norepinephrine and cortisol levels, and norepinephrine and cortisol were also related. Epinephrine was related to proofreading performance, but it was generally not correlated with indices of symptom reporting. Cortisol was related to performance but, overall, was not correlated with symptom reporting either. Norepinephrine, however, was significantly related to all of these measures. Performance was also related to most measures.

While these data suggest that TMI residents experienced greater stress more than a year after the accident than did control subjects, there are several qualifications that must be made. One concerns the fact that it cannot be determined from these data that differences in stress levels are due to the presence of TMI. It is possible that differences between TMI-area residents and control subjects preceded the accident at TMI and have little to do with the accident and aftermath. In an attempt to eliminate this possibility, we obtained permission from TMI and control group subjects to contact their physicians and to gain access to specific data from their records. In doing so, we obtained data on subjects' blood pressure (1978–1981). Although only 2 TMI-area residents and 1 control subject refused to allow us access to their medical records, data were obtained for only 18 TMI residents and 16 control subjects. Data were not available on remaining subjects primarily because subjects had not visited their physicians regularly or because physicians reported that they did not routinely record blood pressure. Only subjects who had visited their physicians at least once between March 1978 and March 1979 and once between April 1979 and April 1980 could be considered in this analysis.

As can be seen in Figure 11.1, data for systolic blood pressure (SBP) provided evidence of a change between pre- and post-accident response among TMI residents. Overall, TMI-area residents had higher SBP than did control subjects, but this effect was qualified by an interaction indicating that while control subjects' readings did not change appreciably over time, TMI residents' readings increased markedly between the year before and the year after the accident. The differences in SBP between TMI and control subjects were significant during the year after the accident but were not significant before the accident, and readings for TMI subjects during the year following the accident were significantly higher than they were before the accident. Diastolic blood pressure (DBP) readings exhibited a similar pattern. Though comparable before the accident, TMI and control subjects' DBP diverge after the accident. While control subjects did not exhibit significant change over time, TMI-area residents' DBP increased significantly during the first year after the accident.

These data suggest that the elevations in symptoms of stress exhibited by people living near TMI have occurred since the accident and are related to it. A possible mechanism underlying this increase in blood pressure could be one involving increased levels of systemic catecholamines. Schneiderman (1983) has reviewed much of the literature indicating that there is an association between increases in catecholamines and hardening of the arteries. Further, increased release of cortisol has been shown to potentiate diet-induced atherosclerosis in monkeys (Sprague, Toxler, Peterson, Schmidt, & Young, 1980). It must be noted, however, that the rise in blood pressure that was observed is

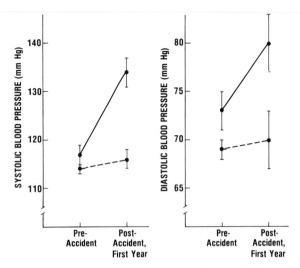

FIGURE 11.1   Systolic and diastolic blood pressure readings for TMI residents (solid line) and controls (dashed line). Pre-accident dates are 1 Jan 1978–27 Mar 1979 and post-accident dates are 28 Mar 1979–27 Mar 1980.

modest; few, if any, of our subjects could be classified as hypertensive, and the post-accident blood pressures are in a high-normal range. Nonetheless, this increase in blood pressure could be an early sign of significant hypertension in some subjects, and such pathology may well result from an interaction of biological predisposition and hormonal changes associated with stress. This same observation can be made about other data as well. Symptom reporting, as measured by the SCL-90, showed clear differences between TMI and control subjects. However, TMI residents' reporting rates remained below clinical levels. That is, their symptom distress was less than has been obtained from psychiatric patients or people experiencing clinical episodes of emotional disturbance.

Self-report measures are susceptible to a variety of biases, including both intentional and unintentional reporting errors. However, data supplied by subjects' physicians seem to confirm the residents' self-reports of somatic complaints. According to physician records, TMI and control subjects had comparable histories one year prior to the accident, but these diverged after the accident, with TMI residents having more problems being noted by their physicians. Further, examination of prescriptions written before and after the accident also showed differences between TMI and control samples. Before the accident, prescriptions were written for both groups in approximately equal numbers. However, after the accident the two groups showed different patterns, with TMI-area residents receiving more prescriptions for medications than control subjects. In addition, both norepinephrine and cortisol (but not epinephrine) correlated significantly with prescriptions written during the year after the accident (see Table 11.3). Norepinephrine also correlated significantly with physician-noted complaints and with SBP. Thus, higher urinary levels of cortisol and norepinephrine were related to a greater number of health complaints as recorded by personal physician, and higher norepinephrine levels were related to both physician-noted complaints and higher levels of SBP. Finally, both SBP and DBP were significantly correlated with physician histories. In all, levels of urinary hormones were related to negative health outcomes, and this paralleled subjects' own self-reports.

Residents of the TMI area also evidenced motivational or concentration problems in their difficulties with the proofreading task, but their scores were comparable to those achieved by college students exposed to acute noise stress (Glass & Singer, 1972). TMI residents' catecholamine levels, though higher than those of the controls, remained within the limits defining normal ranges. Our findings, then, suggest that, as a group, TMI-area residents experienced a moderate magnitude of chronic stress. Residents appeared to be coping with continuing sources of stress and were not debilitated by the problems that they faced. However, constant exposure to threats and problems of the type encountered at TMI should be expected to exact some cost. Although this toll does not appear to be great at the time these data were collected, it is cause for some concern. The ways in which wear and tear on the body and mind unfolds during prolonged exposure to stress remain to be specified, but research has indicated that negative outcomes are possible when stress continues unabated (e.g., Selye, 1976).

It also must be noted that these data are group data—the experience of stress at TMI is by no means universal. Some of the residents in this study appeared to be experiencing stress while others did not. By selecting individuals whose measures of self-report, behavioral performance, and urinary catecholamines uniformly fell above the respective median, 36% of the TMI subjects were classified as high-stress responders, while 34% of the TMI subjects were categorized as low-stress responders by falling uniformly below the median on each system of measure (Schaeffer & Baum, 1982). None of the control subjects could be classified as high-stress responders. A number of coping styles, social support, and perceptions of control have been suggested as mediators of this selective vulnerability (Collins, Baum, & Singer, 1983; Davidson, Baum, & Collins, 1982; Fleming, Baum, Gisriel, & Gatchel, 1982). Clearly, the problems at TMI have not elicited a single response. However, the overall pattern of response suggests that uncertainty is a substantial component of stress at TMI.

Hormonal Correlates of Chronic Uncertainty

As we noted earlier, many potential sources of stress at TMI are related to uncertainty. One of the characteristic victimizations by technological mishaps, such as nuclear accidents and toxic waste spills, is a persistent uncertainty about the nature and extent of harm already done and the threat of further damage by future exposure (Baum, Fleming, & Davidson, 1983). Our studies at TMI have provided evidence of chronic uncertainty; area residents reported continued concern about past and future harm done by radiation, and conversations with subjects suggest that there is uncertainty and apprehension about how and when the reactor will be decontaminated. We have also found that TMI-area residents are, as a group, less confident in their ability to control their surroundings and experience, and that residents reporting low levels of perceived control exhibited higher levels of catecholamines and symptom reporting and poorer proofreading performance (Davidson et al., 1982).

The pattern of catecholamine and cortisol levels also suggests that living at TMI engenders uncertainty and ambiguity. Though the differences in levels of epinephrine between TMI and control subjects only approached significance, the fact that it was higher in the TMI than in the control sample completes the Pattern II response described by Mason (1975). Subsequent findings have bolstered this interpretation. Recall that the data presented in this chapter were collected 15 months after the accident at TMI and before the radioactive gas that had been trapped in the containment building was released. Shortly after these data were collected, the venting of the gas began. The venting was controversial, and it is possible that it provided a focused threat more like those that elicit Pattern I responses. If our interpretation of the hormonal pattern observed was correct, the differences between groups in epinephrine levels during the venting should disappear, while norepinephrine and cortisol differences remain. This is, in fact, what happened. During the venting, control and TMI-area residents exhibited comparable levels of epinephrine, but continued to exhibit differences in norepinephrine and cortisol. Preliminary analyses of urine samples collected during the year following the venting suggest that differences in epinephrine levels returned, while differences in norepinephrine and cortisol levels were maintained. While speculative in nature, this analysis suggests that TMI-area residents have exhibited or approximated a Pattern II response except when confronted by a specific, defined threat or focus of attention.

The fact that the data we have discussed were collected just prior to the venting of radioactive gas from the plant presents some interpretational problems. It is arguable that the measures taken at this time may reflect not only a reaction to the chronic uncertainty of the TMI situation, but also an acute response in anticipation of the release of the radioactive gas. Were these our only data, we would have no way of determining the more important of these causes. However, our research has continued to monitor response at TMI and the control location, not only through the time period of the krypton-85 venting (summer 1980), but also 6 months after the completion of the venting procedure. Preliminary analyses indicated that similar elevations of stress measures at TMI, relative to controls, persisted both 6 weeks after the venting as well as 6 months after its completion. For example, the data summarized in Table 11.4 suggest that TMI-area residents exhibited greater evidence of stress 6 months after the venting than did control subjects. These data increased our confidence that what we were measuring during the first assessment just prior to the venting was indicative of response by TMI-area residents to the chronic uncertainty of this situation at the plant and not just an anticipatory "spike" in their stress-response levels.

The validity of this analysis awaits further research, but this discussion serves to illustrate the applicability of psychoendocrinological approaches to the study of chronic stress, especially when they are part of a multilevel assessment of response to environmental threat or challenge. It also suggests a number of ways in which basic and applied research may benefit one another, and it underscores the importance of joint consideration of biological, behavioral, and environmental contexts of any response or pattern of responses. Finally, the possibility of health-related effects of uncertainty or stress can be considered. The chronic, heightened sympathetic activity and increased adrenal activity that is suggested by our findings may have a number of consequences, ranging from the triggering of a predisposition, to specific illnesses or organ system pathologies, to the wear and tear on bodily tissue that may strengthen or generate such a predisposition. In addition, behavioral consequences associated with loss of control, reduced motivation, and so on, may adversely affect health by modifying important health behaviors. These and other health issues may supersede the restrictions on usable data for impact analysis noted in the recent Supreme Court decision on the consideration of psychological health at TMI.

TABLE 11.4
Mean Levels of Stress Measures 6 Months after Completion of Venting

	Epinephrine (ng/ml)	Norepinephrine (ng/ml)	Symptoms reported	Proofreading errors (%)
TMI	27	45	32	55
Control	13	24	13	68

References

Adler, A. (1943). Neuropsychiatric complications in victims of Boston's Cocoanut Grove disaster. *Journal of the American Medical Association, 123*, 1098–1011.

Baum, A., Fleming, R., & Davidson, L. M. (1983). Natural disaster and technological catastrophe. *Environment and Behavior, 15*, 333–354.

Baum, A., Gatchel, R. J., & Schaeffer, M. A. (1983). Emotional, behavioral, and physiological effects of chronic stress at Three Mile Island. *Journal of Consulting and Clinical Psychology, 51*, 565–572.

Baum, A., Grunberg, N. E., & Singer, J. E. (1982). The use of psychological and neuroendocrinological measurements in the study of stress. *Health Psychology, 1*, 217–236.

Baum, A., Singer, J. E., & Baum, C. S. (1981). Stress and the environment. *Journal of Social Issues, 37*, 4–35.

Bromet, E. (1980). *Three Mile Island: Mental health findings*. Pittsburgh: Western Psychiatric Institute and Clinic, University of Pittsburgh.

Cannon, W. B. (1914). The emergency function of the adrenal medulla in pain and the major emotions. *American Journal of Physiology, 33*, 356–372.

Cannon, W. B. (1929). *Bodily changes in pain, hunger, fear, and rage*. Boston: Branford.

Collins, D. L., Baum, A., & Singer, J. E. (1983). Coping with chronic stress at Three Mile Island: Psychological and biochemical evidence. *Health Psychology, 2*, 149–166.

Davidson, L. M., Baum, A., & Collins, D. L. (1982). Stress and control-related problems at Three Mile Island. *Journal of Applied Psychology, 12*, 349–359.

Derogatis, L., Rickels, K., & Rock, A. (1976). The SCL-90 and the MMPI: A step in the validation of a new self-report scale. *British Journal of Psychiatry, 128*, 280–289.

Dohrenwend, B. P., Dohrenwend, B. S., Kasl, S. V., Warheit, G. J., Bartlett, G. S., Chisolm, R. F., Goldsteen, R. L., Goldsteen, K., & Martin, J. L. (1979). *Report of the task group on behavioral effects to the President's Commission on the accident at Three Mile Island*. Washington, DC.

Duffy, E. (1962). *Activation and behavior*. New York: Wiley.

Durrett, L. R., & Ziegler, M.G. (1980). A sensitive radioenzymatic assay for catechol drugs. *Journal of Neuroscience and Research, 5*, 587–598.

Fleming, R., Baum, A., Gisriel, M. M., & Gatchel, R. J. (1982). Mediating influences of social support on stress at Three Mile Island. *Journal of Human Stress, 8*(3), 14–22.

Flynn, C. B. (1979). *Three Mile Island telephone survey* (NUREG/CR-1093). Washington, DC: U. S. Nuclear Regulatory Commission.

Flynn, C., & Chalmers, J. (1980). The social and economic effects of the accident at Three Mile Island (NUREG/CR-1215). Washington, DC: U. S. Nuclear Regulatory Commission.

Frankenhaeuser, M. (1975). Sympathetic-adrenomedullary activity, behavior and the psychosocial environment. In P. H. Venables & M. J. Christie (Eds.), *Research in psychophysiology* (pp. 71–94). New York: Wiley.

Frankenhaeuser, M. (1978). *Coping with job stress: A psychobiological approach.* Reports from the Department of Psychology, University of Stockholm (532).

Glass, D. C., & Singer, J. E. (1972). *Urban stress: Experiments on noise and social stressors.* New York: Academic Press.

Houts, P. S., Miller, R. W., Tokuhata, G. K., & Ham, K. S. (1980, April). *Health-related behavioral impact of the Three Mile Island nuclear accident.* Report submitted to the TMI Advisory Panel on health-related studies of the Pennsylvania Department of Health, Hershey.

Jenkins, C. D. (1979). Psychosocial modifiers of response to stress. *Journal of Human Stress, 5*(4), 3–15.

Johnson, J. (1973). Effects of accurate expectations about sensations on the sensory and distress components of pain. *Journal of Personality and Social Psychology, 27,* 261–275.

Johnson, J. E., & Leventhal, H. (1974). Effects of accurate expectations and behavioral instructions on reactions during a noxious medical examination. *Journal of Personality and Social Psychology, 29,* 710–718.

Lang, P. J., Rice, D. G., & Sternbach, R. A. (1974). The psychophysiology of emotion. In W. S. Greenfield & R. A. Sternbach (Eds.), *Handbook of psychophysiology* (pp. 623–643). New York: Holt, Rinehart & Winston.

Lazarus, R. S. (1966). *Psychological stress and the coping process.* New York: McGraw-Hill.

Lazarus, R. S., & Alfert, E. (1964). The short-circuiting of threat by experimentally altering cognitive appraisal. *Journal of Abnormal and Social Psychology, 69,* 195–205.

Lazarus, R. S., & Launier, R. (1978). Stress-related transactions between person and environment. In L. A. Pervin & M. Lewis (Eds.), *Internal and external determinants of behavior* (pp. 287–327). New York: Plenum.

Lindsley, D. B. (1956). Physiological psychology. *Annual Review of Psychology, 7,* 323–348.

Mason, J. W. (1975). Emotion as reflected in patterns of endocrine integration. In L. Levi (Ed.), *Emotions: Their parameters and measurement* (pp. 143–181). New York: Raven Press.

Mason, J. W., Brady, J. V., & Tolson, W. W. (1966). Behavioral and endocrine activity. In R. Levine (Ed.) *Endocrines and the central nervous system* (p. 227). Baltimore: Williams & Wilkens.

Mason, J. W., Mangan, G. F., Jr., Brady, J. V., Conrad, D., & Rioch, D. M. (1961). Concurrent plasma epinephrine, norepinephrine, and 17-hydroxycorticosteroid levels during conditioned emotional disturbances in monkeys. *Psychosomatic Medicine, 23,* 344–353.

Nomikos, M. S., Opton, E. M., Jr., Averill, J. R., & Lazarus, R. S. (1968). Surprise versus suspense in the production of stress reaction. *Journal of Personality and Social Psychology, 8,* 204–218.

Riley, V. (1981). Psychoneuroendocrine influences on immunocompetence and neoplasia. *Science, 212,* 1100–1109.

Riley, V., Fitzmaurice, M. A., & Spackman, D. H. (1981). Animal models in biobehavioral research: Effects of anxiety stress on immunocompetence and neoplasia. In S. M. Weiss, J. A. Herd, & B. H. Fox (Eds.), *Perspectives on behavioral medicine* (pp. 371–400). New York: Academic Press.

Rose, R. M., Jenkins, C. D., & Hurst, M. W. (1978). *Air traffic controller health change study* (FAA Contract No. DOT-FA73WA-3211). Boston: Boston University School of Medicine.

Schachter, S., & Singer, J. E. (1962). Cognitive, social and physiological determinants of emotional state. *Psychological Review, 69,* 379–399.

Schaeffer, M. A., & Baum, A. (1982, August). *Consistency of stress response at Three Mile Island.* Paper presented at annual meeting of the American Psychological Association, Washington, DC.

Schneiderman N. (1983). Animal behavior models of coronary heart disease. In D. S. Krantz, A. Baum, & J. E. Singer (Eds.), *Handbook of psychology and health* (Vol. 3, pp. 19–56). Hillsdale, NJ: Erlbaum.

Selye, H. (1976). *The stress of life.* New York: McGraw-Hill.

Sprague, E. A., Toxler, R. G., Peterson, D. F., Schmidt, R. E., & Young, J. T. (1980). Effect of cortisol on the development of atherosclerosis in cynomolgus monkeys. In S. S. Kalter (Ed.), *The use of non-human primates in cardiovascular diseases.* Austin: University of Texas Press.

Stein, M. (1983, June). *Psychosocial perspectives on aging and the immune response.* Paper presented to the Academy of Behavioral Medicine Research, Reston, VA.

Symington, T., Currie, A. R., Curran, R. S., & Davidson, J. N. (1955). The reaction of the adrenal cortex in conditions of stress. In *CIBA Foundations colloquia on endocrinology: Vol. 8. The human adrenal cortex.* Boston: Little, Brown.

Yalow, R. S., & Berson, S. A. (1971). In W. D. Odell & W. H. Daughaday (Eds.), *Principles of competitive protein binding assays.* Philadelphia: Lippincott.

Author Index

Subject Index